P9-APJ-096

Dynamics of Land Use: Needed Adjustment

Dynamics of Land Use: Needed Adjustment

Assembled and published under the sponsorship of the
IOWA STATE UNIVERSITY CENTER FOR
AGRICULTURAL AND ECONOMIC ADJUSTMENT

Iowa State University Press, *Ames,* Iowa, U.S.A.

Other publications of the Center for Agricultural and Economic Adjustment are available as follows, from the source indicated below:

Problems and Policies of American Agriculture, Iowa State University Press, Ames, Iowa, 1959.

Demand for Farm Products, Center for Agricultural and Economic Adjustment, Iowa State University, Ames, Iowa, 1959.

Adjustment and its Problems in Southern Iowa, Center for Agricultural and Economic Adjustment, Iowa State University, Ames, Iowa, 1959.

The Feed-Livestock Workshop, Center for Agricultural and Economic Adjustment, Iowa State University, Ames, Iowa, 1959.

Consumer Preferences and Market Development for Farm Products, Center for Agricultural and Economic Adjustment, Iowa State University, Ames, Iowa, 1960.

Adjustments in U.S. Agriculture: A National Basebook, Iowa State University Press, Ames, Iowa, 1961.

Goals and Values in Agricultural Policy, Iowa State University Press, Ames, Iowa, 1961.

Library of Congress Catalog Card Number 61-14201

Preface

AMERICAN society has wisely invested in development of resources which substitute for land. This investment, represented particularly in research and education for improvement of farming practices, has been highly successful and productive from the standpoint of general welfare and consumer gain. Given a limited land area and a growing population, the nation can produce food abundantly and at relatively low cost. It is not faced with an immediate threat of hunger or population pressure on land resources. Land itself does not restrain agricultural production, and productivity has been increased so greatly that, if all land is used for conventional agricultural products, the farming industry has surplus producing capacity.

The many new forms of capital used in agriculture serve as substitutes for both land and labor. While large amounts of labor have been withdrawn from agriculture, land inputs and the pattern of land use have remained relatively constant over several decades. Consequently, farm surpluses have arisen, and prices and incomes of agriculture have declined relative to other sectors of the American economy. Adaptations in use of land have not been sufficiently dynamic, either in keeping pace with changes in other resource and consumer sectors of a growing economy or in reaction to the pace of technological change in agriculture. Obviously, the American farm problem cannot be solved until further adaptations are made in land use.

This conference, May 3-5, 1960, was planned accordingly. It was structured to inventory the productive potential of the nation's agricultural land, the demand for products from it and the program or policy alternatives which might improve its use and help to alleviate the agricultural problem in a manner equitable to farm owners and operators.

The papers which follow represent an attempt by economists, agronomists and other social scientists to summarize existing knowledge, suggest fruitful hypotheses and stimulate analysis for improving the use of land and eliminating low incomes to agricultural resources generally. The conference is one of several on resources and resource use sponsored by the Center for Agricultural and Economic Adjustment. Other conferences have dealt with labor and capital resources of agriculture.

Earl O. Heady, Director

Center for Agricultural and
Economic Adjustment

Contents

Chapter 1

EARL O. HEADY
Iowa State University

Need for Land and Resource Adjustment

A MAIN CHARACTERISTIC of the American economy in the postwar period has been its sustained growth. Starting from a 1947-49 base period, gross national product increased by 90 percent to 1959. Total disposable personal income increased by 83 percent and income per capita of the non-farm population rose 40 percent. But an equally important characteristic of this economic growth period has been the relative decline of income in the farm sector. Total net income from agriculture declined by 20 percent in the period 1947-49 to 1959. Income per capita from farm sources increased by only 16 percent even though the farm population decreased by 30 percent.

Obviously, then, we have attained a level of economic development and per capita income wherein further progress does not reward farm and non-farm sectors equally. The absolute decline in net income of agriculture resulted partly from diminution of foreign demand, but more particularly because of the rate of growth of farm output and the low demand elasticities for farm products. Farm output grew by 50 percent over the period 1940-59 and 25 percent over the period 1950-59. Output per unit of resource also increased by 50 percent over the 20-year period 1950-59. Given the rate of population growth and the magnitude of foreign markets, a more rapid rate of development in agriculture results in a decline in total income from farming.

INCOME AND RESOURCE PROBLEMS

The relative decline in income from farming promises to continue unless the resource and output structure of the industry is to change. On the surface, low income appears to be the problem of agriculture. But family incomes and resource returns which are lower than in other major sectors is only a result. We must look deeper to find the basic cause or problem. True, income has been depressed because commodity prices are low relative to the prices of the resources which produce them. But following the sequence further, commodity prices and resource returns are low relatively because production is large. Still, not even "overproduction" is the basic problem or cause. Production is in surplus, relative to the magnitude of domestic and foreign markets and commodity prices which have been acceptable to farm people, and accumulates in public storage because the quantity of resources committed to agriculture is large. These are the basic variables or causes of the farm problem.

The quantity of resources now committed to agriculture, or to particular products and geographic locations, is too large to allow returns on resources at levels comparable to other industries, if the full productivity of these resources is utilized in farming and finds its way to the market. Aside from the small likelihood that world institutions and market mechanisms might spring open for humanitarian purposes, there is no prospect that demand expansion will change this picture during the 1960's. Hence, given the demand elasticities which are in prospect for this period, the input of resources for agriculture must be modified through either (1) diminishing the productivity of resources now in agriculture, (2) lessening the quantity of resources used in the industry or (3) diverting the "within agriculture use" of resources among farming alternatives. Must is, of course, a strong word. It is used here in the context of earnings for agricultural labor and investment which are comparable with those for resources of equal quality in other industries. Few persons contest this criterion from the standpoint of (1) the need by or the return to the nation's economy and (2) the welfare and equity position of farm families as resource owners. Agreement is much less firm in respect to whether the resource returns goal is to be tackled from the direction of magnitude of output or magnitude of inputs, or in respect to the specific policy procedures for either. An important purpose of this conference is to help assess the relative short-run and long-run productivity and supply of resources in agriculture. In this particular case, the emphasis is on the land resource. Given greater knowledge in respect to resource productivity and product supply, we can better evaluate the economic feasibility and political acceptability of alternative measures in bringing economic balance to agriculture.

But whatever the approach, the basic variables to be manipulated, controlled or "price encouraged" are resource inputs. Even direct output control can be successful only if it effectively diverts resources from the aggregate production process. There cannot be any output control unless input control exists. Our overflowing public granary provides the empirical evidence and treasury cost of an experiment conducted in scale, proving that production control is impossible without effective control of inputs.

The extreme policy mechanisms for controlling or altering inputs, and hence output, are open market prices and rigid production quotas for each commodity and farm. Between these extremes lie a large number of alternative mechanisms which, as is also true for extremes, can be used as pure strategies or as mixed strategies in restoring returns to resources in agriculture at levels on an economic par with other industries.

SUPPLY OF RESOURCES

Agriculture's fundamental problem is not supply of product but supply or quantity of factors. Persistence of resources to remain in agriculture at low returns in the short run pushes heavily on product supply or output, thus depressing family incomes to levels thought to be inconsistent with standards held by American society. The problem is most severe for labor. But it also is important in respect to the short-run allocation of land among different agricultural crops or between farm products and non-food services. Still, however, labor and land are linked economically, and the existence of excess labor in agriculture certainly has the effect of holding land to more intensive uses and in restraining its shift from surplus commodities. Contrawise, the land resource prices and tax structures which are not geared to the services the consuming society prefers are also important in determining society's employment pattern and the requirements or employment for the labor which is its technical complement. Policy or market mechanisms which cause a reallocation of land from surplus grain or cotton production to less intensive products such as grass, forestry and recreation also must alter the demand for labor in particular soils regions.

It is, therefore, impossible to separate the demand and allocative needs for land from that of the labor and capital resources which serve either as technical complements or substitutes with it. The planners of the conference were aware of this fact, but had several reasons for singling out the land resource for particular concentration:

(1) The long-run needs of, and the problems in, diverting land employment differ greatly from that of labor. Relative to the needs and challenges in economic growth before the nation, land does not have the spatial opportunities of labor. Needs in

respect to labor are especially those of geographic and occupational migration, if economic development is to take place optimally. Opportunities in occupational shifts are much more limited for land and even then are geographically fixed. Hence, the means and alternatives for adjusting land and labor inputs do, at some point, part ways. Public investment to bring about labor shifts can best rest on such mechanisms as improved educational, guidance, employment and market information facilities. Those for land, while affected by those for labor, must be of quite a different nature.

(2) The values of American society allow the institution of ownership in land, but not labor. Labor and individual, the motivating unit in our economy, are inseparable, and means which are publicly acceptable for adapting services of land are not similarly acceptable for labor. Along with acceptance of ownership in land but not in labor, American society has been willing to offer a price for letting land remain idle. The time will not soon come when payments direct to agricultural labor become an acceptable means for reducing or shifting farm output.

(3) During the 1950's, economists and others concentrated on the relative surplus of labor in American agriculture, without parallel emphasis on the relative surplus of land inputs for particular products or aggregate output. The pat remedy of many economists for solving the farm problem has been "reduce the size of the agricultural labor force." Yet, at least in the short run, a reduction in magnitude of the labor force promises little relief in magnitude of farm output. The farm labor force declined by 30 percent from 1940-60; total output increased by 50 percent in the period. This is true because migration of labor from agriculture does not simultaneously cause land inputs to shrink, or even to shift among alternatives. Surplus capacity of labor and machine capital on typical farms is great, and farmers who remain take over the land of those who leave and farm it with equal or greater intensity. Our studies show that remaining operators use a richer mix of capital with this land, and many obtain an even greater output from it than those who leave.

(4) Measures for bringing about an optimal allocation of land should include consideration of the time dimension more specifically than those for labor. Adjustments and programs relating to land need more to concentrate on true conservation problems and alternatives.

(5) Past programs aimed at production control have focused on the land resource. We have been successful only in proving that the policy mechanisms employed for these purposes so far are ineffective in production control. We have created a maze of

programs which simultaneously subsidize improvements of land to (a) increase current production at the expense of the future, (b) pay farmers for withholding land from current production and (c) conserve the services of land for future periods. These programs are justified to the public partly or entirely under the heading of conservation, perhaps as a means of capitalizing on the favorable attitude which now prevails in American society for improving the intertemporal allocation of basic natural resources. Since we have rested so much of our effort to control output on the land resource, and will probably continue to do so in the future, it is important that we attempt to bring better order among the various program elements, particularly when some now in use are a contradiction of each other.

Still, while some features of land and labor resources committed to particular uses in agriculture are separable, the problems in output or product supply which stem from them have common elements in the realm of factor supply. To understand better the mechanisms most readily acceptable and of greatest effectiveness in adapting use of both resources we must first examine the phenomena relating to supply of either the resources or their services. Why, in the short run, are the households which control them willing to commit them to the production process at such low prices or levels of return? In the case of land, particularly, what are the variables or forces which cause it to be held strictly to some uses when the longer-run economic horizon calls for its diversion to other uses?

A complex of other variables also exists which must be analyzed if we are clearly to understand the forces which mold the use of land or which provide potential in directing it into employment which eases the pressure on output, resource returns and family incomes generally. As a starting point in understanding the supply phenomenon of land for particular uses, we need to know more about the stocks of this resource. We make meaningful aggregations of other resources, but we have been unable to do so for land. Is it possible to aggregate land or its services, considering the great variation that exists in soils and climate, against alternatives in technology and capital inputs so that we have a better picture of our national supply of this resource? Until we are able to do so, and relate the potential stock or supply of this resource to the future demand for its services, we have no reliable foundation for planning policies and mechanisms pointed to meshing land use with national developmental needs. More importantly, we lack the basis for selecting consistent programs which will lessen the surplus problem in the immediate years ahead, but provide us with the pattern of land use needed for the longer-run challenges in national economic growth and world responsibilities which face us.

Land supply is a subject which has little concrete meaning. We know the approximate acreage of selected soil types, or that total land used for agriculture approximates 1.4 billion acres while cropland amounts to about 470 million acres. But these aggregates have no great value in national decision making or planning.[1] Needed in soil classification is a method whereby the various soils can be added together to give some operational notion of the total quantity of the land resource and the aggregate production function which attaches to it.

NEED IN ECONOMIC GROWTH

We are extremely in need of a basic and fundamental appraisal of the use of land resources relative to national economic growth and development. Programs need to be designed accordingly, but these must equally recognize the labor resources which have become attached to particular uses of land among different regions. We can push ahead in meshing use of land with prospective economic growth trends only at about the rate we bring about adaptation in use of the human resources now engaged in particular regions. And these human resources are not all engaged directly in agriculture. In farming areas more or less remote from industrial development, employment of persons in business enterprises, public services and social institutions generally is part of the agricultural matrix. These labor resources and households are no less important than those of agriculture in terms of the impact of major shifts in land use on family welfare and potential contribution of these labor resources to the nonfarm growth process which is in prospect for the American economy.

Land Use, Technical Improvement and Economic Growth

The main result or characteristic of economic progress is a rate of increase in national income which exceeds the rate of population growth, with a growth in per capita income accordingly. National economic growth occurs especially because of

[1] For added details in this respect, see Earl O. Heady. Economics of Agricultural Production and Resource Use. Prentice-Hall. New York. 1952. Chapter 10.

(1) technological improvement including improvement of the human resource, (2) capital accumulation, (3) growth in a labor force wherein productivity exceeds consumption and (4) improvement in economic institutions and market mechanisms. All of these have been taking place in the American economy, and there is no doubt that they will continue to do so. But they have different implications for agriculture than for most other industries. Agriculture likely will parallel other industries in technological improvement. Growth in productivity of land and certain associated resources has, in fact, not only kept pace with that of other industries but has outpaced growth in population. The persistent surplus condition stems importantly from this fact.

We do, of course, wish technological progress in all industries as a general contribution to economic progress. Given economic progress and technological improvement in agriculture, however, certain adjustment requirements become unique to land. For the reasons enumerated later, growth in capital and labor employed in agriculture will not keep abreast of the increase for other industries as national economic progress continues. Hence, the major "within agriculture" adjustment to economic growth must fall on land, the immobile and less flexible resource. Adjustments in land use thus become necessary under economic progress if the growth in productivity of land and agriculture exceeds the rate of population growth and the preferences of consumers are to be reflected through either or both pricing and voting mechanisms. This is necessarily true because the pattern of consumer preferences changes as per capita income grows.

First, there are differences among agricultural products themselves. Second, there is a difference between food-fiber products and other products for which land can be used. The magnitudes of income elasticities of demand provide guides for adaptation of land under economic growth. For commodities with income elasticities greater than 1.0, further increases in consumer income are associated with a rate of increase in expenditures which exceeds the rate of growth in income. Unfortunately, no major food aggregates fall in this category, although other important categories of consumer goods and services do.

For commodities with negative elasticities, expenditures per capita actually decline as income increases. This is the situation of cereal products, and as the income elasticity of demand becomes sufficiently low relative to the rate of increase in population, human cereal consumption declines in absolute amounts. With a large enough increase in per acre yield, it is likewise possible for less land to be devoted to this crop. Hence, because of this and other characteristics of demand change under income growth, it follows that the proportion of land devoted to the various major crops also needs to shift under economic development. In general, government programs from 1930 to 1960 served more as institutions to deter these shifts, rather than as mechanisms to aid them and bring about an agricultural or land use pattern consistent with the nation's economic development.

But our main problem is with food in aggregate, and particularly those products serving as the foundation of the feed livestock economy. With an aggregate income elasticity of demand for food of .2 or less, consumer expenditures on food lag far behind the rate of increase in national income and expenditures on non-food products. In fact, the income elasticity of demand for food in physical form is zero, meaning that poundage of food per person does not increase as income increases, even though the composition of the diet may change. Hence, aggregate demand for food in physical form, without regard to the mix of the diet, can increase at only about the rate of growth (is almost a constant function) of population. With a growth in per acre land yield exceeding the rate of population growth, less land is required to produce the nation's food. As Figure 1.1 illustrates, this condition held true from 1940 to 1960 in the United States. Surpluses did not arise during the period of the war and restoration, but they began as soon as the abnormal postwar foreign demand was eliminated by recovery and improvement of agriculture in other nations. While the rate of growth in output has been only slightly greater than the rate of population growth, the price elasticity of

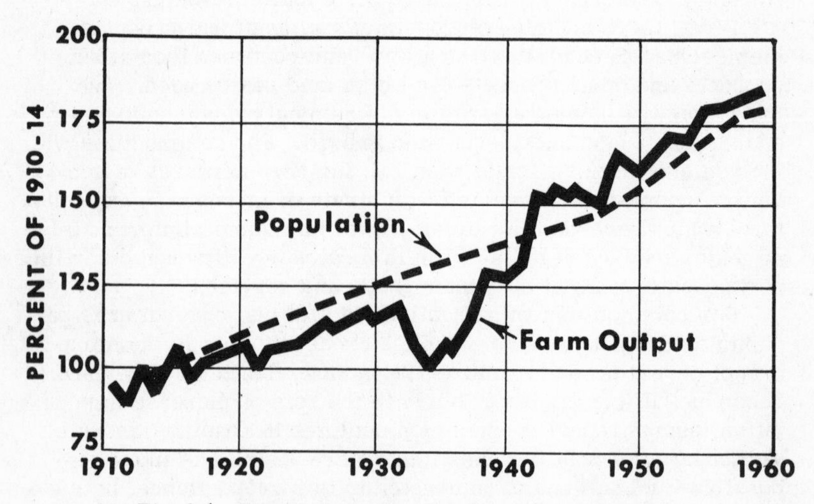

Fig. 1.1. Trends in U. S. population and farm output.

demand for farm products is extremely low. Hence, this small excess depresses prices and incomes by a much greater proportion if it flows "unmolested" into the market. We have, of course, effectively withheld it from the market, or have provided a minimum level to which it could depress prices and income, by storage and price programs for certain basic commodities. Effectively, however, we have not solved our basic land use problem: namely, that of shrinking the magnitudes of inputs for important food products. Storage and price programs of the type used from 1930 to 1960 are not an appropriate means of doing so. They are inappropriate for these purposes, although they can serve usefully for other purposes. The magnitude of stocks and the treasury costs of carrying them are so great that new approaches must be developed. Otherwise, the general public may discredit and eliminate them, even though they can have important uses for stabilizing the farm economy.

Non-food Elasticities

In contrast to the extremely low income elasticity of demand for food product in aggregate, a basic criterion for determining how the use of the land resource should be tempered under further economic growth, the elasticities are much higher for other products of land. Two products with relatively high income elasticities of demand are those of recreation and forest products (e.g. lumber, paper and other products of the latter). Demand for these will grow not only as a constant function of population but also as a function of national income. Other uses of land also have high premiums attached to them as consumer income increases, much higher than for food. Included are highway, airport, residential and similar non-food uses. The latter present, in many ways, less difficulty in respect to the adaptation of land use: they involve a smaller acreage, and non-pricing mechanisms are sometimes used to effect the transformation.

PROGRAMMING NEEDS

The great need is planning and programming of land use in a manner consistent with long-run economic development of the nation. Important guides exist in the income elasticities of demand which have been estimated by market analysis. Their magnitudes can be used to indicate the relative shifts in use of land needed as population and national income progress further.

Concepts and empirical procedures in soil science and production economics can provide a framework, in terms of both economic advantages and physical possibilities, for determining the particular areas which might be shifted. Land tenure and other specialists can prescribe institutions and other mechanisms which are alternatives or appropriate for bringing about the desired shifts needed in gearing land use to national economic development. In general, we have a stock of scientific tools for approaching the problem, although we currently are thin in knowledge of political acceptability among alternative. The tools of these several disciplines, where they are sufficiently developed, should be more effectively and intensively applied to facilitating shifts which are needed for, and can be consistent with, the population and demand patterns of future decades.

It is hoped that this conference can serve as a stimulus in this direction. The collection of sciences represented can provide systematic guidance. The path need not be uncharted to the extent of the past. The framework for analysis should be national economic development, rather than some less appropriate and more restricted realms which could be mentioned.

SUBSTITUTION OF TECHNOLOGY FOR LAND

The American economy has been a dynamic one. It will need to continue so, both to meet the world responsibilities and challenges which face it and to insure reasonably favorable business expectations and employment levels. In contrast to the economic growth which we have experienced and will continue to experience, we could visualize an economy where, except for a few modifications, the general pattern of land use would remain constant. The economy would be one with income growing at only the rate of population and, hence, a constant per capita income over time. Economic growth would be even and at equal rates over the nation. Similarly, technological improvement for agriculture would proceed at the same rate among crops and regions and at the same rate as growth in population. The national land use pattern, once it had been geared to the demand structure at one point in time, could simply be extended into the future, with the only dimension of change being an extended intensity of capital and labor. But growth in the U. S. economy has not been, and will not be, in this pattern. Economic growth has been spatially uneven over the nation, causing the economic advantage to be altered differentially over our land area. Income has increased faster than population, providing a growth in per capita income and changing structure of consumer demand. Technological change in agriculture also has outpaced population and foreign demand growth. It has not been spread equally among regions and crops. Hence, the basis exists for producing our food product with less land, even though our population is increasing.

Technological improvement, or more correctly, the new capital materials which represent it, serve as a substitute for land. So effective has this process been that land has come into a surplus position as far as current food requirements are concerned. Aside from a breakthrough in international markets, this situation will, given technical improvement at rates of the decade 1950-60, continue beyond the 1960's. Some estimates suggest that we could withdraw as much as 15 percent of our cropland, and still produce products in quantity giving no important rise in farm and food prices. The amount may be more or less than this, but our bulging grain bins provide empirical evidence that the land input devoted to food is greater than needed. Even while surpluses have continued to accumulate, we have had over 25 million acres in acreage and conservation reserves. Too, further technological advances and rearrangements are known and could be applied to more farms. Irrigation, continuous corn with high level fertilization and application of more fertilizer on additional farms are examples.

We have not been sufficiently aware of the fact that technological improvement (or more particularly the new capital forms or materials representing it) serves as a substitute for land. But this is true whether the innovations so represented apply to crop or livestock production. For example, an innovation in nutrition which improves feeding efficiency allows us to get a given output of livestock product from less feed. Since less feed is required, less land also is required. The feed addition serving as the innovation in nutrition is thus a substitute for land. Innovation in livestock breeding and sanitation, crop breeding, insecticides and others serve similarly and have a varying rate of substitution for land, depending on the mix and rate at which they are used on soils of different types. The application is generally the same for all of these biological innovations, but we will illustrate the possibility with fertilizer. Suppose that the per acre response equation or production function for fertilizer applied to land is that in (1) where Y is yield per acre and X is fertilizer input per

$$Y = a + bX - cX^2 \quad (1)$$

acre. For farms of typical size, this same production function or response outcome can be realized on all acres of the given soil.

Hence, considering only land and fertilizer, the production function for the entire area of the farm becomes that in (2) where $\bar{Y}$ is total production and A is number of acres.[2]

$$\bar{Y} = aA + bAX - cAX^2 \tag{2}$$

Now, setting $\bar{Y}$ at a particular level, we can derive a production isoquant for the farm as in (3). The corresponding equation of marginal rate of substitution of fertilizer for land then is (4).

$$X = b(2c)^{-1} \pm \sqrt{[4c(A - Y) + Ab^2](4c^2A)^{-1}} \tag{3}$$

Quite obviously, the marginal rate at which fertilizer substitutes for land, in producing a given output, depends on the level at

$$\frac{dA}{dX} = -\frac{bA - 2cAX}{a + bX - cX^2} \tag{4}$$

which fertilizer is used. As increasing quantities of fertilizer are used for a given state of technology, the rate of substitution will decline. But as other technologies are developed which increase the productivity of fertilizer, the marginal rate of substitution of land for fertilizer will increase.

Price of Substitute Inputs

The rapid use of inputs which substitute for land has not "just happened." The innovations so represented have been put into use because they were profitable. If farmers were not limited on capital and risk aversion in credit use were absent, even more of the materials representing innovations could be used at profit by individual farmers (although this would not hold true for agriculture in aggregate). Why have these innovations proved so profitable? Because the price of the materials representing the innovations has been low relative to prices of the commodities they

[2]This production function, one for an individual farm, is used to illustrate the possible outcome for a single producer. Yield or total production is a linear function of acreage but not of fertilizer. This is essentially the condition which holds true for individual farms, since the response they can obtain on one acre of a particular soil they can also obtain on other acres. Typical farms are not so large as to preclude this possibility. However, if we forgot about individual farms and considered a national production function, it might be of different form in respect to changing marginal productivity of land. Yet the same general substitution relationships would exist. While only one algebraic form has been used to illustrate the situation for an individual farm, the same general conditions in respect to substitutability and changing rates of substitution would hold true for other algebraic forms.

produce. Price structures, particularly in the postwar period, have favored the substitution of new technology for land. The rate of substitution has been more rapid than the withdrawal of excess land inputs from the commodities for which the new innovations have been used.

Prices of materials representing new technologies have been low relative to farm commodity prices because of the pricing structure of the former and because of the support levels of the latter. Prices of innovation materials have been low relatively because of research in and efficiency of the firms and industries which produce them. Competition in these industries will likely serve as a force causing this effort to continue, in order that the volume of inputs might remain large and/or increase. Even if the rate of technological improvement slows relative to population growth, the substitution process can still continue. However, it would continue at a rate which might slow the speed with which innovation materials are substituted for land. The quantity of innovation materials which a farmer can profitably apply per acre is a function of the production relationship in (1) (more exactly the derivative of this equation or the marginal productivity of the innovation material) and the price of the material relative to the price of the product.[3] Should we reach a time when the rate of population increase is greater than the rate of technological improvement in agriculture, the price of farm commodities would rise relative to the price of innovation materials. Substitution of these for land would then be extended, even with a decline in the marginal rate of substitution. But for the 1960's, it is likely that substitution will continue at rates causing land to be made surplus relative to current food uses.

NEW TECHNOLOGY AND THE PRODUCTION PROCESS

New technology does not represent an "act" apart from other concepts of the production process. Instead it represents a process of identifying the various resources which have a productivity greater than zero in the production process or production function. At a given time we have knowledge of only a limited number of these resources or of their productivity. There are

[3]In the absence of capital limitation and with sufficient knowledge, the farmer could maximize profits by equating the derivative of (1) with the ratio formed by dividing the price per unit of the innovation material by the price of the product. As the price of the product rises relative to the price of the material, the latter can be used in larger amount and until it has a smaller productivity. Under limited capital, the criterion is different but the marginal productivity and price ratios are still the relevant quantities, in comparison with the same ratios for other products.

literally thousands of these different resources, many of which are yet unknown. As in the production function of (5), we may know of the existence and productivity of resources X through X_r

$$Y = f(X_1, X_2, \ldots X_r, X_{r+1}, X_{r+2}, \ldots X_n) \tag{5}$$

– including nitrogen, soil of particular characteristics, moisture, sunlight, a particular seed variety and others. Now we identify the resource or material X_{r+1}, or its productivity. It can now be included in the "knowledgeable" physical function, along with other resources or materials. It will be substituted for others, including land, if its productivity is sufficiently high and its price is sufficiently low.

As we extend technological knowledge thus, we both increase the possible product from a given land area and raise the rate at which aggregate capital (due largely to its new forms representing innovation) substitutes for land. The long-run tendency for this substitution to occur is illustrated in the decline in farm land prices relative to the prices of farm products and relative to the price of other inputs. Given a fixed supply of land, one would expect, apart from the offsetting forces mentioned here, population growth to cause land price to rise relatively. The same would not hold true for inputs such as fertilizer, machinery and other items which might more nearly have a constant supply price (in contrast to land which would have a steeply rising supply price if we tried to increase it in aggregate). Yet relative to farm product prices, the real price of land has declined by almost 20 percent since 1910. This decline emphasizes the relative increase in the "effective" supply of land services since the earlier period. The real price (i.e. price of resource relative to price of farm products) of fertilizer has declined even more, or by around 35 percent, a development which has itself encouraged the substitution of fertilizer for land. In contrast, the real prices of farm labor, farm machinery and farm supplies in general have increased since 1910. The decline in real price of fertilizer has taken place not because it has been reduced in relative importance in the production process (the opposite has held true) but because of technical improvement and competition in the fertilizer industry. The decline in real price has caused it to be "demanded" in larger quantities. In contrast, however, land is not used in larger quantities (its stock is fairly well limited) and has declined in relative price because other resources have increasingly substituted for it, thus increasing its effective supply against national food demand.

Increasingly, the product of agriculture is becoming less a

function of the services of land and labor and more the product of the services of capital items representing improved technology. The capacity of agriculture to produce is less limited by our land area and depends more on other sections of the economy. Capacity has been added through development and expansion of the industries which furnish the agricultural inputs substituting for land. Relative to our population and the productivity of soil our supply of land is relatively larger than it has been at any time since 1885. It appears that this situation will continue for some time, and likely will be accentuated by chemical and biological developments in prospect. While agricultural output once had an effective restraint defined by land area or a spatial limit, this is no longer true. Agriculture is now similar to industries such as filling stations, department stores and others where space or area is not the restraining force for output. We must learn to live with this surplus capacity, a fortunate development since the nation has obtained "food capacity" by producing it, rather than by conquering it as has been an historic approach of many nations.

Unfortunately, we have not been sufficiently aware of the fact that new technology (e.g. the new capital resources which represent it) is a substitute for land. We have not planned programs, of either an educational or action nature, which encourage and allow diversion of surplus land inputs for particular uses as the substitution process takes place to those services and uses which are consistent with long-run economic growth and conservation needs. It is time we did so, to help erase the price and income problems of agriculture and for more complete attainment of the longer-run needs and goals of the nation.

We have a definite public policy for developing resources which substitute for land. This systematic and vigorous effort is represented by our public investment, through Land Grant Colleges and the U. S. Department of Agriculture, in developing new technology to substitute for land. This course is the safe and prudent one for a nation faced with population and economic growth. But we have not completed the public decision when we fail to aid the conversion of land to other uses, once it has been replaced or caused to be surplus relative to present uses.

PRICE POLICIES AND SPATIAL ADJUSTMENT

Numerous policies can be used to better mesh the agricultural plant with economic development. Policies of the past have generally been unsuccessful because they have been tied too loosely to national economic growth. We need to develop and use policies which are more consistent with the economic development in prospect. These policies must also be politically acceptable. But acceptability of various policies also is a function of education and knowledge of means and ends, or of alternatives and consequences. We have done much less to inform and educate farm and other people on the basic nature of economic growth, in relation to land use needs, than we have in educating farmers on how to use and substitute other inputs for land. To be certain, we need the latter as part of our economic development investment and because of the world challenges which face us. Leaving out the possibility of war, the major competition between East and West will be in promoting internal growth, partly as a means of aiding growth elsewhere over the world. It will benefit mankind if this proves true, and the likelihood is great that it will. Still, it makes little sense to invest in research and education to show farmers how to substitute other inputs for land, without a parallel effort to help them understand the connection between this process and economic progress. It also makes little sense to aid the substitution of capital inputs for land, causing immense output pressure to grow up in agriculture, without providing understanding and market or institutional mechanisms so that this pressure can be relieved to (1) lessen the depression of resource returns in agriculture and (2) allow greater society realization of the gains which are made possible through the substitution of new technology for land and labor in agriculture.

Production control and land diversion programs of the past have generally been unsuccessful as attempts to eliminate surpluses and low resource returns in particular sectors of agriculture, partly because they have been forced into a tight spatial restraint. They have not sufficiently recognized that economic growth and development, within both agriculture and other industries, does and should take place at differential rates over the nation if our natural resources are to be developed most efficiently. The same program elements have generally been applied to all soils and locations, probably because the policy focus has been that of income equity and short-run welfare considerations. In some manner, we must break away from this spatial restraint, while retaining income and equity considerations deemed relevant by American society. We need to shift the use of land in different geographic and soil regions in line with its physical production possibilities and relative economic advantage as technological progress in agriculture, national income and consumer preferences progress over time. To do so would mean concentration of major land use adjustments in particular locations. It would mean a much less intensive agriculture and a further and more rapid shrinkage in farm and non-farm populations in these locations.

But even this problem is tied closely with rates of economic development in particular areas. For example, in some areas of the Southeast where industrialization is progressing at a rapid rate, a shift of land from annual crops to forestry need not require a major population shift because job opportunities exist in the community. In contrast, however, a shift from wheat to grass in marginal areas of the Grain Plains entails a much more severe adjustment. Industrialization often does not exist as a means of reemployment of people who are replaced from farming, and the entire business and social structure is affected as geographic migration occurs. These considerations are important, and both short-run and long-run policies need to be adapted accordingly. For short-run policies, it is important that the economic interest and compensation possibilities of all people in the community be considered, with programs structured accordingly so that more basic adjustments will be encouraged. For long-run policies, opportunities for improved use of the human resource now attached to land needs to be given particular emphasis.

Education is especially important in this scheme. With uneven economic growth over the nation, it is important that society invest appropriately in education of youth, so that those in regions declining in a relative economic sense acquire the skills and knowledge for productive application upon migration to more rapidly growing regions. Education and other migration aids relate closely to adjustments in the national pattern of land use. So far we have handled this complex of problems inadequately, largely because we have tried to segregate and isolate solutions on the farm front from economic development forces. The economic growth tides are simply too great for us to do so, unless we are willing to live with farm surplus and income difficulties of magnitudes as large or larger than those which now exist.

Margin of Adjustment

Adjustment in land use will be brought about directly by adjustments in capital and labor resources used with land. Land use can be adjusted at either the intensive or extensive margin. Adjustment at the intensive margin would leave land allocated to present crops or uses, but cause fewer capital and labor inputs to be used with it. Adjustment in the extensive margin generally would mean a shift to crop alternatives other than those now emphasized on less productive soils. It would require a diminution in land inputs for major field crops. If land use were shifted into line with prospective demand and growth trends of the nation, some regions would need to make such major shifts as from wheat to grazing or from annual cash crops to forestry. Some regions would be converted largely to recreational areas. Our national policies have attempted to avoid these shifts through programs encouraging or forcing comparable curtailment of land inputs for all farms or regions.

These short-run policies, or modifications of them, may be needed to avoid the extreme burdens which would fall on particular persons and communities if the longer-run shifts were telescoped into an extremely short time span. We probably have the choice, in the realm of welfare economics, of either (1) providing compensation to those who suffer a capital loss or depression in earning power as the pattern of agriculture is changed in particular regions or (2) extending the span of time over which adjustments are made and concentrated in particular regions. Recent price and income policies contribute to both. They have not eliminated migration of people from farming; they have largely retarded the shift of land in problem areas, while providing compensation directly to farmers, and indirectly to other businesses, within these areas. Later chapters throw light on the means that are possible and publicly acceptable for better meshing the reallocation of both human effort and land to the products needed most under economic development.

Society could, of course, decide that adjustments to mesh agriculture and land use with national growth should not take place and try to create a "national agricultural museum." The museum would be represented by policies to "keep the structure of agriculture the same as in the past," so that we could see farming in its historic dress. But speaking through the market, society has not chosen to do so. It has voted higher prices for labor which has migrated from the most "burdened" sectors of agriculture to other regions and industries. Labor has left agriculture most rapidly in those regions where agriculture is least adapted to the future. Society has not created legal or institutional barriers to keep it from doing so, although it has not always provided optimum facilities for migration. In this sense, we must believe that society chooses regional adaptations over the long run. Current policies slow the process and lessen the pain for those who remain. They prevent an adaptation of land much more than they prevent an adaptation of labor.

Inevitably, then, even if due to labor transfers, differential adjustments are going to be made among regions in land use. We need to decide on the best pricing, institutional and compensation means for facilitating these adjustments. As an illustration of the patterns of change which might be expected, we cite some tentative results from a study in production economics underway by the writer and Al Egbert of the U. S. Department of Agriculture. The details and qualifications of the study will not be cited here because they are given elsewhere.[4] The empirical analyses apply to grain production, since this is the realm of greatest surplus and land use adjustment needs.

The Models and Results

Regional adjustment programs require determination of regions that should stay in and that should go out of production. Several programming models were developed. Our results apply to production of wheat, corn, oats, barley and grain sorghums since these are the commodities of greatest storage burden. We determined which regions should continue to produce these grains and which should shift to other products to make annual output approximate annual "requirements" or disappearance of these products. The year 1954 served as the basis for relating output to requirements because the research was initiated at that time. Requirements are considered to be "discrete" quantities representing disappearance of grain in 1954 adjusted for normal exports, livestock populations and food requirements. We assumed farming techniques to be those of 1954 and supposed, to make the computational burden manageable, that requirements coefficients were constant within each region. The results would be modified with up-to-date technology but the general pattern would remain the same.

Production patterns resulting from three programming models are presented in this section. The United States was broken down into 104 producing regions, each with these three activities: feed grains, wheat for food and wheat for feed. Restrictions included land or acreage constraints for these crop activities in the 104 regions, plus two restrictions for total United States feed grain and food wheat demand. Without slack variables for disposal activities, the coefficient matrices are of 106 x 310 order. The model allows us to consider the comparative advantage of different regions in producing food and feed grains. The objective in two models is that of minimizing the cost of meeting

[4] Earl O. Heady and Alvin C. Egbert. Programming regional adjustments in grain production to eliminate surpluses. Jour. Farm Econ. 41:4:718-33. Nov., 1959.

demand requirements. Maximizing profits is the objective in one model.

Model A. The objective function for this model is

$$(6) \quad \text{Min. } f(X) = C_1X_1 + \ldots\ldots + C_kX_k + \ldots\ldots + C_rX_r$$

where C_k is a subvector of per unit costs, containing n elements to represent costs of producing feed grains and wheat in the k-th region; and X_k is a subvector of crop outputs, with n elements representing production levels in the k-th region. In this case, c_{jk}, the unit cost of producing the j-th crop in the k-th region, includes only the labor, power, machine, seed, fertilizer and related inputs for each grain. It does not include rent and farm overhead or fixed costs. The restraints of (7) where x_{1k}, x_{2k} and x_{3k} refer respectively to outputs of feed grains (barley, corn, oats and grain sorghums), feed wheat and food wheat in the k-th region and p_{1k}, p_{2k} and p_{3k} stand for the per unit land inputs for these activities in the k-th region; while S_k is a vector of acreage

$$(7) \quad x_{1k}p_{1k} + x_{2k}p_{2k} + x_{3k}p_{3k} \leq S_k$$

restrictions in this same region. The production possibility relations include 104 inequalities such as those in (7). The restrictions in S_k are the largest acreages devoted to grains in the 8 years prior to computations. In addition to these acreage restraints, there are two discrete demand restrictions:

$$(8) \quad x_{11} + x_{21} + x_{12} + x_{22} + \ldots + x_{1k} + x_{2k} + \ldots + x_{1r} + x_{2r} = d_1$$

$$(9) \quad x_{31} + x_{32} + \ldots + x_{3k} + \ldots + x_{3r} = d_2$$

In (8), a national "demand" restriction for feed grains, the coefficients of all x_{jk} are 1 because units of output are in terms of a feed equivalent expressed in corn. The feed grain demand restriction is measured in this same unit, with total units representing the 1954 level of feed grain disappearance adjusted for normal livestock production. Coefficients in (9), a national demand restriction for food wheat, are also 1. For requirements restrictions in both (8) and (9) an equality was used to indicate that annual output must exactly equal annual requirements, with requirements at the 1954 level adjusted for normal livestock production, exports, population and feed uses, as corn and small grains are grown in fixed rotational proportions in regions such as the Corn Belt.

Model B. This model is the same as A, except that land rent

is included in c_{jk}, the per unit cost of producing the j-th crop in the k-th region. The model represented by B was used because only grain crops are used as competitive alternatives. Inclusion of rent in B gives some weight to alternative crops. Since grains are the major crops in the regions delineated, rents are largely based on grains. Hence, the estimates arising under models A and C are likely more appropriate than those of B.

Model C. This model is the same as A in terms of nature and number of activities, restrictions and production costs, except that it gives some recognition to transportation costs to demand regions. Instead of minimizing costs as in (6), we maximize profit since C_k is now a vector of net prices for the k-th region. We use differentials in net prices in each region to account for transportation costs to consuming regions. Prices in each region are equal to those in a central market, less the cost of transportation from the region.

Assumptions of Model A result in regions being withdrawn from production of all grains in southeastern Colorado, eastern New Mexico, northern Utah and eastern Wyoming and Montana. Some regions scattered over Texas, Nebraska, Oklahoma, Missouri, Kansas and New York also would be withdrawn. In the Southeast, regions representing a large acreage would be withdrawn from production of grains (Fig. 1.2). The major wheat and

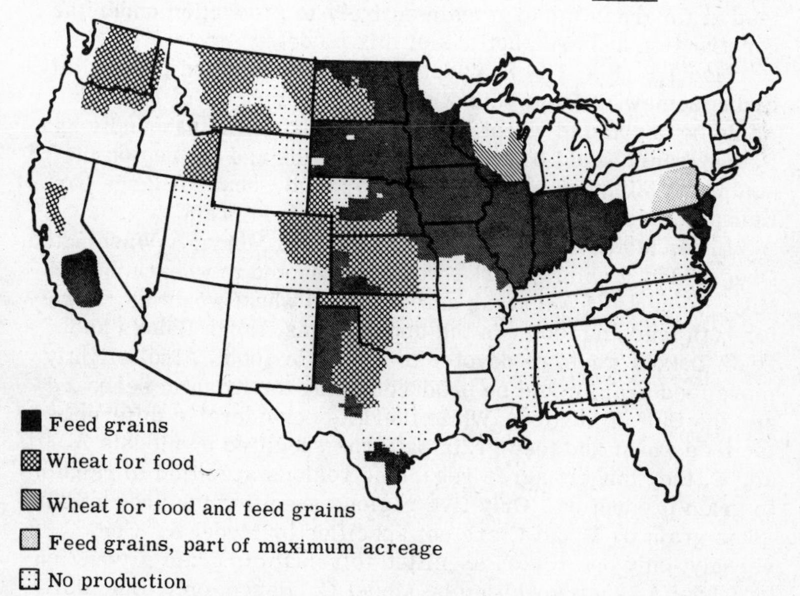

Fig. 1.2. Production pattern specified by Model A.

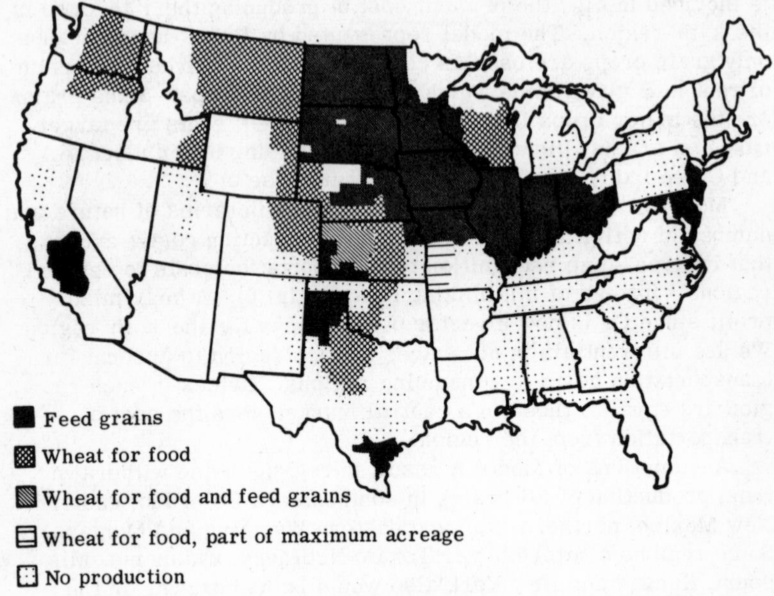

Fig. 1.3. Production pattern specified by Model B.

feed grain areas would remain entirely in production under the construction and assumptions of this model.

Model B (Fig. 1.3) provides a spatial production pattern differing somewhat from both A and C. Under B, all of Montana would be devoted to wheat for food, the Oklahoma panhandle and Pennsylvania would be shifted out of grains and the region in southwest Missouri would be used for food wheat. A large part of Kansas would be used for both wheat and feed grain.

Under Model C (Fig. 1.4) large parts of Montana, Washington, Oregon, Idaho and Nebraska would be devoted to wheat for feed only. In parts of Nebraska and Colorado wheat would be grown for both feed and food. In the upper plains, North Dakota and South Dakota would be devoted to wheat for food. Also, slightly more feed grain would be produced along the Atlantic seaboard and the Gulf of Mexico. While there is considerable difference in the food wheat and feed grain patterns specified by models A and C, they largely agree regarding regions specified to remain in grain production. Only five regions specified for production of some grain by Model C are not specified by Model A. Conversely, only one region specified to remain in grain production by Model A is not specified by Model C. Hence, only four more of the 104 regions would be needed to meet feed grain and food

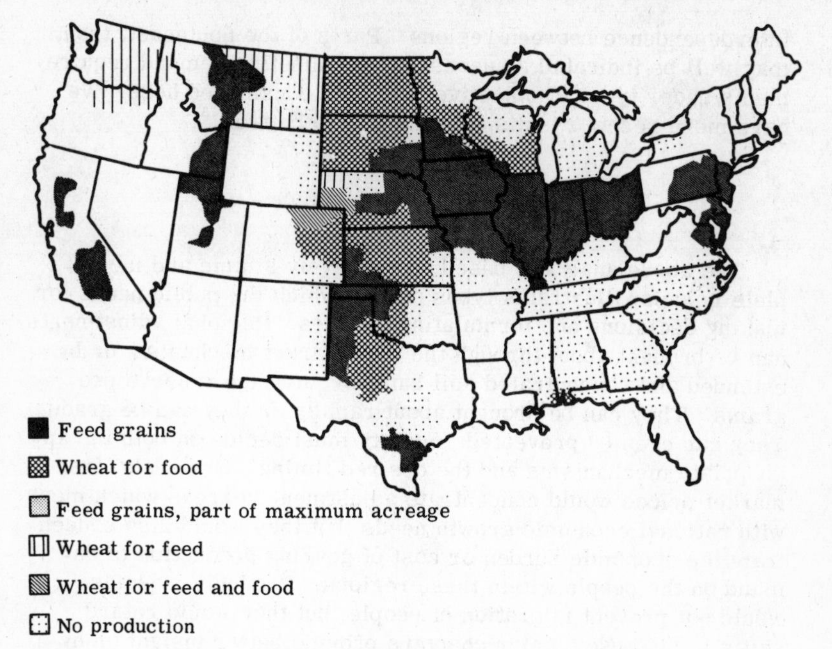

Fig. 1.4. Production pattern specified by Model C.

wheat requirements in Model C than in A. The five additional regions for fulfilling feed or food requirements under C include regions in eastern Virginia, northeast Ohio, western Kansas, southern Alabama and northern Utah. The region specified by Model A, but not by C, is in northeast South Dakota. Thirty-five entire regions and part of a small region in western Kentucky would not be required for grain production in Model C. The pattern is the same, except for the six regions noted above, for Model A.

The three models are consistent for 88 of the 104 regions. They specify 88 regions that should remain in grain production or shift completely out of grains. Hence, disagreement among the three models existed only for 16 regions. Consistency between models A and C, the two models deemed most appropriate, existed for all but six regions.

The results, computed with average regional coefficients and current farming techniques, illustrate both needed data and the types of analyses possible with today's principles and computing facilities. Use of "today's techniques" provides the reason that the entire Southeast is indicated as "not required" to meet annual demand requirements. It is likely, of course, that technical improvements on the horizon will change the degree of interdependence between regions. Parts of the Southeast, then, may well be indicated as necessary for meeting demand requirements under types of objective functions considered here. We have more recent results showing this to be true.[5]

Program Elements

The above analysis, based on relatively simple and incomplete models, illustrates types of data which the public needs for making decisions and formulating policies. Regional adjustments can be brought about through the free market mechanism or by extended and concentrated soil bank and acreage reserve programs. They can be brought about rapidly or they can be gradual. They can even be prevented. Society must decide on both the appropriate mechanisms and the desired timing. Obviously, free market prices would concentrate adjustment in areas which mesh with national economic growth needs, but they would also concentrate the economic burden or cost of gearing production to demand on the people within these regions. Production quotas would not prevent migration of people, but they would retard shifts in land use. Later chapters provide better insight or hypotheses for public choices in these directions.

But regardless of the decision which the public makes on policies, it needs to include the appropriate supplement policy measures for ends deemed relevant. For example, a shift from wheat to grass entails upwards of five years. A shift to forestry involves a longer period and one generally beyond the planning span of middle-aged operators who depend solely on farming. Even a shift from wheat to grass requires added capital, and income drops sharply in the transition period. Hence, special credit programs to allow conversion and farm enlargement may be necessary. Programs to supplement incomes during the transition period may also be necessary. These are elements of an overall program needed to facilitate land use shifts consistent with the present developmental and income trends of the American economy. If broad regional adjustments were to be made, choice also would need to be exercised among such alternatives as (1) using free market prices for the purpose, (2) government purchase of the land, (3) renting the land from farmers, (4) purchasing

[5] It is recognized, of course, that not all land in the "going out" areas would be shifted or all that in the "staying in" areas would remain under present uses. The degree of aggregation and the linear structure of the model bring about these conditions. But the models are for broad diagnostic purposes. They need to be extended in more detail by soils specialists and production economists.

farmers' rights to produce surplus crops, (5) paying farmers to use their land only for particular commodities. These are the types of alternatives to be analyzed in later chapters dealing with the public mechanisms available and the political acceptability of alternatives.

CONSISTENT PROGRAMS

Our efforts touching upon adjustment of the land resource are highly segmented. Aggregatively, they are not tied sufficiently to the economic growth trends of the economy. Individually, they are not sufficiently consistent in respect to purpose. On the one hand, we use conservation and acreage reserve payments to induce farmers to withdraw all capital from land, causing the land to be withdrawn from market production in order to reduce output. On the other hand, we provide ACP payments to farmers to use more capital items on their land, causing output to be increased in the immediate future. We provide conservation payments and assistance to help save land which is in danger of erosion but may be needed for future generations. But we also provide payments and assistance to aid farmers on level land who have no true conservation problem.[6] We make payments and provide assistance to drain level land, to irrigate level land, to use soil amendments on level land, most of which speed up the rate at which we use stock resources in the soil and add to output when we already have a surplus of farm products.

It is time that we incorporated our problems and programs of economic development and conservation into a comprehensive and systematic model for the land resource. Public investment in our segmented, and often inconsistent, approaches to land use and adaptation has been great from 1930 to 1960. Undoubtedly, the investment, including a large portion of that concentrated on the surplus problem, has been large enough to have allowed attainment of major adjustment needs, had our sights been on systematic and long-run economic development. We are at a stage in surplus accumulation and world responsibilities where we must begin to plan accordingly. We must see land use in its broader context and fit our research, education and action programs into a consistent economic growth and general equilibrium model. The conference was planned to bring together agronomists,

[6]For a distinction between production practices and conservation practices or investment, see Earl O. Heady. Economics of Agricultural Production and Resource Use. Prentice-Hall. New York. 1952. Chapter 27.

economists, political scientists and others representing the variables which appropriately belong in such a model or approach. It is not expected that it will provide all the answers. But it should provide suggested directions and appropriate hypotheses. We hope that it will serve as an aid to research workers, educational specialists, program administrators and agricultural leaders, providing better images of the adjustment problem, technological and economic growth trends, prospective developmental trends and program alternatives.

Chapter 2

JAMES W. KNOWLES
Joint Economic Committee
United States Congress

Growth Prospects for the American Economy

DURING the 1940's and 1950's the use of long-range projections of the growth possibilities of the American economy became standard practice in many areas of public and private decision making. Its use has become commonplace in the areas of agricultural policy, water resource development — both power and irrigation, planning of large public works programs, forestry policies and various other public programs — federal, state, and local, which must be planned in the light of prospective conditions extending over long future periods. In the private sectors of the economy the use of long-range projections as a guide to capital investment has grown in importance and has extended into new areas including research and development and personnel planning. The use of long-range projections in connection with the debate over postwar economic policies during the 1940's led to a more widespread knowledge of this tool, and was the largest single stimulus to the expansion in its use.[1]

Such projections are of a calm, routine character compared to the controversies of the 1950's and earlier. While the scientific basis for the making of long-range projections has progressed a long way since the 1920's, there still remains much cause for caution in their construction and use.

We cannot be too careful in making sure that any projection which is prepared as a basis for private and public policy decisions is designed so as to provide the sort of evaluations of

[1] The expansion in the use of long-range full employment projections has been strongly influenced by the persistent and outstanding work in this field by the National Planning Association. Beginning with "National budgets for full employment" in 1945, their series continued in 1952 with "The American economy in 1960," by Gerhard Colm with the assistance of Marilyn Young. In 1956 the National Planning Association obtained a grant from the Ford Foundation to develop improved methods for long-range projections and to carry forward the 1952 estimates to 1970. Its results appeared in October, 1959, in "Long-range projections for economic growth: the American economy in 1970" (Planning Pamphlet No. 107). NPA has developed for organizational members and subscribers a National Economic Projection Series published in annual and quarterly editions.

prospects suitable for the particular decisions at issue. I have emphasized this point before[2] but I also emphasize the point here to warn that the general projections of economic growth possibilities presented in this chapter may need to be adapted in various ways to the problems of land use and needed adjustments in public and private policies at which this book is aimed.

It is especially appropriate that these first chapters should be devoted to analysis of the long-range growth prospects of the economy as a whole as well as those sectors and aspects with peculiar relevance to the land use problem. As I have stated elsewhere:

> Confidence in the Nation's potential for future economic growth has been the fundamental assumption upon which public and private economic policies have been based in the United States since its founding. Though occasionally challenged during unexpected reverses, as during the 1930s when concepts of economic maturity and stagnation were brought into the debates over economic policies for a time, this basic belief in the possibilities or opportunities for future increases in employment, output, and in per capita, real purchasing power for a rising population, has survived all vicissitudes of public debate to provide the foundation for public and private economic policies.[3]

Anyone assessing the growth prospects of the American economy in the 1960's must do so on a basis of somewhat different assumptions than he could have legitimately made 30 or 40 years earlier. Projections of output, employment, income and demand are usually made on the assumption that in the future conditions are likely to prevail which approximate reasonably full employment of the economy's resources. The near universality of this assumption in long-range projections stems in large part from the fact that achievement of such conditions has been incorporated into the Employment Act of 1946 as part of America's national economic objectives. The Employment Act does not purport to guarantee or insure full employment, an adequate rate of growth and a stable rate of prices, but it does commit the federal government, in cooperation with other public and private agencies, to utilize all its plans, functions and resources to promote the accomplishment of these objectives.[4]

---

[2] "Relation of structure and assumption to purpose in making economic projections," a paper presented at the Annual Meeting of the American Statistical Association, September, 1957. See Amer. Stat. Assoc. Proc., Business and Econ. Stat. Sec., 1957, pp. 279-83.

[3] Study Paper No. 20, "The potential economic growth in the United States," by James W. Knowles, assisted by Charles B. Warden, Jr., prepared in connection with the Study of Employment, Growth, and Price Levels, for the Joint Economic Committee, January, 1960 (hereinafter cited as Study Paper No. 20).

[4] Employment Act of 1946, Sec. 2.

With this commitment as the basis of public policy, it is not unreasonable to assume that on the average, reasonably full employment of resources will be achieved within the framework of a stable level of prices and an adequate rate of growth.

While this assumption seems legitimate, and indeed the most useful one for the purposes of this book, several cautions should be kept in mind in using such a projection. Although it is legitimate to assume that public and private policies will strive toward these goals, recognition must be given the fact that unqualified success is not at all certain. In designing policies, allowance must be made for some degree of human error. Furthermore, allowance should be made for the fact that the statistics by which the performance of the economy is measured are far from perfect and, ex post, may reflect some rise in average prices and a somewhat slower rate of growth than in fact occurs. The indexes of output and prices do not appear to be free of bias. Lastly, even if we succeed largely in achieving these objectives, full employment will not necessarily be achieved each and every year from now until eternity. If fluctuations in employment, prices, output and the rate of growth can be held within reasonably narrow limits, this will be success indeed, and no one, I am sure, will be so impractical as to view modest fluctuations in activity as major policy failures.

From the foregoing it follows that in the projections presented below, the following assumptions have been made explicitly:

(1) Prices are assumed to remain reasonably stable during the 1960's and 1970's, the price level being measured in terms of the implicit price deflator for gross national product as computed by the Office of Business Economics, United States Department of Commerce.

(2) The economy is assumed to operate at reasonably full employment with an absence of either war, other disturbing international catastrophies or large and persistent depressions during the period of the projection (1959-1980).

(3) For purposes of this chapter, full employment is defined as representing a state of labor markets such that unemployment as a percent of the civilian labor force will average about 4 percent.[5]

I should, at this point, give a brief explanation of the meaning I attach to a term used throughout this chapter — namely, potential output. In accordance with past usage by myself as well as the staff of the Joint Economic Committee, I shall refer to a "full"

---

[5]Projections given in this chapter are consistent with those in Chapter 4 of Study Paper No. 20 (op. cit.).

employment gross national product measured in constant dollars as potential output. Potential output is not the upper limit to which the economy's rate of output can be pushed and, therefore, it is not a measure of capacity. The distinction here drawn is considered at somewhat greater length in my study for the Joint Economic Committee, and I refer to Chapter I of that paper, especially pages 6 and following, for further development of this point.

The potential output level represents the amount the economy could produce at some stipulated rate of use of the labor force and of capital, and under the assumption that productive resources are used at something approaching the economy's notion of a least-cost combination of inputs. That is, capacity, however conceived, is being operated so as to produce output at the least cost per unit of output, in accordance with the best practices possible with existing management, capital and training and knowledge of the labor force. It is, in a word, a measure of what practical man can do under the usual operating conditions maintainable over long periods of time without excess strain or breakdown, on the one hand, or, on the other, excessive, wasteful slack in the system, particularly prolonged, involuntary unemployment of labor.

In the light of this framework, I shall present projections of the economy's potential output for the years 1960-1980 by five-year intervals. The next step will be the analysis of possible developments on the demand side consistent with this potential output; and, finally, I shall examine some implications of alternative projections.

GROWTH IN POTENTIAL OUTPUT TO 1980

It has been common practice in making long-range projections to derive the estimate of possible output in the target year from projections of population and the corresponding labor force, combined with an assumed rate of change in hours of work and in output per man-hour. Projections are usually made separately for agricultural, governmental and private non-agricultural output, though sometimes the private non-agricultural sector has been further subdivided. This procedure implicitly assumes some type of production function relating output to inputs of labor, capital and other productive resources.

The present projections are made by use of an explicit production function which was derived as the central part of my recent study paper on potential economic growth. The production function was developed as a tool for estimating the economy's output under conditions of sustainable "maximum employment, production and purchasing power." It therefore was designed to have the following characteristics:

1. It should incorporate measures of as many of the identifiable productive resources as is possible in light of availability of data, especially

   (a) labor
   (b) tangible capital: plant, equipment, etc.
   (c) the state of technology and its changes and
   (d) other intangibles such as research, health, education, etc.

2. It should incorporate a procedure for separating changes associated with cyclical and other short-run fluctuations from changes reflecting secular influences.

3. Provision should be made to separate changes in output due to shifts in the production function itself in response to changes in techniques, etc., from changes in output reflecting increases in the supply of the productive services of labor and capital.

4. A procedure is needed for allowing for influences on aggregate output and on the productivity of inputs arising solely out of shifts in demand between goods and services with varying requirements for productive resources — i.e., between those with higher or lower requirements for capital, and higher or lower requirements for labor.

5. If possible, specific provision should be made to measure the influence of changes in quality of inputs and outputs on the production function.

6. Since the absolute magnitudes of the measures of inputs and outputs for the economy as a whole will depend on the particular price structure used to price inputs and outputs and on various conventions of mensuration, these absolute levels will be of little significance. Primary attention must center on changes between time periods — year to year — and on relative proportions between measures in each period. Therefore the form of the function should be chosen so as to operate in terms of rates of change.

The equation for the derived production function was expressed in logs in the following form:

$$\log O_m = -5.43104 + \log L_p + .9104 \log (L_a/L_p) - 3.39[\log (L_a/L_p)]^2 + .35 \log (K/L_p) - 5.6411 \log k + 10.356 (\log k)^2 + X + .00884t$$

where: O_m = computed gross national product in constant 1954 dollars

L_p = potential labor input in man-hours

L_a = actual labor input in man-hours

K = stock of private productive capital exclusive of housing and gross of depreciation in constant prices

k = the average age of the capital stock

X = index adjusting for the influence of changes in the composition of demand on productivity of inputs

and t was measured in years with 1909 as the origin.

The potential output O_p can be computed from the same formula by simply dropping out the cyclical terms involving the ratio L_a/L_p. By using this formula, allowance can be made for the influence on potential output of changes in availability of supplies of labor and capital, in the average age or technological condition of the capital stock, in the progress of technology as measured by the time trend (t) and in the demand mix. The time trend indicates a rate of technological progress of about 2.1 percent per year. The projections, therefore, depend not merely upon the trends in population, labor force and productivity as in the usual projections but also upon explicit assumptions concerning the course of capital investment and the composition of demand.

The projection presented here (corresponding to the medium, or "B" projection in Study Paper 20) assumes that our economic affairs are managed in both the private and public areas so as to attain reasonable success in maintaining maximum employment. It assumes that no deep or prolonged depression will occur and no war, as noted above, but does assume that there will be occasional recessions such as have disturbed the course of economic growth since World War II.

The projection of the labor force, therefore, is derived from a medium projection of the population combined with participation rates which would represent a continuation of recent trends. The labor force projection, therefore, is in about the middle of the range of such projections, particularly those of the Department of Labor.[6] The total labor force, including the armed forces, is

---

[6]See U. S. Bureau of the Census, series P-25, No. 187, Nov. 10, 1958, "Illustrative projections of the population of the United States, by age and sex, 1960 to 1980," and U. S. Bureau of Labor Statistics, Bul. 1242, "Population and labor force projections for the United States, 1960 to 1975."

assumed to rise from about 73 million in 1960 to about 103 million in the year 1980. This increase is equivalent to an annual rate of about 1.7 percent per year. Since a constant rate of unemployment of 4 percent is assumed, total employment, including the armed forces, increases also at a rate of 1.7 percent a year.

Average annual hours of work have tended to decline from 1910 to 1960 at a rate of about 0.6 percent per year. The rate has been considerably faster in recessions or deep and prolonged depressions, such as in the 1930's, and slower in the more prosperous periods. A somewhat slower rate of decline from 1960 to 1980 is assumed, or about 0.5 percent per year.

The combination of the 1.7 percent per year increase in the total labor force, including the armed forces, and an average rate of decline of about 0.5 percent per year in average hours of work produces an assumed average rate of increase in total man-hours of about 1.2 percent per year.

During the 1910 to 1960 period, the stock of private plant and equipment in constant prices has increased about 2.2 percent per year. The rate has varied widely, depending on economic conditions. The rate is substantially higher in prosperous periods and lower in recessions, even declining in the depression of the 1930's. For these projections, the rate of capital accumulation has been assumed to be somewhat more modest than could reasonably be achieved but still consistent with the assumption that serious depression will be avoided, or about 2.7 percent a year. Consistent with this, the average age of the capital stock is assumed to decline almost imperceptibly, or by about 0.1 percent per year — mostly as a result of a faster rate of growth of equipment than of plant.

Changes in the composition of demand tended to add an average of about 0.1 percent per year to the rate of growth in output. In considerable part, this has been a result of the shift from agricultural to non-agricultural production and of shifts between private and public employment. The assumption is made that changes in composition of demand during the 1960's and 1970's would be almost neutral.

These assumptions, when combined through the formula previously cited, produce a rate of growth of potential gross national product in constant prices of about 4 percent per year. Since in 1959 output was about 7 percent below the computed potential for that year, the rate of growth from the actual output of 1959 would be higher than 4 percent per year. This projection gives a rate of growth one-third higher than that achieved in the 1910 to 1960 period. Why? The foremost reason is to be found in the basic assumption that deep, prolonged depressions will be avoided in the 1960's and 1970's. Growth was interrupted between 1929 and 1941 by such a depression. The assumption that this will not be repeated has a pervasive influence on the projections. It affects the rate of growth of the labor force, the rate of decline in hours of work, the rate of accumulation of capital, the speed with which new technology is incorporated in actual production processes and the composition of demand.

For example, during the 1910 to 1960 period the average rate of increase in the capital stock has been only about 2.2 percent a year because of the long period of low investment during the 1930's. In fact, from 1930-31 until 1945 the growth in the gross capital stock was barely sufficient to keep pace with the rise in potential labor input so that the capital-labor ratio remained almost constant for over a decade. There was capital widening but no capital deepening. The assumption that deep and prolonged depression will be avoided in the 1960's and 1970's raises the average rate of growth of the capital stock such that even on the rather modest assumption of a capital stock growth of 2.7 percent a year the capital-labor ratio rises by an average of about 1.5 percent per year. Furthermore, since 1910 the average age of the capital stock has risen in part because of the depression of the 1930's, whereas, on the average, it is likely to fall slightly during the 1960's and 1970's if our assumptions prove to be an accurate reflection of subsequent events.

In general, the assumptions underlying this projection are conservative. Competent students have prepared analyses of historical tendencies and future prospects under reasonably prosperous conditions which, on the basis of the formula used in this chapter, would lead to even higher rates of growth. In Study Paper No. 20 a growth rate of 4.6 percent a year was at the high end of a potential range of possibilities, and the lowest figure that seemed reasonable, if serious depression is avoided, came out only as low as 3.5 percent per year.

Before proceeding further, it should be noted that these projections do not assume any radical or fundamental changes in our economic system. The projected output can be achieved without instituting elaborate controls and without having the government impose a pattern of consumption or a forced-draft high rate of capital accumulation.

If this projection should be realized, then, assuming prices to average the same as in 1949, the potential gross national product would rise from about $514 billion in 1959 to $532 billion in 1960, then to $1,175 billion in 1980. By five-year periods, the figures run as follows:

Years	Potential GNP In 1954 dollars	In 1959 dollars
1959	456 billion	514 billion
1960	473	532
1965	577	649
1970	703	791
1975	856	964
1980	1,044	1,175

DEMAND POSSIBILITIES IN A GROWING ECONOMY

The development of acceptable assumptions respecting the possible future growth of potential output under full employment conditions is a formidable assignment, but to perform the equivalent task for demand presents an even more difficult and hazardous assignment. Not only are there difficulties relating to the detection of trends in expenditures generated by changes in incomes, population and relative prices, there is the further and more challenging task of dealing with the foreseeable fact that most of the goods and services which will be purchased by consumers, business and government 20 years hence have no close counterpart at the present time.

Would a forecaster in 1940 have been able to perceive that in 1960 consumers would be spending very substantial proportions of their budget on such items as television or swimming pools? This difficulty accounts, in part, for the fact that long-range projections are much more likely to be too low than to be too high.

Total government expenditures for goods and services – federal, state, and local – in 1959 amounted to $97.6 billion, or about 20 percent of the gross national product. If past trends prevail during the 1960's and 1970's, this total could increase to about $240 billion, or about the same proportion of the potential gross national product in 1980. Although the proportion of gross national product may be about the same in the two years, the internal composition is likely to change considerably. Unless the international situation changes materially, federal expenditures on national defense programs are likely to increase at a moderate rate – a safe assumption would be approximately $55 billion compared to the 1960 levels of about $45 billion. This assumes that, in spite of the increasing complexity and cost of major defense weapons systems, national defense expenditures can decline from 1960 levels of about 9-10 percent of the gross national product to about 5 percent or less in 1980. In addition to national defense, the federal government faces the prospect of an increase in other civilian expenditures for goods and services as population increases, since most of the civilian programs are directly dependent on the size of the population and the level of personal incomes. These civilian programs, which were about 1.8 percent of gross national product in 1959, are assumed to be only about 1.7 percent by 1980, or perhaps $20 billion. As noted, this does not include transfers.

The major impact of rising demands for government services by a larger and wealthier population is likely to fall upon those types of services which traditionally have been handled mainly by state and local governments. Therefore, state and local government expenditures for goods and services, which have been running a little over 8 percent of gross national product, may increase in two decades to almost double their present share. For present purposes, the share is assumed to grow to about 14 percent, or about $165 billion by 1980. Such an increase is hardly an unreasonable expectation in view of past trends and the prospective increase in population requiring police, fire, court and related services as well as a demand, through a great increase of children and young people, for educational services.

At times when actual output closely approximates potential output, that is, when there are reasonably full employment conditions, there has been a tendency for the share of consumption in total output to be rather stable. As a percentage of the gross national product, it has varied within the limits of 63 to 70 percent, with much of the variation being in the durable goods area. Taking into consideration the prospects for growth of income and population consistent with the projection of potential gross national product, consumer expenditures might average about 67 percent of the gross national product by 1980, which would yield a total of $790 billion in terms of the 1959 price level, or almost two-thirds again as much as the entire gross national product for 1959. If realized, this would mean a rise in per capita consumption from $1,761 to $3,147 in 1959 dollars, or an increase of 79 percent in real per capita consumption over a period of 20 years.

The introduction of new products, changes in social aspirations or tastes, growth in the number of households headed by retired workers, more leisure and changes in the proportions of the population in different age-sex groups are likely to result in substantial changes in consumption patterns. It seems probable, however, that the broad general division of consumption between durable goods, nondurable goods and services will roughly correspond to the relative proportions of high employment years. In this chapter no attempt is made to spell out consumption patterns in detail since this book is mainly concerned with foods, fibers and other products derived from land, and these prospects will be gone into more thoroughly in other chapters.

The growth in potential output at a rate of 4 percent a year during the 1960's and 1970's would require substantial investment each year in new plants, equipment and inventories. Population growth, rising incomes, results of research and development expenditures and competitive pressures, both domestic and foreign, will vastly expand investment opportunities. It must be recognized, however, that just as output per man-hour increases, so it is likely that a long period devoid of war or serious depression would be accompanied by a rise in output per unit of capital. The potential output projections to 1980 of 4 percent a year imply a rate of increase of about 2.8 percent a year in output per man-hour for the economy as a whole. But they also imply a rate of increase of about 1 percent a year in output per unit of capital.

The additional investment for expansion will be a smaller percentage of gross national product in 1980 than it is in 1960. At prices assumed to be at 1960 levels, a 4 percent a year expansion in potential output for the economy as a whole requires an additional investment in business plant and equipment equivalent to about 4.1 percent of gross national product and replacement of old assets about 5.2 percent, or a total of 9.3 percent of gross national product. By 1980, expansion of output at 4 percent per year would require investment of only about 3.0 percent of gross national product and replacement about 4.5 percent, or a total of about 7.5 percent of potential output.

On this basis, business expenditures for plant and equipment could be expected to rise from about $44 billion in 1960 to about $88 billion in 1980. In addition the increase in the potential output would be accompanied by annual additions to inventories, which is assumed to average about 0.5 percent of gross national product, or about $6 billion per year.

A rise in population with accompanying increases in annual family formation can be expected to create substantial demands for residential housing both in total and per family or per person as per capita incomes also rise. If such increases run in line with the expectation of most experts in the field of housing, then in terms of 1960 prices, total expenditures, as we find them in the national income and output accounts, could average about $46 billion per year, or about 4 percent of gross national product.

An important factor in the estimate of future demand is the question of net exports. This is a very difficult area in which to develop assumptions about future growth possibilities. Growing incomes and populations will obviously create growing demands here for both raw materials and finished goods from other countries. It seems safe also to assume that high rates of growth, both in the developed countries, such as Western Europe, and in the underdeveloped countries, are likely to create larger demands for American exports. Certainly this latter would seem likely if general expectations are realized — that many of these countries which in 1960 have per capita incomes below the United States will raise their outputs and incomes at a faster rate per year than does the United States. But though it seems easy to make generalized assertions, the reduction of the possibilities to a consistent and explainable quantitative estimate is beyond my resources. I therefore have assumed arbitrarily that net exports will be slightly under 0.5 percent a year — not far from past experience.

The sum of these estimates of demand possibilities — since they have been largely based on population and income prospects consistent with the potential output already developed — will add up to a gross national expenditure of $1,175 billion.

SOME IMPLICATIONS AND ALTERNATIVES

The first implication of this analysis is that a 4 percent rate of growth is, after all, very conservative. In the past, the United States has been able to devote as much as 10 to 13 percent of the total gross national product to the replacement and expansion of the stock of private plant and equipment. The projections assume that by 1980 only about 7.5 percent will be so used if potential output rises at 4 percent per year. An increase in the rate of growth would raise replacement requirements only slightly and slowly so that devotion of a larger percentage of gross national product to gross investment in plant and equipment would make possible a significantly higher rate of growth. Even the 4.6 percent a year, which was the high estimate presented in Study Paper No. 20, is rather conservative in the light of both past experience and the nation's increasing technological and managerial know-how.

Second, the problem of scarcity of savings, about which there has been so much discussion, may not be a very likely future prospect if conditions work out along the lines outlined above. The potential cash flows to business under the assumed conditions and the flow of personal savings imply savings enough for all private demands. Hence, tight conditions in capital markets would be likely to develop only if the demands for funds to finance by new indebtedness some of the rising costs of state and local governments become too large. If, at high employment levels, ways and means are found to maintain a surplus in the federal budget (which under projected conditions would not be difficult), and state and local governments do not finance too high a proportion of their annual capital outlays by borrowing, then the federal surplus should offset the state and local deficits. The flow of savings should be adequate, therefore, and, indeed, it would be not unexpected if interest rates more often tended to be weak than strong, with the long-run trend toward declining rates reasserting itself.

Finally, I would like to emphasize the implications of these projections for the problem of taxation and state and local financing. If we are to continue to finance the government services for our rising population through state and local channels, substantial innovations clearly will be needed. Newer methods and newer institutions will need to be explored and developed to practical usefulness. Furthermore, state and local tax structures will demand close study. One of the most important automatic stabilizers which contributes to offsetting tendencies toward inflationary expansion, on the one hand, and recession, on the other, is the total federal, state and local tax and expenditure structures which tend to shift from surplus to deficit and back again more rapidly and to a greater proportionate extent than the changes in output, employment and income to which they respond. But this is largely the result of federal rather than state and local fiscal operations. If, during the 1960's and 1970's, the share of the federal government in gross national product declines, as here assumed, and the share of state and local governments rises, the potential contribution of governmental receipts and expenditures to the automatic stabilization of the economy will be seriously impaired.

One of the important problems of stabilization policy, therefore, seems very likely to be the development of new techniques for dealing with these tendencies. This is particularly true in view of the prospective demands upon state and local governments and the sources from which they can raise additional revenue. Though much attention is given, and rightly, to needed reforms in the federal tax structure, it seems likely that reforms in state and local tax will be a much more difficult and important problem, while reform of the federal tax structure is likely to grow easier and perhaps to be of lesser significance. This conclusion, of course, is readily apparent from the practical consideration that federal tax reform can be made within the framework of a series of tax reductions, while state and local authorities face the more difficult task of bringing about tax reforms in the face of a need for ever larger receipts from taxes to finance continually rising expenditures.

Chapter 3

NATHAN M. KOFFSKY
Agricultural Marketing
Service, USDA

Potential Demand for Farm Products

THE PURPOSE of this chapter is to translate the kind of economic growth projected by James Knowles into the potential demands for farm products over the next several decades. In the post-war period, we have realized a somewhat faster rate of economic growth than in our previous history — marred only by relatively mild interruptions or recessions. We have gained confidence in our economic potential from the prosperous fifties and have entered into the "golden sixties." We look ahead now some 20-25 years under the basic assumption of a continuing prosperity, a process that has been aptly described as the "art of crawling on the ceiling." We should note that with our new projection, we encompass some 40 years or so of rapid economic growth — a period of time approaching that associated with the long-run economic cycle described in business cycle literature. This is only to suggest that as we go along in the years ahead we may need to be concerned even more with how to maintain rapid growth. Fortunately for agriculture, consumer incomes have been well maintained during the post-war recessions and the demand for food was not significantly affected.

The last several years have witnessed a flowering of long-term projections for agriculture. We now have on hand projections of demand for farm products for 1965, 1975, 1980, 2000 and 2010. These include:

Prospects for Agriculture in a Growing Economy, by Barton and Daly, projecting to 1965 and 1975, presented at the Conference on Problems and Policies of American Agriculture in October, 1958.[1]

A 50-Year Look Ahead at U. S. Agriculture. U. S. Department of Agriculture, June, 1959, projected to the year 2010.

[1] Published in Problems and Policies of American Agriculture. Iowa State University Press, Ames, Iowa, 1959, pp. 28-46.

Land and Water Potentials and Future Requirements for Water. A report made by the department at the request of the Select Committee on National Water Resources, United States Senate, December, 1959, projecting demands to 1980 and 2000.

The projections of potential demand for farm products which follow are for 1980 as developed for the report to the Senate mentioned above. Let me acknowledge that they are not essentially different from the 1975 projections presented by Daly and Barton in 1958, but do coordinate in time with the other projections presented in this book. The Daly-Barton paper was well documented in terms of the data and relationships and procedures used, and I will not attempt to repeat what they have done. Rather, let me indicate the major rules or guide-lines for projecting demand which provide a sort of do-it-yourself kit.

1. Population growth. How fast our population grows will largely determine the potential demand for farm products. The domestic market for U.S. farm products accounts for some 90 percent of the total market, and food uses account for about 90 percent of the total domestic market. By 1960, population was increasing about 1.6 percent a year. By 1980, according to the projections of Resources for the Future, which provided the basic framework for the Senate Committee Study, population of the U.S. could range from a low of 225 million to a high of 278 million, depending on possible future rates of fertility, net immigration, etc. (This is a somewhat wider range than the Census Bureau projections of from 231 million to 273 million.) The medium projection of 244 million persons is at about the middle of the range. Thus, population could increase by 50 to 100 million persons by 1980, or from 30 to 60 percent. Since 1940, population has increased some 35 percent. It is worth noting that the possible range in population that might be forthcoming by 1980 is much wider than the excess of farm output over commercial takings of farm products in the 1950's.

There is a corollary question as to whether the changing age composition of the population will have a significant effect on the per capita takings of food. Much of the increase in population will likely come in the younger age groups, particularly heavy-eating teen-agers, but also in the older age brackets. By and large, these would appear to be offsetting in their effect on average per capita food consumption.[2]

2. Economic growth and per capita consumption of farm

[2]R. Lifquist. Jour. Farm Econ. Dec., 1958, p. 1289.

products. The effect of economic growth and rising consumer incomes on food consumption per person is relatively small and appears to be diminishing. Total pounds of food consumed per person remain much the same, but there has been a substantial upgrading in the average consumer diet and considerable shifts among the several foods (Fig. 3.1). In 1960 we ate on the average over 100 pounds more meat and livestock products than in 1935, but less cereals and potatoes by an equal amount. Shifts and trends such as those illustrated in the chart have been influenced by the search for better nutrition, by innovations in production and marketing and, particularly in the case of butter and margarine, by the price factor.

This upgrading in diet is reflected in the Department's index of per capita food use, inasmuch as it is a price-weighted index giving allowance to the trend toward more expensive foods — a factor which has meaning for the farmer since more resources are required to produce a pound of meat than a pound of grain. Thus, since 1940 the index of per capita consumption of food has risen about 10 percent. In the post-war period, there are some indications, as Daly reported in 1958, that the long-term income elasticity of demand for domestically produced food of about 0.20 may be getting smaller. The same may be the case for price elasticities — and prices appear to be somewhat more sensitive to changes in supplies than before World War II. It is logical that as purchasing power rises (at the rate of 2 percent or more a year), more and more people are eating the kinds of food they want to eat. If we apply this income elasticity of food consumed to the projected 45 percent increase in real income per person, per capita food consumption might rise an additional 9 or 10 percent by 1980.

There is some support for this estimate from the cross-section analysis of the 1955 Survey of Food Consumption.[3] When we compare indexes of per person food consumption for the average income group, $4000 to $5000, with the group some 50 percent higher, the latter shows an increase of 8 percent. These cross-section indexes also show a leveling off at about that income level, suggesting that after 1980 further gains in food consumption per capita might well be quite negligible.

As our trend chart has indicated, the response to income growth varies among the major food groups. Table 3.1 shows the historical income and price elasticities for major groups of farm food products. All that is new here as compared with the Daly

[3]USDA, National Food Situation, July, 1959, p. 17 ff.

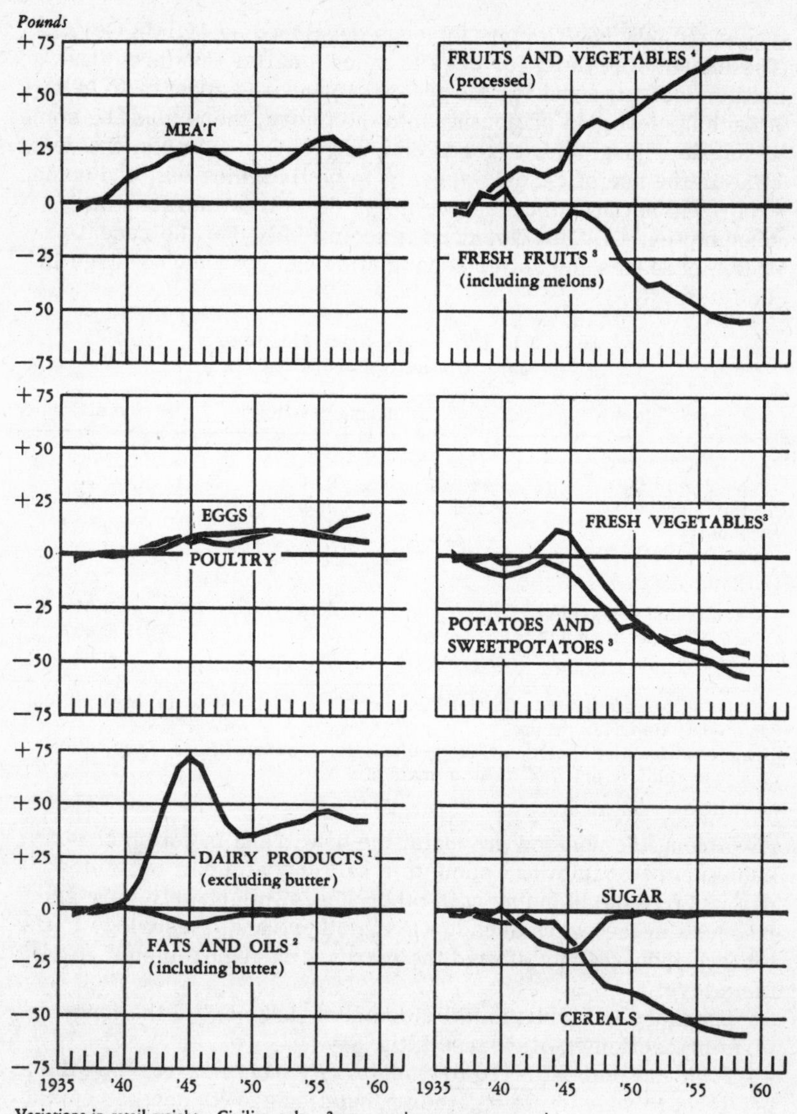

Variations in retail weight. Civilian only. 3-year moving average centered.

[1] Product weight, except milk and cream content of ice cream.

[2] Fat content.

[3] Includes home garden produce.

[4] Includes frozen concentrated citrus juice on single strength basis.

Fig. 3.1. Changes in food consumption, from 1935-39 average per capita.

paper are new coefficients for eggs developed by Martin Gerra.[4] The income elasticity for eggs is much smaller than previous studies indicated and for all practical purposes appears to be approaching zero. In projecting into the future, there must be some measure of judgment. Trends do change. For example, the decline in the use of cereals appears to be flattening out, and some experts in nutrition suggest we might do well to increase our consumption a little. Nor does it seem likely that the recent sharp increases in broiler consumption can continue as large in the future.

Table 3.1. Income and Price Elasticities
For Major Groups of Farm Products

Item	Income elasticity	Price elasticity
Livestock products		
Meat animals	0.48	-0.30
Dairy products [a]	0.09	-0.05
Poultry	0.62	-0.50 [c]
Eggs	0.04	-0.10
Crops		
Fruits and vegetables	0.16	-0.06
Cereals, potatoes and beans	-0.23	0.002
Other crops [b]	0.16	-0.02

[a] Based on price weighted combined consumption of fat and nonfat milk solids.
[b] Excluding imported crops.
[c] This equation also included a cross elasticity of demand for poultry with respect to relative price of meat animals of 0.05.

Among the nonfood products, the downtrend in cotton consumption per capita has come to a halt and with new technology, particularly the blending with other fibers, might well show some increase in the years ahead. On the other hand, technology in the tobacco industry has slowed the increase in requirements at the farm level.

So, there is a substantial element of judgment in the long-term projection do-it-yourself kit.

3. Total domestic requirements. We have now reached the point where we can put together population growth and per capita consumption and arrive at some total domestic requirements for farm products (Table 3.2). According to the rate of population growth assumed, domestic use of all farm products might increase

[4] Martin Gerra, "The demand and price structure for eggs," USDA Tech. Bul. 1204.

from 50 to 80 percent by 1980, with meat animals showing a larger rise. However, feed requirements do not rise as much, reflecting the trend toward rising feeding efficiencies per animal. Nonfood uses are projected to rise somewhat faster than food uses. This could well occur in view of the expanding research effort in this field.

Table 3.2. Total Requirements For Farm Products, 1954 and 1958, and Projections to 1980

(Index numbers, 1954=100)

Item	1954	1958 total	Projections 1980 total		
			Low	Medium	High
Population	100	107	139	150	171
Domestic utilization of					
all farm products	100	106	157	169	192
Food	100	107	155	167	189
Nonfood	100	101	171	185	211
Livestock products:					
Food	100	107	156	168	190
Meat animals	100	104	162	175	199
Dairy products	100	107	148	160	182
Poultry	100	129	168	182	206
Eggs	100	99	137	148	168
Nonfood	100	86	105	114	129
Crops:					
Food	100	107	152	165	188
Cereals and potatoes	100	102	129	136	151
Fruits and vegetables	100	113	164	176	201
Nonfood	100	113	138	150	171
Feed and seed	100	117	131	143	162
Other	100	100	164	177	201
Exports total	100	136	172	172	172
Livestock exports	100	126	100	100	100
Crop exports	100	138	188	188	188

Source: "Land and water potentials and future requirements for water," a report by USDA to the Select Committee on National Water Resources, U. S. Senate.

These projections of consumption assume a price situation over-all much the same as we have had in recent years — that is, a price index for farm products of 240-250 on a 1910-14 base.

4. Foreign requirements. Our colleagues in the Foreign Agricultural Service developed estimates of the potential foreign commercial demand for U. S. agricultural products for the purposes of the Senate Committee report. These were based on projections by the United Nations of population growth in the rest of

the world, some increase in real per capita income and some improvement in diets in underdeveloped areas. They also assessed the likely trends of production in other surplus-producing areas and their ability to meet world needs. Summarizing very briefly, the major opportunities for increases in commercial channels appear to be for fats and oils, particularly in low-income areas, and for feed grains in Europe, where an increasing volume of imports will be required for an expanding livestock industry (Table 3.3).

Table 3.3. Foreign Commercial Demand For Selected United States Agricultural Products, Average 1950-54, 1954 and 1956, and Projection 1980

Commodity	Unit	Exports[a] Average 1950-54	1954	1956	Projection 1980
Cotton	Mil. bales	4.0	3.8	7.6	7.6
Tobacco	Mil. lbs.	474	462	510	440
Wheat	Mil. bu.	330	274	546	390
Rice	Mil. cwt.	13.8	8.9	26.3	21
Feed grains	Mil. cwt.	100	155	136	305
Fats and oils[b]	Mil. lbs.	2,882	2,897	4,950	8,500
Index[c]	1950-51 to 1954-55=100	100	99	161	186

[a] Year beginning January 1 for tobacco, July 1 for wheat and feed grain, August 1 for cotton and rice and October 1 for fats and oils.
[b] Including oil equivalent of oil seeds.
[c] Index calculated on market value basis.

Source: "Land and water potentials and future requirements for water," *op. cit.*

On this basis, an increase in our exports of some 25 percent is projected from 1958 to 1980 (also Table 3.2). With economic growth proceeding rapidly in Europe, some additional optimism over commercial export potentials has been generated, particularly for feed grains and poultry which have shown substantial gains during 1960. Further, it is difficult to assess how the role of food might develop in the economic cold war between East and West and the needs of newly emerging countries. To keep perspective, we need to remember that we export about 10 percent of our production, including a substantial amount under Public Law 480. While events may turn out that exports might rise appreciably beyond those projected, the effect on total requirements — the sum of domestic and foreign — would not be large. For example, we could double the level of exports by 1980, and total requirements would rise 5 percent or less. Further, the possible alternative levels of exports that might prevail 20 or 25 years ahead will probably depend to a considerable extent on how well domestic demands are met. In other words, if our population increases relatively slowly, a higher level of exports is more likely than if population and domestic requirements increase rapidly.

Total Requirements

Table 3.4 summarizes for major crops the projected requirements, domestic and foreign, for 1980 according to the 3 population projections. It can be seen that for some commodities, production in 1958 was within or above the range of projected requirements. These include wheat, rye, potatoes, soybeans, flaxseed, grain sorghums and, in 1959, corn. Pasture production would need to increase by 30-60 percent from 1958 to support the increase in output required in the livestock sector.

Table 3.4. Production of Major Crops, 1954 and 1958, and Projected Requirements in 1980

Commodity	Unit	Production		Projected requirements 1980		
		1954	1958	Low	Medium	High
Corn	Mil. bu.	3,058	3,800	4,310	4,643	5,234
Oats	Mil. bu.	1,410	1,422	1,551	1,683	1,905
Barley	Mil. bu.	379	470	720	769	858
Sorghums	Mil. bu.	235	615	354	381	428
Hay	Mil. tons	108	122	137	149	170
Cotton	Thous. bales	13,890	12,059	21,296	22,247	24,507
Tobacco	Mil. lb.	2,244	1,758	2,697	2,734	3,001
Wheat	Mil. bu.	984	1,462	1,217	1,287	1,411
Rye	Mil. bu.	26	32	28	30	33
Rice (rough)	Mil. cwt.	53	43	64	66	71
Potatoes	Mil. cwt.	220	266	257	278	317
Sweetpotatoes	Mil. cwt.	17	17	27	28	32
Sugar (raw):						
Beets	Thous. tons	2,186	2,202	2,654	2,654	2,654
Cane	Thous. tons	610	579	757	757	757
Dry beans	Mil. lb.	1,694	1,898	2,079	2,254	2,567
Soybeans	Mil. bu.	341	574	512	532	568
Flaxseed	Mil. bu.	41	40	37	39	43
Peanuts (farmers' stock)	Mil. lb.	1,008	1,886	2,283	2,449	2,744
Cottonseed	Thous. tons	5,709	4,798	6,889	7,467	8,502

Source: "Land and water potentials and future requirements for water," *op. cit.*

In view of the surplus situation and prospective continuing feeding efficiencies, total farm output would need to increase about 35 percent from the 1958 level to meet requirements for the low population projection, about 45 percent for the medium projection and 60 percent for the high projection. Also, in 1958 some 27 million acres were in the acreage reserve and conservation reserve of the Soil Bank.

We have not made allowance for possible changes in requirements for stocks. Clearly in the case of wheat, there would be no need for a higher "normal" carryover than presently — and very substantially below the existing carryover stocks level. For corn, "normal" stocks in 1980 might well be 30-50 percent greater than present needs — but again still substantially below what we actually have. For cotton, we might well consider an increase of 50 percent in our "normal" stock level by 1980 — perhaps not much different than the level of stocks we have at present.

SUMMARY

What have we learned from our exercise? In essence it is that agriculture faces a wide range of possibilities. If population grows slowly, there is little prospect, in view of current technology and persistently rising costs, for demands to rise fast enough to alter significantly the current situation of surpluses and lagging incomes in agriculture. If, on the other hand, population increases rapidly, we may be hard put to meet requirements, and the low price elasticities for farm products which are agriculture's weakness today, could become a source of strength in terms of the prices and incomes that farmers might then realize. Crop and livestock inventory requirements could add some further tightness. We might well have to find room not only for 100 million more people, but also for 100 million more livestock.

Considering the range in possibilities, it is very difficult to be dogmatic. To narrow the range appreciably, we need to be able to project population with closer tolerances. Perhaps as a nation we should aim at the mid-point as being the most likely, recognizing that demands could be plus or minus some 10 percent or so. In our programs, we might hope to retain enough flexibility so that if either eventuality occurs, we would not be unduly embarrassed.

Chapter 4

MARION CLAWSON[1]
Resources for the Future
Washington, D. C.

Potential Demand for Nonfarm Products and Services Provided by Agricultural Lands

THE AWKWARD TITLE of this chapter reflects the difficulty of finding a simple word or phrase to describe the subject. The other chapters will deal with agriculture (including grazing) and forestry. I shall single out for treatment three other kinds of land use: for urban purposes, for recreation and for transportation. These three uses are alike in that each is small in area compared to the large amount used for agriculture, grazing and forestry; each is alike in great importance, if measured in terms of the monetary values involved and numbers of people affected; and each is alike in that the area used has been growing rapidly in the past and will continue to grow in the future. Moreover, each of these land uses may have a significant indirect effect upon the larger uses for agriculture and forestry.

LAND FOR URBAN PURPOSES

The United States is an urban nation, and will become even more urbanized in the future. From less than 10 percent of the total population in cities during the first half century of the nation's existence, the cities have grown until they include two-thirds of the total population (Table 4.1). By the year 2000 they will include over 80 percent. Impressive as is this growth in terms of total population, the cities have grown in other and less easily measurable ways. Probably an equal proportion of physical wealth is situated in the cities, and likewise an equal proportion of gainful employment. In terms of economic and political power, the cities have grown also. Certainly cities are centers

[1]The views expressed herein are entirely personal, not those of the author's organization. The analysis draws heavily on the publication, Land for the Future, by Marion Clawson, Burnell Held and C. H. Stoddard, published by the Johns Hopkins Press, 1960.

Table 4.1. Total and Urban Population, Number and Average Size of Cities, and Area of Cities, By Census Periods 1790 to 1950, and Projections to 1980 and 2000

	Population[a]			Cities[a]		
Year	Total (1,000)	Urban[b] (1,000)	Urban as percent of total[c]	Number	Average population[c]	Area in cities[d] (1,000 acres)
1790	3,929	202	5	24	8,420	54
1800	5,308	322	6	33	9,760	80
1810	7,240	525	7	46	11,400	116
1820	9,638	693	7	61	11,400	154
1830	12,866	1,127	9	90	12,300	241
1840	17,069	1,845	11	131	14,100	375
1850	23,192	3,544	15	236	15,000	720
1860	31,443	6,217	20	392	15,900	1,200
1870	39,818	9,902	25	663	15,000	1,958
1880	50,156	14,130	28	939	15,100	2,785
1890	62,948	22,106	35	1,348	16,400	4,190
1900	75,995	30,160	40	1,737	17,300	5,545
1910	91,972	41,400	45	2,262	18,300	7,450
1920	105,711	54,158	51	2,722	19,900	9,535
1930	122,775	68,955	56	3,165	21,800	11,780
1940	131,669	74,424	56	3,464	21,500	12,800
1950-						
old	150,697	88,927	59	4,023	22,100	15,040
new	150,697	96,468	64	4,741	20,300	16,750
1980	240,000	185,000	77	8,100	22,900	30,300
2000	310,000	255,000	82	10,400	24,500	41,000

[a] Data from census publications. All data apply to the 48 continental states.
[b] In towns and cities of 2,500 and over, except for the 1950 "new" which includes some smaller urban places.
[c] Slide rule divisions.
[d] Estimates made by author, described in Land for the Future, (in press) Johns Hopkins Press, 1960. These data are primarily for cities as political units; they exclude some land used for urban purposes outside of cities, but probably include some land inside of cities used for other purposes. Standard metropolitan areas are roughly 10 times larger, and include much farm, forest and other nonurban land. See discussion in book.

of finance, insurance, marketing and many other economic activities. In spite of a system of government which heavily overweights rural areas in political strength, both nationally and in most states, the greater population of the cities will shortly submerge the rural areas entirely, as far as political strength is concerned. Because we were so much more rural in the past, our society and even our economy is still rural value-oriented, but this, too, is changing. As one who grew up in rural and small-town areas, and who yet dislikes large cities, I recite these facts without enthusiasm; but facts they are, nonetheless.

It is obvious to even the casual observer that cities and suburbs have taken much land. There has been much misunderstanding about this, some from agricultural people. Occasionally there has appeared some anti-city sentiment, as though the city were an enemy of the country. The fact is, it has been population growth, not city growth as such, which has taken so much land from agricultural production for site purposes. Had the increased population been spread mostly in open country, far more land would have been required for site uses. If we must have much larger populations, then cities are the most efficient place to put people, if we want to save land. There has been confusion in other directions also. Growth of city population has increased the market for farm commodities, and this in turn has stimulated agricultural output and, to some extent, development of land for agriculture. It should be recalled that one of the few serious studies of the withdrawal of land from farms to city use found that the area of land in farms actually increased for all metropolitan areas as a whole, from 1929 to 1954.[2] If the agricultural technological revolution of the first half of the 1900's had occurred while total national population was remaining constant, how much land would we have had in crops by 1960? The relations between urban growth and agricultural land use are more subtle than merely putting last year's field into this year's subdivision.

Over the decades, the number of cities has increased, and their average population has grown larger also. From an average population of slightly over 8,000 at the first census, the average city had grown to over 22,000 in 1950 (by the same definition). Small cities grew to middle sized ones, and the latter to large ones, while hamlets were becoming small cities, for this long period. The definition of urban population changed in 1950, and strict comparisons are not possible with earlier figures. Our calculations are that the average size of city will rise further in the future. As we shall see in a moment, this affects land use by cities.

When it comes to the area of land used for urban purposes, we are seriously handicapped by lack of accurate and relevant data. One reason why data are so deficient is that we lack useful

---

[2] Donald J. Bogue. Metropolitan Growth and the Conversion of Land to Nonagricultural Uses, published jointly by Scripps Foundation for Research in Population Problems, Miami University, and Population Research and Training Center, University of Chicago, 1956.

concepts or definitions of urban land use. Two ideas need distinguishing: (1) the city (or its inhabitants) use land, for private and public purposes of many kinds; and (2) they withdraw land from other uses, but do not use all of it. As nearly as I have been able to determine, the withdrawn but idle area is almost as large as the used area. That is, as far as other land uses are concerned, the total area withdrawn by the city is unavailable to their use, but only half or a little more of it is actually used for urban purposes. The rest consists of vacant lots, leap-frogged areas and idle fringes around cities, where mounting land values, taxes and other charges have driven agriculture out. A second difficulty is that we need data for cities as economic units, whereas most data are for cities as political units. Some cities, as legal political units, include farm or other non-urban land; but they also exclude much urban land.[3]

In Table 4.1 we find estimates of the area within cities, from the earliest census to the present, and projections for 1980 and 2000. These most nearly conform to withdrawn area, rather than to used area, and are for political rather than for economic cities. Some urban land is omitted and some non-urban land is included; thus to some extent errors or deficiencies in data balance each other off. The data probably are a good index as to changes in area, and a reasonably good estimate of the magnitude of the withdrawn area. The total area in cities was small during our early history, reaching a million acres only a few years before the Civil War. It has increased more rapidly in recent decades, and by 1960 stood at roughly 1 percent of the total land area of the nation. On the basis of the projected population increases, land in cities will nearly double between 1950 and 1980 and will increase further by 2000. Even at the latter date, the total area will be only a little more than 2 percent of the total land area.

If the data on urban population and city area were plotted on semilog paper, or converted to index numbers, it would be seen that the area has not risen as rapidly as the population. The average density of all cities rises as their population increases.[4] This has been true since 1900, for all cities for which we have data on area as well as population, and the relationship has stayed remarkably constant. As a city grows, its density changes in its older parts, as well as spreading to new territory. Small cities

[3] The data problem is more complicated than there is space here to discuss in detail. The interested reader is referred to footnote 1.

[4] In 1950 the relationship between urban population density and city size can be expressed in the formula $Y = 3295 \log X - 10{,}500$, where Y is per persons per square mile of city area and X is total number of persons in the city.

are our most lavish users of land. In 1950 cities of less than 25,000 used half the total area in all cities, although they had only about a fourth of the urban population. Many observers have assumed that average city densities have declined because the suburbs, where population growth is most clearly evident, have a lower average density than older parts of the same cities. But this overlooks the increases in density of the older parts of cities, as old homes are converted to slum apartments, as new and larger apartment buildings rise, and as other changes occur. It also overlooks the fact that the population growth in suburbs to a large extent takes the place of growth which otherwise would occur in small towns and cities, where densities are still lower.

As we look to the future, we can be fairly sure that cities will take away from agriculture, and from most other land uses, just about any land they want. Urban use of land is so much more intensive than agricultural use, that city people can and will outbid farm people for land, whenever the land is in real demand for city use. Moreover, I think we must concede that the projected expansion of urban area does not pose any real threat to agriculture as a whole, nor does it suggest a shortage of food and fiber because of lack of land. Urban expansion will create agricultural disturbances in those areas where urban growth is rapid. But, in my opinion, attempts to stop urban expansion are doomed to failure; farmers themselves are too eager to get the higher prices for their land which urban expansion usually brings, to cite but one reason.

The real issues, it seems to me, are different. The real question is, what kind of cities are being built on the land taken from other uses? Few observers are satisfied with the kinds of cities we are building. They have been attacked as inefficient, unnecessarily costly, unaesthetic, subject to high obsolescence and otherwise less than they could be. We cannot get into a comprehensive critique of the modern city here, even were I capable of making it. But we can point to the inefficient use of land by the typical city. By careful land use planning and sound urban development, all of the projected increase in urban population could take place on 35 instead of 41 million acres by 2000; perhaps even on 30 million acres. A saving of 5 or 10 million acres of land, when we now have a farm surplus of perhaps 40 million acres, may not seem large, or important. But it should be borne in mind that this potential saving in urban land is located in some of the most important and strategic areas of the United States.

If agricultural people have a right to demand that city people make a more efficient use of the land they take, they also have a responsibility to help provide the institutional and legal framework necessary for sound urban development. The modern city, as a political unit, lacks the legal powers necessary for it to assume its proper economic responsibilities. This is especially marked for the large metropolitan centers, typically made up of several cities. There is no legal entity with power to carry out planning and development for what is a single economic unit. By and large, our rural-dominated state legislatures have been unwilling to give cities the tools with which to use land efficiently, or otherwise to develop on sound lines. If we are really concerned about loss of farm land to suburban development, let us tackle the needed remedies.

LAND FOR RECREATION

In a modern high-income society, recreation may become as important as food, shelter, clothing or other so-called basic expenditure items. Moreover, it may be argued that the use of leisure has been as influential in forming a social structure and an economy as has been the form of work. Whatever we may think about the psychological or other need for recreation, by the average citizen, we can be sure that he will demand it, if allowed to spend his income as he chooses. Recreation includes many kinds of activities; I shall focus here on public outdoor recreation, as a user of land. We have very little data on use of private land for recreation; the area of land so used is likely to be included in statistics on forestry or on agriculture.

Four factors capable of statistical expression have together led to a greatly increased usage of outdoor recreation areas. First, total population has risen, as we all know. The trends toward greater urbanization and toward more older people in the population have also perhaps affected the demand for outdoor recreation. Secondly, increases in real income per capita have greatly increased the demand for recreation. Apparently a larger percentage of income is spent for recreation as income rises, and certainly a larger total sum is so spent. Thirdly, there has been a great increase in leisure as the average work week has declined so greatly over the past century. Fourth, improved travel facilities have led to greatly increased movement of people, much of which is for recreation purposes. The trend in each of these four factors has been upward for many years, and at something like the same general rates. Hence, it is almost impossible to separate the effects of each. The usually accepted outlook is for further upward trends for each — more people, higher real incomes per person, more leisure and greater travel. Other factors perhaps have been or will be important also but are less readily capable of statistical expression.

It is helpful to separate all outdoor recreation into three general classes. First, there is user-oriented outdoor recreation. This must be located near where people live, so that it can be used after work or after school. City parks and playgrounds are the best example of such areas. Second, there are resource-based areas. Here, the superb quality of the scenery and other features is sufficient to draw people from long distances. The time and cost of getting to such areas means that they are usually used for vacations. National parks and seashore areas are illustrative of this class. Thirdly, there are intermediate areas — intermediate as to location, intermediate as to quality. Most such areas must be within two hours, and preferably within one-half hour, travel time of most users. They are mostly day outing areas. Many state parks fall into this category. These broad classes are not clearly separate and distinct, but represent major divisions on a continuum according to location, time of use, natural quality, cost of use and several other factors.

The trend in use of user-oriented areas has apparently been about 4 percent increase annually. (I say apparently because our data are poorer for this type of area than for others.) This is twice the rate of increase in total population, or about equal to the increase in total population times the increase in per capita income. The trend in usage of both other major types has been in the general magnitude of 10 percent annually. These rates of increase have prevailed for as long a period as we have data — since 1910 for the national parks and for shorter periods for other areas. The rates of increase have been remarkably constant on semi-log paper, except for the war when gasoline and other rationing reduced recreation travel greatly. Even major depressions have reduced the rate of growth comparatively little. There is no real evidence of a slowing down in rate of growth of usage of these areas.

The situation for 1956 and 2000 for each of the three major types of areas is shown in Table 4.2. The area available in 1956 in each case was less than specialists consider desirable, although no specific estimates of the latter have been made for resource-based areas. The projected increases in usage between 1956 and 2000 are large — an increase of 4 times for user-oriented areas, of 16 times for intermediate areas, and of 40 times for resource-based areas, or an over-all increase of 10 times. These may seem like very large increases. The reader should be warned that most recreation specialists think my estimates are too high; but they will also concede that all their past

Table 4.2. Recreation Use and Area, 1956 and 2000

Use and area	Type of recreation: User-oriented[a]	Intermediate[b]	Resource-based[c]
1956			
million visits	1,000 plus	312	116
actual area - million acres	0.7	9[d]	45[e,g]
adequate area - million acres	2.0	15[f]	
2000			
million visits	3,750 plus	5,000	5,000
adequate area - million acres	5.0	70[h]	60[i]

[a] Using city and county parks as an index of this type.
[b] Using state parks and federal reservoirs as a measure of this type.
[c] Using the national park system, national forests and federal wildlife refuges as a measure of this type.
[d] State parks, 5.1 million acres; remainder, federal reservoirs.
[e] Includes area of national park system, federal wildlife refuges and national forests used primarily for recreation; additional areas are available for recreation and add value to specialized recreation areas.
[f] Assuming area of state parks doubled and of federal reservoirs unchanged.
[g] No estimate made.
[h] Assuming reservoir areas of 20 million acres and state parks of 50 million acres.
[i] Assuming some increase in federal areas used primarily or solely for recreation.

estimates have been too low, and that a mere projection of past trends will lead to much larger figures than these.

It is possible, though difficult, to estimate an "adequate" area of each type for 2000. Whether such an area will be provided or not is primarily a political rather than an economic question. Decisions about park and recreation areas in the past have not been decided primarily on economic grounds, and it seems unlikely that they will be in the future. If the area actually provided falls too seriously short of the adequate, then some of the demand will not eventuate, because over-crowding will reduce the attractiveness of the areas greatly. But there will be a demand, in at least some senses of the term, for much larger areas than now.

The user-oriented areas are now mostly included within the statistics for urban area, and this is true also of the increased area required. Hence no major additional drain on agricultural land will arise from this source. A large part of the additional resource-based areas will come from land not now in farms — much of it in federal ownership now, used for forestry or grazing, or not used at all.

Our attention thus focuses on the increases in intermediate

type areas. I have argued elsewhere that it is especially important that these areas expand, for that will go far toward taking the pressure off the national parks.[5] The increase in federal reservoir area from about 4 million acres in 1960 to about 20 million in 2000 will be primarily for purposes other than recreation — municipal and industrial water, storage to maintain low flows for waste disposal, flood control and others. But such areas will have great value for outdoor recreation, especially for those kinds using water surfaces. I consider desirable a tenfold increase in state park area. It is possible to make good state parks. The recipe goes like this: Take a piece of rolling countryside, perhaps somewhat eroded, with a modest valley that has 10 to 50 square miles of drainage area; build a low, fixed-outlet dam to create an artificial lake of a few hundred acres with a constant shore line; plant trees on the surrounding areas, if necessary; add roads, picnic facilities and the like; and in 20 years you have a really nice outdoor recreation area. It will not rival Yosemite or Yellowstone or Grand Canyon, but it will provide good swimming, boating and fishing. Hiking and picnicking and camping will be possible and enjoyable. There are several such state parks in most states, and there could be scores more. Such areas, if located within an hour's travel time, or less, would fill a very real role in the outdoor recreation needs of this country.

If the increase estimated as desirable should take place in recreation areas, this would add about 75 million acres to public recreation (excluding the city parks, which are included in urban area also). Probably no more than two-thirds of this would be in farms, and perhaps less than half of the latter would be in crops. After all, the topographic and other qualities which often make for good parks frequently mean poor farmland. Thus, even at my estimates — considered large by most recreation specialists — something on the rough order of 25 million acres of cropland would be required. This would include the land flooded by reservoirs as well, if the latter have recreation values. In light of the total cropland situation, and the possibilities of substantial surplus areas, these requirements for recreation do not seem unattainable.

My estimates are for 2000. If they are to be realized, by and large a disproportionate percentage of the needed area should be reserved during the 1960 to 1980 period. The area of land owned primarily for private recreation may also increase; but in the future, as at present, such land is likely to be included in statistics on forest or other land use.

---

[5]Marion Clawson. "Our national parks in the year 2000," National Parks Magazine, July, 1959.

LAND FOR TRANSPORTATION

Transportation facilities are one major means whereby land is given productivity and value. In our commercial economy, products of the land must be transported to market if they are to have value; and production goods must be brought to the land from their place of manufacture. The land taken out of direct production for transportation purposes may thus be the most productive of all land.

In the United States, for as long a period as we have tolerably accurate records, the really significant trends have been toward modest increases in area of land for transportation purposes, combined with large increases in output of transportation facilities (Fig. 4.1). The area of land taken for railroad rights-of-way must have increased greatly from 1830, when railroads first began, until 1890, when the railroad network of the nation had about reached its present extent. After that date there was a modest increase in area of right-of-way, and then a still more modest decline in mileage and area as local railroads were abandoned. Railroad freight tonnage reflects changing business conditions to a major extent, but a strong over-all upward trend is evident. Passenger traffic on railroads has had a more erratic but more strongly downward trend, on the whole, since 1920.

The area of land in road rights-of-way increased from 1904, when the first data are available, to 1921. Since the latter date, the increase in area has been very modest indeed. This is contrary to a common impression. Another part of the story is that the quality of roads has increased vastly over this period. Roads have been widened, straightened and hard surfaced. This has taken some additional area. Not as obvious has been a reduction in unimproved road mileage, especially in areas which experienced major land use changes. In the Great Plains, northern Lake States and other areas where land once farmed has now become grazing or forest land, some roads have been abandoned. Never highly improved, their area has rather quickly reverted to grass or trees. These have offset in part the large increases for superhighways and other major roads. Roads often lie in valleys, where land is usually good for agriculture; but some rights-of-way include hilly areas of low productivity. In contrast, the volume of passenger traffic on roads has mounted steadily and rapidly, with only a modest interruption during the "great depression" and a larger one during the war when travel was rationed in various ways.

The area in airports increased considerably from 1930 to 1960, but is still small, relative to either road or railroad area,

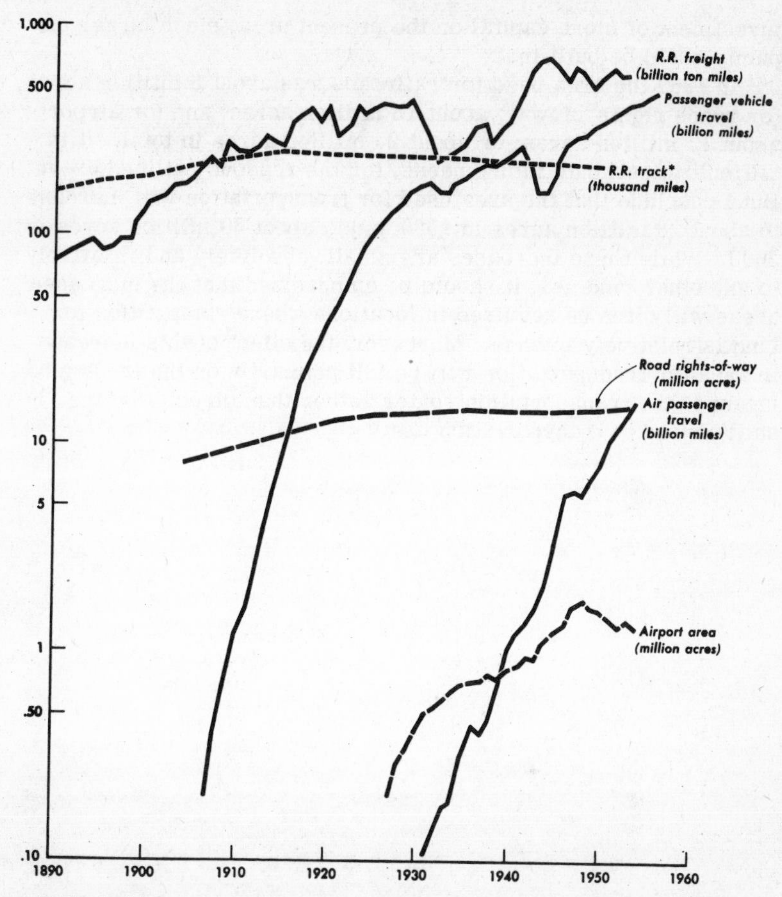

**Railroad mileage "owned"; miles of trackage operated is greater due to double and triple trackage.*

Fig. 4.1. Area and output of major transportation systems, 1890 to date.

and still smaller compared to other major land uses. The trend in air passenger travel has been steeply upward, roughly paralleling the trend in auto travel of 25 or 30 years earlier. While the rate of increase in auto travel has slackened off considerably, the rate of increase in air travel shows no such slackening.

There is good reason to believe that each major form of transportation has large excess capacity, as far as land area is concerned. By very modest additions to land area, and in some cases with none at all, capacity of the transportation system could be increased very greatly. In fact, there is often excess capacity, with existing physical facilities other than land; and by investment of more capital on the present area, much larger capacity could be built in.

In 1960 the area used for railroads was about 8 million acres; for roads rights-of-way, about 16 million acres; and for airports, about $1\frac{1}{2}$ million acres; or about 25 million acres in total. It is difficult to estimate future needs, for the reasons outlined above. But I conclude that the area used for transportation will increase to about 28 million acres in 1980 and to about 30 million acres in 2000. While these increases are small, absolutely and relatively to any other land use, it should be emphasized that the increased areas will often be required in locations where competition for land is relatively intense. Moreover, the effect of this increase in area for transportation will be felt primarily on the lands adjacent to the transportation routes rather than directly by the shift of land to transportation use.

Chapter 5

W. D. SHRADER
F. F. RIECKEN
Iowa State University

Potentials for Increasing Production in the Corn Belt

UNDER 1960 prices the demand for corn was about 3.8 billion bushels, but production in 1959 was some 4.3 billion bushels (11). Some 28 million acres of cropland are withdrawn from production in the acreage control programs, and it has been suggested that 45 to 70 million acres be withdrawn from cropland use. The differences between various estimates indicates a critical need for more valid estimates of production potentials. If production of the needed quantity of corn is to take place with maximum efficiency, what lands will remain in production and what lands and what acreage should be withdrawn?

In this chapter we shall endeavor to illustrate how soil survey information can be used to appraise the crop production potential of a region. The probable effect of changing technology on corn production on different soil conditions will be examined in some detail, and a tentative evaluation of the corn production potential of the Midland Feed Region or Corn Belt will be made.

THE CORN BELT

The Midland Feed Region or Corn Belt has 11.5 percent of the total land area of the continental United States and about 34 percent of the cropland. It produces more than two-thirds of the corn, oats and soybeans. Corn is grown on more than 44 million acres (6).

This region is not uniform, however, in the amount of corn grown in all of its parts. Different suitability and productivity for corn is caused by soil, topography or climatic differences, singly or in combination. In Figure 5.1 the Midland Feed Region or Corn Belt[1] has been subdivided into 5 sub-regions. The land

[1] It includes north central Ohio, Indiana, Illinois and Missouri; Iowa; northeastern Kansas; eastern Nebraska; southeastern South Dakota; southern Minnesota, Wisconsin and Michigan.

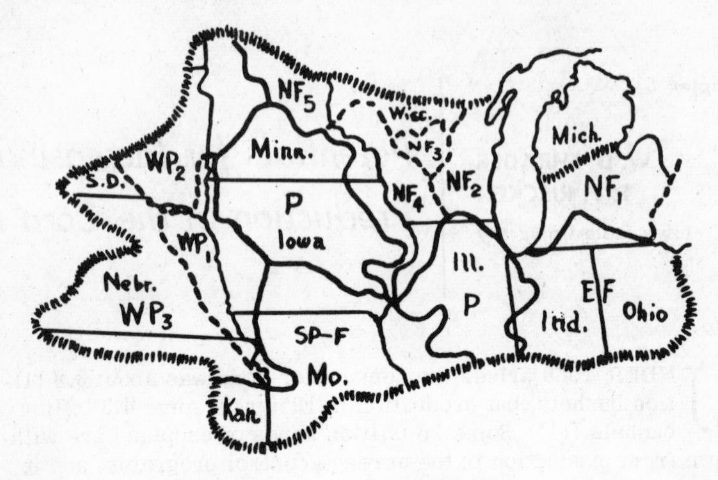

PRAIRIE

P. CENTRAL PRAIRIE SUBREGION
WP. WESTERN PRAIRIE SUBREGION
WP_1 MISSOURI VALLEY HILLY AREA
WP_2 DAKOTA-MINNESOTA AREA
WP_3 NEBRASKA AREA

PRAIRIE-FOREST

SP-F SOUTHERN PRAIRIE FOREST

FOREST

EF. EASTERN FOREST SUBREGION
NF. NORTHERN FOREST SUBREGION
NF_1 SOUTHERN MICHIGAN AREA
NF_2 EASTERN WISCONSIN AREA
NF_3 CENTRAL WISCONSIN SANDY AREA
NF_4 MISSISSIPPI VALLEY HILLY AREA
NF_5 NORTHERN FRINGE AREA

Fig. 5.1. Sub-regions of the Midland Feed Region adapted from Soil, the 1957 Yearbook of Agriculture, page 536.

use, based on the 1955 census, is given in Table 5.1. The Central Prairie, Western Prairie and Eastern Forest sub-regions are highest in present use for corn, with the former ranking first. This is illustrated in Figure 5.2. These sub-regions have been described elsewhere as to soil, topography and land use and corn-yielding capacity, based mainly on 1946 to 1955 census data (6).

CORN PRODUCTION TECHNOLOGY

As described elsewhere (2, 6), the early systems of soil management in the Corn Belt revolved largely around lime, legumes and livestock. Generally this meant for cropland acres a cropping system which included about equal acreages of corn, a small grain (mainly oats) and a legume-grass meadow. Legumes,

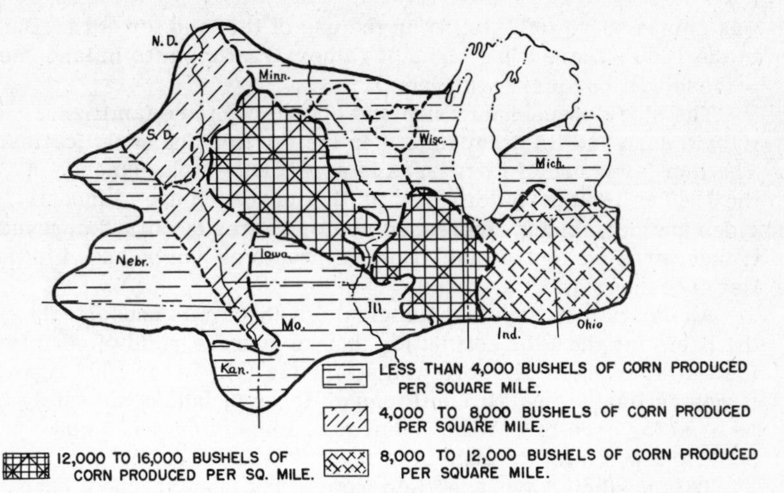

Fig. 5.2. Intensity of corn production in the Midland Feed Region.

Table 5.1. Present Land Use of Farm Land in the Midland Feed Region[a]

Sub-regions	Size Millions of Acres	Corn	Oats	Soy-beans	Wheat	Hay	Pasture	Forest
				(Percent)				
Central Prairie	40	33	17	13	1	10	20	5
Western Prairie	60							
Missouri Hilly Valley		28	14	3	2	8	35	9
Dakota-Minnesota		24	25	4	2	12	31	1
Nebraska		22	6	-	17	12	41	2
Prairie-Forest	36	13	5	6	5	9	45	16
Forest								
Eastern Forest	30	26	8	10	10	12	23	11
Northern Forest	52	11	12	1	2	16	36	22

[a] Based on a 20 percent sample from 1955 federal census.

manure and the soil were the main source of nitrogen for the grain crops. Deviations occurred, but on the whole about 30 to 50 percent of the cropland acres were used for corn. Generally, this was the land use pattern for the Corn Belt from the turn of the century to the 1955 to 1960 period. During this period there was comparative inflexibility in the use of the land for corn. But in the 1950's there were signs of rather drastic shifts in land use — these will be referred to later.

The story of mechanization and hybrid corn are familiar. Hybrid corn had its great impact in the thirties and early forties. The increased use of fertilizers is a well known phenomenon of the 1940 to 1960 period, as well as the increased use of insecticides and herbicides. Increased planting rates of corn, improved tillage, erosion control and drainage practices can be added to the list of technological advances.

Application of such technological advances was undoubtedly the basis for the 1952 estimation that an average yield of corn for Iowa of 85 bushels per acre was attainable (1). In the 1952 report it was estimated that 10.7 millions of acres of land could safely be used for corn by 1955. A number of lines of evidence now point to a potential acreage of at least half again as much.

This predicted average yield has not yet been reached, but the significance of the technological advances may well be not so much in the direction of increased yield per acre, as in the changes in land use. Legumes and oats may well be shifting on many soils from a complementary position in the cropping system to a non-essential one or to a competitive position as far as acreage of corn is involved. The agronomic feasibility of such a shift in production practices is indicated by the data presented in Table 5.2. The studies reported in this table indicate that, on land where rotations are not needed to control erosion, as high yields of corn can be obtained with adequate nitrogen under continuous corn culture as when a rotation containing a legume is used. The percentage of the time that corn occupies the land commonly changes from 33 or 50 percent to 100 percent as a shift is made from rotation to continuous cropping. Thus, on a given tract of land the quantity of corn produced may be doubled or tripled by such a shift in land use. The data in Table 5.3 illustrate the impact of this on potential corn output. A number of technological advances undoubtedly have made this possible, but the substitution of fertilizer nitrogen for the legume-supplied nitrogen undoubtedly will be the key technology.

TECHNOLOGICAL POTENTIALS

Previously the authors have made some preliminary analyses of the implications of the complex of new corn production technologies for several selected counties in Iowa (7, 10). In Appanoose County it was estimated that the corn production could be

Table 5.2. Relative Yields of Rotation and Continuous Corn Based on 1955 to 1959 Average Yields

Experimental field and soil type	Rotation corn[a]	Continuous corn	
		No nitrogen fertilizer	Nitrogen fertilizer used[b]
		(Percent)	
Carrington-Clyde (Kenyon silt loam)	100	--	108
Clarion-Webster (Webster silty clay loam)	100	48	98
Pasture Improvement (Belinda silt loam)	100	79	82
Soil Conservation (Marshall silt loam)	100	90	104
Southern Iowa (Edina silt loam)	100	49	123
Howard County (Cresco silt loam)	100	79	90

[a] Yields of first year corn (corn following a legume-grass meadow) were taken as 100 percent for each location.
[b] All nutrients except nitrogen were supplied as needed to all areas. The maximum nitrogen treatments were 160 pounds per acre at all locations except in Howard County where 90 pounds per acre were used and in southern Iowa where it was 240 pounds per acre.

increased from 1.4 million bushels to 3.2 million bushels, or an increase of about 1.8 million bushels. This county has only a small amount of nearly level land suited to frequent or continuous corn production. Most of the cropland would require use of erosion control practices which would involve legume-grasses in the rotation.

But in Hamilton County we estimated that corn production could be increased about 6 million bushels by applying the technology available in 1957. We now consider this figure too low, and estimate that a 12 million bushels per year increase in corn production in Hamilton County is physically possible (over the pre-1957 production). This large potential increase in corn production in Hamilton County, where there are dominantly level to nearly level soils of high-yielding potential, can result primarily because increased acres can be used for corn largely in an almost continuous corn system of farming.

This example of applying new technology illustrates that not only do differences in corn production exist but also that a very high corn production potential is physically possible in some counties. But it is necessary to consider other factors too. Many

Table 5.3. Estimated Annual Physical Corn Production Potential of Corn Suitability Class A, B and C Soils for Selected Counties of the Central Prairie, Southern Prairie-Forest and Missouri Valley Hilly Sub-Regions

Sub-region	County	Present corn production	Estimated corn production potential[c]				
			Class A+B soils[d]		Class C soils[e]		Class A+B+C soils
			(Acres)	(Bushels)	(Acres)	(Bushels)	(Bushels)
Central Prairie	Hamilton, Ia.	8,530,000[a]	302,000	19,970,000	19,000	895,000	20,865,000
	Calhoun, Ia.	6,070,000[a]	320,800	22,980,000	10,300	384,000	23,364,000
	Christian, Ill.	3,280,000[b]	296,500	17,069,000	39,400	135,000	17,204,000
	Faribault, Minn.	8,315,281[b]	344,506	20,551,700	36,503	1,414,500	21,966,200
	Steele, Minn.	3,613,730[b]	185,760	9,712,500	85,037	2,474,300	12,186,800
Southern Prairie-Forest	Ringgold, Ia.	2,457,000[a]	55,706	3,684,000	62,618	1,504,000	5,188,000
Missouri Valley Hilly (of Western Prairie)	Shelby, Ia.	6,650,000[a]	59,300	4,059,000	206,700	9,644,000	13,703,000

[a] Iowa Farm Census, 1953-57 average.
[b] Federal Census, 1954 only.
[c] On present cropland only.
[d] Includes the soils best adapted to corn production and suited to continuous corn culture.
[e] Fair corn soils, but not suited to continuous corn production.

of the soils in other parts of the humid region might conceivably be used for crop production, but on many of them yields would be very low and production costs high. On many soils the full complex of the new technologies could not be applied efficiently because of limitations of size and uniformity of soil patterns. Therefore, any realistic appraisal of corn production potential must take into account not only the various technological and economic aspects of corn production, but it must consider whether or not the technologies can be efficiently applied to various soils. Among the facets involved are yielding capacity of soil types, slope or lay of the land, size and shape of uniform soil areas. For example, a farm with some highly productive soils, but which occur in small fields suitable for efficient use by 2-row equipment, would be poorly suited for 4-row and 6-row equipment. Thus it is evident that aggregate acreages of various kinds of land cannot be used as the only criteria in evaluating corn production potential. There must be supplemental studies or perhaps complete replacement with field-by-field or farm-by-farm analysis. The need for these kinds of studies is urgent, and too few have been made.

PRODUCTION POTENTIALS IN SELECTED COUNTIES

We recognize that some of these and other considerations must be brought into the picture if serious estimates are to be made of corn production potentials in the Corn Belt. Clearly, such details are beyond the scope of this chapter. However, we did introduce some of these elements in making corn production estimates for selected counties within three sub-regions in the Corn Belt. The estimates are given in Table 5.3. A brief elaboration of the method and a discussion of each county follows. In Table 5.3 the soils are ranked according to their "relative suitability" for corn production. Briefly, Class A soil areas are the "ideal" condition, which consists of medium textured, easily tilled, level to nearly level soils. Muscatine silt loam is a representative soil. Class A soils occur in large, uniform areas and are capable of producing average corn yields in excess of 70 bushels per acre per year with moderate fertilization. They occur dominantly in association with Class B soils. Class B soils are only slightly less desirable in one or more characteristics but are still very highly desirable soils for corn production. Class C soils are mostly too sloping for use for continuous corn or may have other undesirable characteristics. They are capable of high sustained production with suitable management and conservation practices as needed. Class D land is marginal for corn production, and under present conditions Class E land probably is not suited for corn.

Corn production is considered to be the cheapest per bushel of product on suitability Class A soils, and most expensive on Class E soils. Only cropland in the counties considered was classified. The amount of Class A soils, the "ideal" corn soil, is limited, but large areas in the Central Prairie Region are classified as Class B soils.

In a county such as Shelby County, Iowa, there is a potential for a large increase in corn production, but mostly on the Class C land. In other words, the sloping soils of Shelby County are not as well adapted to utilizing existing corn production technology (i.e., frequent use with high yields) as are the level, uniform soils of Calhoun and Hamilton counties, Iowa, or Christian County, Illinois.

Present techniques and economy favor corn production on the class A and B soils. The data presented in Table 5.3 for Hamilton, Calhoun, Faribault and Christian counties indicate that there are large areas of class A and B soils in the Central Prairie sub-region. Other large areas of favorable soils occur in the Eastern Forest sub-region of northern Indiana and Ohio.

These few case studies are sufficient to indicate why there may be no apparent relationship between acreage of land removed from production and the amount of a given crop produced. Average annual corn production (yield per acre times the percent of the time that the land is in corn) on the class A and B lands is about 70 bushels per acre. On Class C land average annual production is estimated at about 35 bushels per acre, and on Class D land it is only about 14 bushels per acre.

Any bushel reduction that might result from removing 100 acres of Class D land from production could be compensated for by shifting about 40 acres of Class B land from a corn-corn-oats-meadow rotation to continuous corn.

IMPORTANCE OF SOIL CLASSIFICATION

The classification of all cropland into 5 general classes enables us to make some general statements about the relative suitability of different areas for corn production. It is obvious that corn can be produced more cheaply on areas where large-scale equipment can be used and where, with an expenditure of perhaps $12 to $15 per acre per year for fertilizer, average yields of 70 to 90 bushels of corn can be obtained, as compared to areas where yields are low and costs are high. However, it is important also to know where and how many acres of different classes of land there are. This is needed in the aggregate, but it is also needed on a field-by-field and farm-by-farm basis. It is needed for broad regions, and for small areas. We cannot stress too strongly that such information on classes of soils can be gained only from modern, detailed surveys; and these are too few in number and the current rate of progress is too slow.

MODEL OF CORN PRODUCTION POTENTIAL

If such soil class information were available for all potential cropland, it would make possible detailed predictions as to the amount of corn that could be profitably produced over a range of prices and an estimation of the amount and kind of land that would be required. Such information would make possible development of a realistic corn production model.

Such a model for the corn production industry as a whole can be visualized from Figure 5.3. The existence of the knowledge that would be necessary to construct such a model would not insure that corn would necessarily be produced on the land where it could be produced most efficiently, but it would furnish a framework of information within which rational plans would be possible either at the farm or national level.

As shown in Figure 5.3, to produce P amount of corn requires only A acres; this production is shown as all taking place on land of S suitability. As production is increased, land of lesser and lesser desirability must be used. To produce P_2 amount of corn, A_2 amount of land must be used, a portion of which is of S_2 suitability. Eventually a point is reached, P_n, at which all land would have to be used regardless of quality.

It is our purpose to determine in a general way our present location on the supply line A-Z. Are we approaching the point Z, or are we still to the left of point A?

CORN BELT POTENTIALS

An estimate of the corn production potential for the Central Prairie sub-region is given in Table 5.4, and an estimate for the entire Corn Belt Region is given in Table 5.5. Under the assumptions made, it is estimated that a corn production potential of about 4.6 billion bushels of corn exists in the Corn Belt. This contrasts with a present production of 2.1 billion bushels (1955 production).

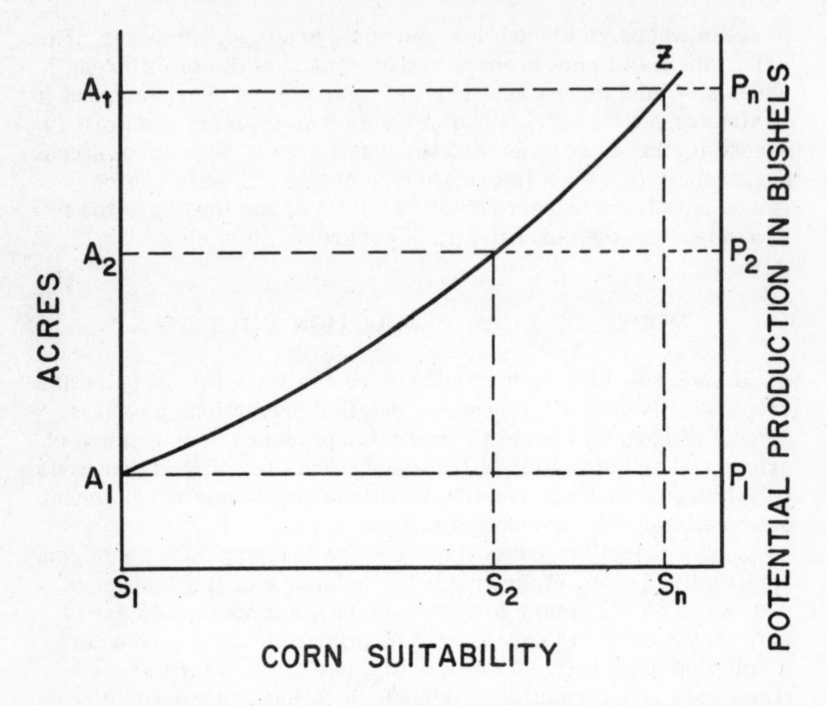

Fig. 5.3. Relationship of relative suitability of land for corn production to acres needed for a given amount of production.

The methods and assumptions need brief elaboration here. About a 20 percent randomly selected county sample was chosen for each of the sub-regions. Available county-wide soil survey and statistical soil survey or land capability information was studied. Then the complex of new corn production technology was evaluated for its suitability for the different soil or land capability situations within each county. Attainable corn yields were next estimated for the different soil and land capability situations. A corn production potential for each county was then computed. The corn production for each sub-region was then obtained by expanding the 20 percent county sample. The estimates obtained by this procedure have their limitations and could be improved appreciably by better data. However, with the admitted limitations, the estimates given are considered to be of the right order of magnitude and direction.

Table 5.4. Corn Production Potential on Highly Suitable Soils in the Central Prairie Sub-Region

State	Approximate area in Central Prairie sub-region acres	Percent of area with soils highly suitable for corn (Corn suitability classes A and B)[a]	Estimated average production in bushels per acre per year	Potential corn production in bushels per year
Indiana	1,300,000	30	80[b]	32,000,000
Illinois	15,000,000	71	80[b]	848,000,000
Iowa	14,400,000	59	75[c]	637,000,000
Minnesota	8,500,000	52	52[d]	229,000,000
		61	73	1,746,000,000

[a] Present cropland only considered.
[b] Yield estimate based on estimates given by McKenzie (3, 4).
[c] Yield estimate based on estimates by Shrader *et al.* (9) as applied to a 90 percent sample of Land Use Capability Classes I and II in the sample counties.
[d] Yield estimates based on information furnished by Dr. R. H. Rust, Department of Soils, University of Minnesota. Estimated average yields per acre are comparable with these for Iowa but recommended intensity of cropping is somewhat less.

SUB-REGION IMPLICATIONS

It is to be noted that highly favorable soils of the Central Prairie sub-region have an estimated corn production potential of 1.7 billion bushels, or about one-half of the total U. S. corn needs.

The estimated production potential for the Central Prairie sub-region is listed by states in Table 5.4. This table indicates the yield estimates used and the source of these estimates. This study indicates that the concentration of good corn land is highest in northern Illinois and next highest in northern Iowa. It appears that there is an enormous potential for expanded corn production in the Central Prairie sub-region.

The estimates given in Table 5.5 are for the entire Corn Belt. The estimates of acreage of good corn land are based primarily on the county summaries of land use capability classes which were available for most of the area. These acreage estimates are believed to be reasonably accurate. The estimates of yields for the various sub-regions are, in some cases, based on very limited information and should be considered only as general guides to the probable magnitude of potential production.

Table 5.5. Estimates of Corn-Producing Potentials of the Midland Feed Region Based on the Acreage of Land Use Capability Classes I and II

Sub-regions	Present corn production[a]		Land use capability		Potential corn production on land use capability		Estimated percent of U.S. needs (1960)
			Class I	Class II	Class I	Class II	
	Millions of bushels (1955)	Percent of U.S. production (1955)	Millions of acres	Percent of area	Yield per acre	Millions of bushels	
Prairie							
P. Central Prairie	900	25	24	61[b]	73	1750	46
W.P. Western Prairie	500	14	26	43[b]	40	1000	26
Prairie-Forest							
S.P.-F. Southern Prairie-Forest	100	3	6	13[c]	60	360	9
Forest							
E.F. Eastern Forest	400	11	17	57[b]	65	1100	29
N.F. Northern Forest	200	6	11	21[b]	40	400	11
Subtotals	2100	59				4610	121

[a] 1954 Federal Census.
[b] 20 percent sample of entire area (1/5 of counties, randomly selected).
[c] 20 percent sample of Kansas and Iowa, and 5 percent in Missouri (1/5 and 1/20 of all counties, randomly selected).

The Southern Prairie-Forest sub-region has an estimated corn production potential of 0.36 billion bushels. The Prairie-Forest sub-region includes an area of more than 55 counties in southern Iowa, northern Missouri and adjoining parts of Illinois. Though this study did not evaluate in adequate detail the effect of field size and shape, or efficiency of adapting the complex of new technology of corn production in the Southern Prairie sub-region, it seems that much of this sub-region would continue to be at a considerable disadvantage as regards efficiency of corn production. The lower estimated corn yields (60 bushels per acre) would also seem to indicate that corn production in the Southern Prairie-Forest sub-region would be at some efficiency disadvantage compared to the Central Prairie or Eastern Forest sub-regions.

The Western Prairie and Northern Forest sub-regions have a large potential increase, percentage-wise, in corn production. Low yields and also a smaller field size in the Northern sub-region would seem to indicate the complex of new technology would be less efficient in these sub-regions.

Yields in the Western Prairie sub-region can be markedly increased through irrigation. However, there is evidence (5, 8) that yields on the plains under irrigation average about the same as non-irrigated yields in Illinois, Indiana or Ohio. Therefore, it appears that on a purely competitive basis the Western Prairie sub-region is not as suitable a place to produce corn as in the eastern part of the region.

Soil and climatic conditions and the status of technology all favor the intensive production of corn in the 40 million acre Central Prairie sub-region of northern Iowa and northern Illinois, and the 26 million acre Eastern Forest sub-region of northern Indiana and Ohio. Existing information indicates that under conditions approaching maximum efficiency a total of approximately 3 billion bushels of corn could be produced annually in these two sub-regions.

It is highly unlikely that all of the best corn land in these regions will ever be used for corn or that corn production will be eliminated in the other areas, but it is possible that long-time trends in adjustments will tend in this direction.

LIMITATIONS

This study is very obviously made with incomplete data. Samples are missing from large portions of the area studied. Numerous assumptions are made which the authors consider to be valid but for which no rigid proof exists. It is, for example, assumed that land use capability classes 1 and 2 define in a general way the same areas as corn suitability classes A and B. Studies made on individual counties indicate that there is good agreement between these two estimates of land quality in the Central Prairie sub-region but poorer agreement in some of the other sub-regions.

In this paper no notice is taken of the corn production potential of the rest of the nation outside of the Corn Belt. Although several promising areas such as the Mississippi Delta and sections of the southeastern United States are known to exist, they were considered as being outside the range of this study.

IMPLICATIONS AND CONCLUSIONS

This study indicates (1) that if we are to arrive at a valid estimation of production potential for a crop, it must be made on the basis of soil survey information; (2) that the sampling technique used in this study offers promise for furnishing information on a regional basis of considerable accuracy and at a reasonable cost; (3) that the position of a soil on the landscape must be considered in evaluating its production potential; (4) that more complete and valid estimates of yields than are now available are needed and (5) that before such a study can be used as a basis for action it will be necessary to determine the present level of adoption of various technologies by farmers.

Incomplete though this study is, it does indicate that a very large potential for increased corn production exists within the Corn Belt and that the opportunities for increasing production without loss of efficiency are greatest in the Central Prairie and Eastern Forest sub-regions. It appears that at least 70 percent of the nation's needs for corn could be produced on the highly favored soil in these two sub-regions.

LITERATURE CITED

1. An Appraisal of the Agricultural Production Capacity in Iowa. AN 153 (mimeographed). Feb., 1952. Iowa State University, Ames, Iowa.
2. CRICKMAN, C. W. The Use of Land in the Corn Belt. Yearbook of Agriculture, 1958, pp. 122-28.
3. McKENZIE, L. J. Potential Productivity of Illinois Soils. Ill. Agr. Exp. Sta. SP 17, 1957.
4. McKENZIE, L. J. Potential Productivity of the Soils of Northwestern and East-central Illinois. Ill. Agr. Exp. Sta. SP 19, 1957.

5. Minutes of North Central Drainage and Irrigation Committee NCR-12 for 1960. Mimeographed report on file at Dept. of Agron., Iowa State University, Ames, Iowa.
6. PIERRE, W. H., and RIECKEN, F. F. The Midland Feed Region. Yearbook of Agriculture, 1957, pp. 535-46.
7. RIECKEN, F. F., DUMENIL, L., THOMPSON, H., and ENGELSTAD, O. Land Use Crop Production and Soil Resources (in southern Iowa). Seminar on adjustment and its problems in southern Iowa, pp. 11-26. C.A.E.A. Report 4, Iowa State University, Ames, Iowa. 1959.
8. RHOADES, H. F., and NELSON, L. B. Growing 100-bushel Corn With Irrigation. Yearbook of Agriculture, 1955, pp. 394-400.
9. SHRADER, W. D., SCHALLER, F. W., PESEK, J. T., SLUSHER, D. F., and RIECKEN, F. F. Estimated Crop Yields on Iowa Soils. Special Report No. 25. Iowa State University, Ames, Iowa. April, 1960.
10. SHRADER, W. D., and RIECKEN, F. F. Adjustments in the Cropping Pattern of Iowa Agriculture. Basebook for Agricultural Adjustment in Iowa, Part II, pp. 26-30. Iowa State University, Ames, Iowa. Special Report No. 21.
11. The Feed Situation. Feb., 1960. AMS, USDA.

Chapter 6

ANDREW R. AANDAHL

Soil Conservation Service, USDA[1]

Potentials for Increasing Wheat Production in the Great Plains

THE GREAT PLAINS STATES produce about 60 percent of all wheat grown in the United States from about 70 percent of the acreage of harvested wheat (Table 6.1). The United States produces about 15 percent of the world's wheat production (Table 6.2).

Table 6.1. Acreage of All Wheat Threshed in the Great Plains States and the United States in Selected Years

Area	1954	1949	1944
		(Million acres)	
North Dakota	7.6	10.2	9.6
South Dakota	2.6	3.9	3.0
Nebraska	3.0	3.9	2.6
Kansas	9.5	13.4	11.2
Oklahoma	4.5	6.3	5.1
Texas	3.0	5.6	4.4
Montana	4.3	4.6	3.7
Wyoming	.2	.4	.2
Colorado	1.6	2.5	1.2
New Mexico	.1	.5	.3
Great Plains States	36.3	51.3	41.4
United States	51.4	71.2	58.3

Source: Bureau of the Census, U.S. Department of Commerce.

The annual disappearance of wheat in the continental United States, 1946-55, averages 665 million bushels.[2] This includes wheat used for food, seed, industry and feed. This ranged from 754 million bushels in 1947 to 589 million bushels in 1955.

[1] The heads, Departments of Agronomy and/or Soils, Experiment Stations, Great Plains States, and selected members of their staffs provided valuable assistance.

[2] "The wheat situation," Feb., 1960, AMS, USDA.

Table 6.2. Wheat Production in the United States and the World, Five-Year Averages, 1925-59

Year of harvest	United States	World	Percentage of world
Five-year Averages		(Million bushels)	
1925-29	823	5,310	15
1930-34	732	5,560	13
1935-39	759	6,084	12
1940-44	926	5,800	16
1945-49	1,202	5,898	20
1950-54	1,094	6,975	16
1955-59	1,095	7,916	14

Sources: For 1925-49 – Foreign Agricultural Trade Statistical Handbook, Stat. Bul. No. 179, Aug., 1956, USDA. For 1950-59 – "The wheat situation," Feb., 1960, AMS, USDA.

THE GREAT PLAINS

The Great Plains is that dominantly level, treeless, semiarid and subhumid area between the Rocky Mountains and the 98th Meridian. The boundaries are really transition zones. To the Spaniards of the Southwest, it was a land to be avoided. They did not know how to survive, much less live there. To the early explorers, it was the Great American Desert. This was land not fit for human occupation but which must be crossed to reach the fair lands of the West. To the buffaloes it was their true home. They roamed the Plains in herds estimated in the millions. To the American Indians, it was their last retreat. To us, it is home. Its many moods, its capricious nature and its extremes are challenges to us.

We are learning how to live in the Plains; we expect to learn how to live here better in the future. This is a unique area – different from the arid Southwest and the humid East and not a transition from one to the other. In arid areas one is not tempted to grow crops; in the humid areas one grows them with security.

The pioneers of the Plains should have "thrown the book away" before they came. The knowledge, the experiences, the institutions, the ways of living that it contained were not for the Plains. One needs to look only at the Homestead Act to recognize this fact. Our forefathers learned this the hard way, but we are still struggling to write our own "book." One of our difficulties is that many people, both in the Plains and elsewhere, do not realize that we need our own "book."

Climate

The climate of the Plains really is not semiarid or subhumid; it is sometimes subhumid, sometimes arid, sometimes humid and sometimes semiarid, but always unpredictable. Palmer[3] classified the climate of central South Dakota as arid 3 percent of the years; semiarid, 51 percent; dry subhumid, 40 percent; moist subhumid, 3 percent, and humid, 3 percent.

Many people still remember the dry years of the thirties, the "dirty thirties"; more people remember the dry years of the fifties in the Southern Plains. Although no definite cyclical pattern exists, there is some tendency for wet years and dry years to occur together. This tendency makes our problem of adjustment more difficult. People tend to become too optimistic during the wet years and too pessimistic during the dry years.

The normal annual precipitation of the spring wheat area of the Northern Plains ranges from about 14 to 20 inches. The range for the winter wheat area of the Central Plains and Southern Plains is from about 16 to 36 inches. The variability of the precipitation is reflected in the wheat yields shown in Figure 6.3.

During these periods of high rainfall and frequently high prices, farmers were too optimistic. The result was the plowing of much native grassland and planting crops on soils not well suited to cultivation. We have 12,000,000 to 14,000,000 acres of land under cultivation, which the Soil Conservation Service places in capability classes V, VI and VII. A similar amount is placed in capability class IV.

Wind, drought, hail — these are the troublemakers of the Plains. Winds and droughts combine with poor farming to give us dust storms. These not only affect crop production but also make living unpleasant for a time. Ask a lady of the Plains about them, but don't do it just after one! Crop damage from hail is much higher in the Plains than it is in the humid East.[4]

The chinook, the norther and the real blizzard are wind phenomena almost unique to the Plains.[5] An extreme chinook can evaporate the snow and leave dry ground. They are common to the Northern Plains near the mountains. The norther, common to the Southern Plains, can drop the temperature 20 to 30 degrees within a very short time and fill the sky with dust. The blizzard is the grizzly of the Plains.

---

[3] W. C. Palmer. Weekly Weather and Crop Bulletin, U. S. Weather Bureau, 44 (1A), 1957.

[4] S. D. Flora. Hailstorms in the United States, University of Oklahoma Press, Norman, 1956.

[5] W. P. Webb. The Great Plains, Ginn and Company, 1931.

Most winds are dry, but some are hot and dry. These can reduce crop yields drastically within a few days. The severe one from the southwest in 1953 left its mark on the corn as far northeast as Ames, Iowa.

Perhaps the more serious but less noticeable effect is the higher evaporation with its resulting lower efficiency of water use. The wind velocity of the Plains is 30 to 50 percent more than that of the humid East.[6]

The Soil

The soils on which most of the wheat is raised are medium-textured (loamy) ones of the Chernozem, Chestnut, Calcium Carbonate Solonchak, Reddish Prairie, Reddish Chestnut and Brown great soil groups. Most of these are level or nearly level, and perhaps less than 15 percent have slope gradients of more than 5 percent. In the Northern Plains these have formed mainly from drift, loess, alluvium and residual materials from sandstones and shales. In Kansas and adjacent states, loess is the most extensive parent material, but there are many soils formed in alluvium and residual from shales and sandstones.

THE WHEAT LANDS

The location of the land used for growing wheat in the Great Plains States and the United States in 1954 is shown in Figure 6.1. The Sandhills of Nebraska, in general, separate the spring wheat areas of the Northern Plains from the winter wheat areas of the Central Plains and Southern Plains. Little or no spring wheat is grown south of the Sandhills, but some winter wheat is raised in Montana and South Dakota. More winter wheat can and likely will be raised in these areas in the future.

The obvious reason for the large acreage of wheat in the Great Plains States is that the farmers believe it is one of their best alternatives. Other alternatives, however, when compared with those of the humid East, are not numerous. They include native and tame grasses, cotton, sorghum, corn, flax, barley and other small grain and feed crops.[7]

Wheat is a good alternative in the Plains, partly because the quality here is high.

---

[6] S. S. Visher. Climatic Atlas of the United States, Harvard University Press, Cambridge, N. J., 1954.

[7] Other alternatives involving irrigation are not considered here.

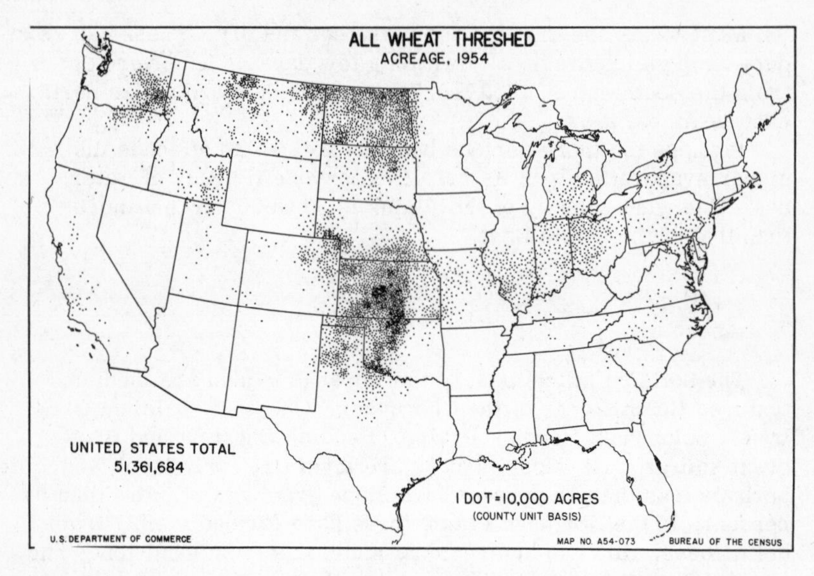

Fig. 6.1. Location of the land used for growing wheat in the Great Plains States and the United States (1954).

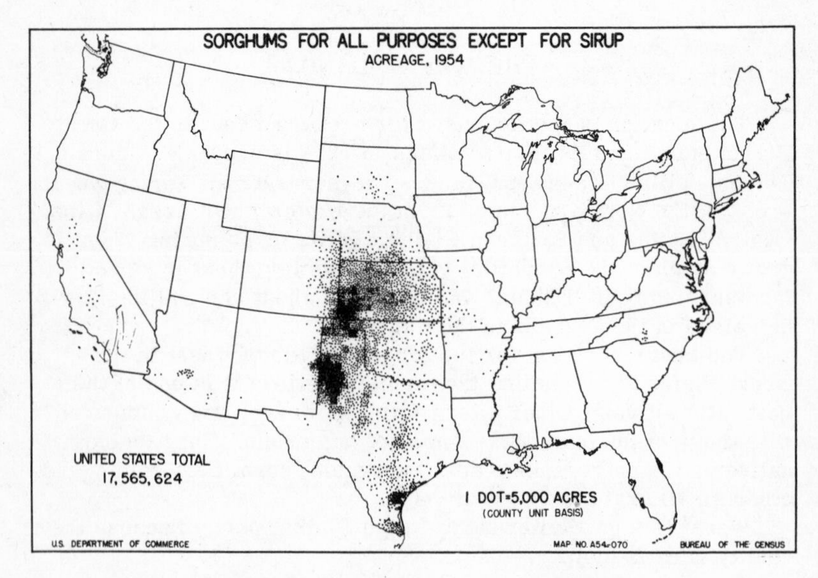

Fig. 6.2. Acreage of sorghum (1954).

Wheat farmers have time to do other things because most of the work of growing wheat is concentrated during the time of planting and harvesting the crop. During other periods, there is little that farmers generally can do to improve the crop. This fact makes the alternative of growing wheat more attractive to many people because it permits them to be active in other business ventures.

Where the rainfall is lower, as on the western edge of the wheat lands, grasses are the better alternative. Sorghum competes with both grass and wheat in the southern transition between the two, especially on the sandier soils.

The status of sorghum as a competitor of both wheat and cotton has improved greatly. Yields have increased for several reasons. Hybrid varieties have been developed, and the yields of these are about 20 percent higher. Farmers are using more nitrogen and phosphorus fertilizers. They are using lower planting rates, and the resulting thinner stands produce better during dry years. These stands thicken during wet years. Surface planting with its lower seedling losses is replacing listing. Seed treatment is becoming more common. All these factors contribute to the higher yields. As a feed, sorghum is about 90 percent as efficient as corn. The 1954 acreage of sorghum is shown in Figure 6.2.

The acreages of sorghums for seven Great Plains States and the United States in 1944, 1949 and 1954 are given in Table 6.3. The 1960 estimate for the United States is 19,800,000 acres. While the acreages have fluctuated greatly, future acreages of

Table 6.3. Sorghum for All Purposes Except for Syrup in Seven Great Plains States and the United States in Selected Years

Area	1954	1949	1944
		(Million acres)	
South Dakota	.1	.1	.5
Nebraska	.8	.3	.7
Kansas	5.4	2.3	3.6
Oklahoma	1.6	1.1	2.4
Texas	7.4	4.6	7.9
Colorado	.8	.6	.7
New Mexico	.4	.5	.7
Great Plains States	16.5	9.6	16.4
United States	17.6	10.1	17.2

Source: Bureau of the Census, U.S. Department of Commerce.

sorghum are likely to remain high. They may increase, especially if more livestock feeding develops in the Central States and Southern Plains States.

The transition between cotton and wheat is usually narrow, with wheat losing in the competition where the season is long enough for good cotton growth. In southwestern Oklahoma and adjacent areas in Texas, however, there is a large area where both cotton and wheat are grown.

Corn dominates the cropping pattern in eastern Nebraska and southeastern South Dakota. There is no reason to believe that excellent wheat cannot be raised in this area, but the farmers have a definite preference for growing corn. There may be a human element here, in addition to the monetary advantage favoring corn, because the settlers in this area, to a large degree, came from the Corn Belt. Also, this area is near Omaha, the world's largest livestock market.

Flax, barley and other feed crops provide several alternatives to wheat in the spring wheat area. The acreages of some of these in North Dakota for selected years are given in Table 6.4. In recent years, barley and flax have been the more common substitute for wheat. Safflower, a relatively new crop, has shown considerable promise.

A study in 1955 of cropland acres diverted from wheat on 927 farms in Kansas, Montana and North Dakota showed 63 percent in west-central Kansas going to grain sorghum; 40 percent to barley and other grains, and 36 percent to flax in north-central North Dakota; and 85 percent to barley and other grains in north-central Montana.[8]

Table 6.4. Acreages of Selected Crops and Cropland in North Dakota in Selected Years

Crops	1954	1949	1944
		(Millions of acres)	
Wheat	7.6	10.2	9.6
Barley	3.0	1.6	2.6
Rye	.3	.2	.1
Oats	2.1	1.6	2.5
Flax	3.1	1.8	.8
Total (5 crops)	16.1	15.4	15.7
Cropland (harvested)	21.2	20.4	20.8
Cropland (total)	27.7	27.6	25.1

Source: Bureau of the Census, U.S. Department of Commerce.

[8] C. W. Nauheim, W. R. Bailey, D. E. Merrick. "Wheat production," Agr. Info. Bul. No. 179, ARS, USDA, March, 1958.

Alternatives in the Great Plains are not as numerous as in the humid part of the United States, and shifts in the short run are often difficult. The establishment of grasses, for example, may require two or three attempts, depending upon the weather. Long-run shifts to more feed crops and more feeding of livestock can be accomplished. These, however, would require considerable change in the living habits of the farmer and his family. There would be a substantial sacrifice of freedom and time to do other things. The net results financially may be more favorable than generally recognized.

POTENTIAL WHEAT PRODUCTION

Increased production of wheat in the Great Plains States could be accomplished by (1) diverting acres in other crops and uses to wheat and (2) increase the yield per acre. Both of these will now be explored, but there is no implication that the possibilities of the first method should be done. As we all know, the country has been trying to do the opposite.

The acres of wheat harvested in the Great Plains States in 1949 were 51.3 million (Table 6.1). The number of acres of wheat that could be harvested is probably over 60 million. For our purpose we will assume that 55 million acres can be harvested. This is about 19 million acres more than in 1954. Most of these could come from the following sources:

Sorghum	8 million
Flax	2 million
Barley	3 million
Corn	2 million
Oats	1 million
Wild hay	1 million

Most of the land in wild hay which is suitable for cultivation is in North Dakota and South Dakota.

Wheat yields per seeded acres for the Great Plains States from 1920 to 1960 are given in Table 6.5 and in Figure 6.3. Although the variations from year to year were great, the upward trend was rather definite.[9] An estimated present average yield of 14 bushels per harvested acre is conservative. The yields given in Table 6.5 are for seeded acres, and average abandonment in the Great Plains is more than 10 percent.

---

[9] Ibid., pp. 33.

Table 6.5. Wheat Yields Per Seeded Acre for the United States and Two Major Wheat Regions, Ten-Year Averages, 1920-59

Ten-year average	United States	Major wheat regions	
		Hard winter wheat[a]	Spring wheat[b]
	(Bushels)	(Bushels)	(Bushels)
1920-29	12.7	11.5	11.6
1930-39	10.7	9.0	7.1
1940-49	15.7	13.8	14.7
1950-59	17.1	13.3[c]	14.8[d]

[a] Hard winter wheat region includes Kansas, Nebraska, Oklahoma, Texas, Colorado, Wyoming and New Mexico.

[b] Spring wheat region includes Montana, North Dakota and South Dakota.

[c] For 1957-59 winter wheat yields were used after multiplying by the factor .8 to make them more comparable with the yields by wheat regions.

[d] For 1957-59 spring wheat yields were used after multiplying by the factor .96.

Sources: "Wheat production," Agr. Info. Bul. No. 179, March, 1958, ARS, USDA. "The wheat situation," Feb., 1960, ARS, USDA.

HARD WINTER WHEAT

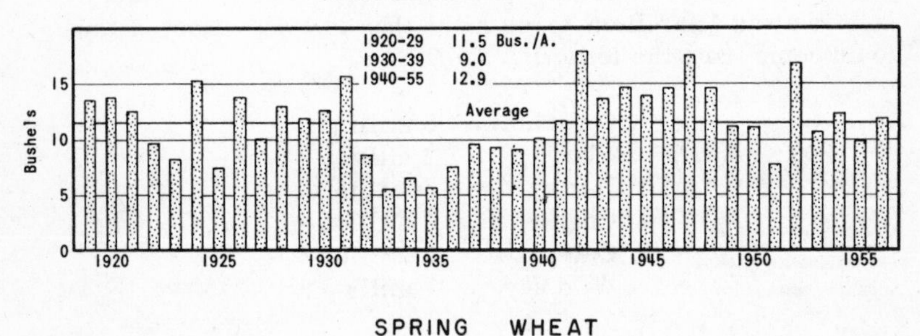

SPRING WHEAT

1920-29 11.6 Bus./A.
1930-39 7.1
1940-55 14.2
Average
Bushels
0
5
10
15
1920
1925
1930
1935
1940
1945
1950
1955

Fig. 6.3. Wheat yields per seeded acres for the Great Plains States from 1920 to 1960.

Potential production from 55,000,000 acres of wheat yielding 14 bushels per acre is 770,000,000 bushels. This is more than the average total disappearance of wheat in continental United States, which is 665,000,000 bushels.

This potential production can be increased further by greater adoption of improved technology. Considerably more nitrogen and phosphorus fertilizers can be profitably used. More drought-resistant and otherwise better varieties are available for use. Better residue management and tillage methods can be used by many farmers. Greater control of weeds, insects and diseases is possible. Some spring wheat, especially in South Dakota and Montana, can be shifted to winter wheat which produces 5 to 10 bushels per acre more. Better erosion control will decrease crop losses. The combined effect of these are reflected in the yield predictions given in Table 6.6. Roughly, the average of

Table 6.6. Predicted Wheat-Acre Yields Under Average and High Management for Level to Gently Undulating Phases of Selected Soil Families in the Spring Wheat and Hard Winter Wheat Areas of the Great Plains States

Soil family[a]	Management level	
	Average	High
	(Bushels)	(Bushels)
Spring wheat area		
Aastad (loam)	18	24
Barnes (loam)	14	20
Bearden (loam)	18	28
Williams (loam)	10	14
Hard winter wheat area		
Amarillo (fine sandy loam)	12	16
Colby (silt loam)	10	14
Crete (silty clay loam)	14	20
Dalhart (fine sandy loam)	8	12
Goshen (silt loam)	16	20
Hastings (silty clay loam)[b]	18	26
Hastings (clay loam)[c]	12	16
Holdrege (silt loam)	16	22
Judson (silt loam)	20	28
Kirkland (silt loam)	14	20
Lancaster (loam)	10	16
Pullman (clay loam)[b]	14	18
Pullman (clay loam)[c]	10	14
Sharpsburg (silty clay loam)	20	30
Teller (loam)	14	22
Vebar (fine sandy loam)	12	16
Williams (silt loam)	12	16

[a]Prediction based upon texture indicated.
[b]Eastern part of area. [c]Western part of area.

these yield increases is 40 percent, being slightly higher in the more humid areas.

These yield predictions are based upon those given in soil survey reports, in the interpretations of key or benchmark soils and in other publications.[10] They are the results of the combined judgment of many people who evaluated the available information.

Increasing crop yields 40 percent on the average appears to be possible. If the past trend of increasing yields continues, however, it will be about 1990 before the average yield per harvested acre will be 20 bushels.

If technology were understood and practiced by all farmers, the average annual potential production of wheat in the Great Plains States could be more than a billion bushels.

---

[10] The interpretations of key and benchmark soils, when completed and kept up to date, will provide basic yield predictions for studies of potentials and other uses. They also will provide the basic interpretations needed for other purposes, such as conservation planning by farmers and ranchers. The philosophy of key or benchmark soils is to provide an approach which makes possible the maximum contribution by people in experiment stations and elsewhere to soil interpretations. Unfortunately, only a start has been made.

Chapter 7

R. W. PEARSON
Agricultural Research
Service, USDA

Cotton Production Trends

COMMERCIAL COTTON CULTURE in the United States is limited to areas having 200 or more frost-free days. Thus the Cotton Belt lies generally south of the 37^0 N parallel, except on the West Coast where it extends somewhat farther north. The location of major centers of production within the Cotton Belt, their potentials for production and the shifting pattern of cotton culture are a result, however, of a number of factors in addition to climate. A brief review of geographical shifts in cotton production in the past will show how trends set in motion many decades ago are strongly influencing the pattern today.

Cotton was introduced along the Atlantic Seaboard by the earliest settlers, and by the middle of the seventeenth century its culture formed an important part of the agriculture of this region. As the settlers moved westward, cotton became the main cash crop, first in the Piedmont, then in the Southeastern Coastal Plain and later in the South Central States.

By the time of the Civil War, the center of production had shifted from the worn-out soils of the Carolinas to the newer lands of the mid-South. Alabama and Mississippi then accounted for nearly one-half of all cotton grown in the country. The Civil War, with its destruction of the marketing, financing and transportation complex, was followed by development of the sharecropping system, and increasing numbers of small family-operated farms. The introduction of fertilizers and their increased use made possible the reclamation of many abandoned farms in the older areas. This also increased the yields in the newer sections. But the westward migration in search of new and cheap land continued. The period from 1880 to the advent of the boll weevil was marked by a very rapid expansion in cotton production throughout the Old Cotton Belt and in Louisiana, Arkansas, Oklahoma and Texas.

Figure 7.1 shows that the period 1920-58 was marked by a drastic decline in production in the rolling to hilly areas of the

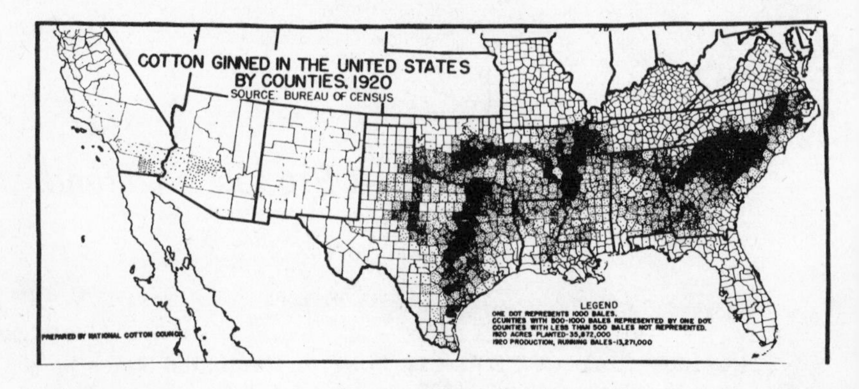

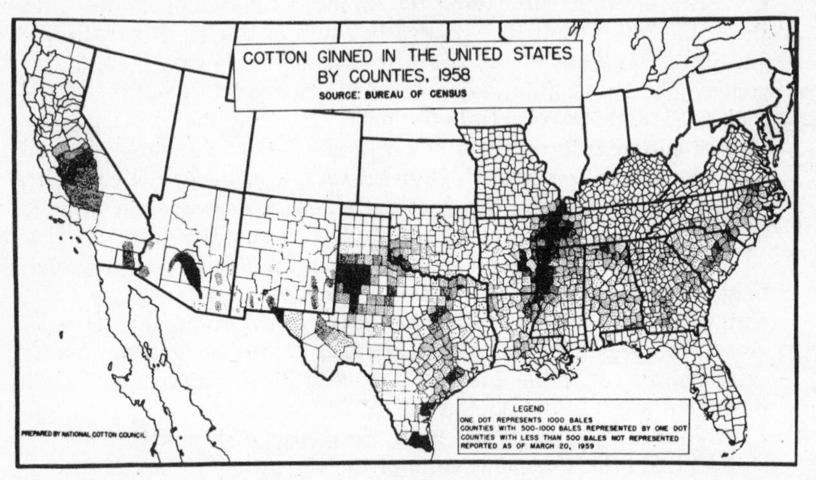

Fig. 7.1. Distribution of cotton production in the United States in 1920 and 1958. (Prepared by the National Cotton Council of America.)

Carolinas, Texas and Oklahoma, accompanied by a tremendous expansion in the Texas High Plains and the irrigated valleys of California, Arizona, New Mexico and Texas. These changes from 1940-60 are expressed in acres and percent shift for selected groups of states in Table 7.1. During this period, cotton acreage in the predominantly upland states of the Southeast has declined 69 percent. The Delta States have lost 57 percent of their acreage and Texas and Oklahoma 44 percent. The western states, in contrast, have gained 101 percent in cotton acreage. It should be noted, however, that the 1958 cotton acreage in the Southeast was the lowest in history, and that it increased in 1959 by about 60 percent. In contrast, acreage in the West changed little from

Table 7.1. Changes in Cotton Acreage in Different Sections of the Cotton Belt During the Period 1938-58 (4)

Section	Harvested cotton, 1,000 acres			Percent increase or decrease during period
	1938	1948	1958	
Ala., Ga., S.C.	5,310	4,039	1,263	-69
Miss., Ark., La.	5,777	5,815	2,504	-57
Texas, Okla.	10,440	9,638	5,805	-44
Calif., Ariz., N. Mex.	638	1,294	1,285	+101

1958 to 1959. Increased per-acre yields since 1920 have gone far toward maintaining total production on the declining acreage in the Old Cotton Belt. The Delta States produced the same amount in 1957 as in 1920, and on less than half the acreage, and the rest of the Southeast produced nearly one-half as much on one-sixth the acreage.

While this gives a gross picture of the movements of cotton culture within the entire Cotton Belt, it does not bring out important shifts within the various sections. In the Southeast, cotton acreage in the Delta Region of Mississippi, Arkansas, Louisiana and Tennessee has declined relatively little in comparison with the loss of the upland areas of those states. This is reflected to some extent by the difference in percentage reductions between Alabama, Georgia and South Carolina, and Mississippi, Arkansas and Louisiana. Similarly, while the total acreage of Texas and Oklahoma decreased 44 percent, there was a tremendous expansion in the High Plains, and the extreme upper and lower Rio Grande counties at the expense of the Black Prairie and Coastal Plain areas. It has been estimated, for example, that the High Plains alone will produce around two million bales in 1960, or one-half of Texas' total production.

Distribution of production in 1958, as given in Table 7.2, shows that the center of gravity of cotton production lies definitely in the Southwest. However, California and Arizona, with only 10 percent of the total cotton acreage, accounted for 20 percent of the production. The present core areas of production in the United States are located in the San Joaquin and Imperial Valleys of California, the Gila Valley of Arizona, the Pecos and Upper Rio Grande areas of New Mexico and Texas, the Texas High Plains, the lower Rio Grande and the Arkansas, Mississippi and Louisiana Delta.

Table 7.2. Distribution of Cotton Production in the United States by Regions, 1958 (4)

Region[a]	Harvested acreage	Production
	(Percent of U.S. total)	
Southeast	40	37
Southwest	50	43
West	10	20

[a] Southeast: States east of the Texas-Arkansas line; Southwest: Texas, Oklahoma and New Mexico; and West: California and Arizona.

FACTORS INFLUENCING LOCATION OF MAJOR COTTON PRODUCTION AREAS

A number of factors have played a part in the westward movement of cotton. Not the least of these have been the Federal production control programs begun during the thirties, and indirect subsidies such as cheap water provided by reclamation and irrigation programs in the West. The impact of these factors on cotton production is beyond the scope of this chapter and are merely recognized here as being potent influences.

The southwestern and western areas have some advantage in efficiency of production, however, to account in part for the shift. In general, these advantages derive from the facts that moisture is under the farmer's control, and that large-scale, mechanized production is the rule. Throughout the Southeast, excessively wet conditions at planting time frequently delay establishment and early growth of cotton, hinder weed control and encourage nitrogen loss by leaching and volatilization. When periods of deficient rainfall occur during the summer months, the low water-storage capacities of many of the soils make them unable to meet plant demands for moisture. During the harvest season, wet conditions often cause storm damage to the fibers and delay harvest.

Production in the arid region is totally dependent upon the availability of irrigation water and the land's suitability for irrigation. Large-scale operation, and the adequate credit and financing that goes with it, make specialized management and mechanization possible. In the humid region, the only cotton production center that has held its own in recent years is the Delta. This area is characterized by relatively level topography, larger operational units and more fertile soils than are found in the rest of the Southeast.

Several specific problems and characteristics that have had a bearing on the cotton industry should be mentioned.

Climate

A number of climatic factors are important to cotton production along with the length-of-growing-season requirement already mentioned. For example, spring mean temperatures must be high enough to insure rapid germination and early growth to avoid seedling diseases and resultant poor stands. An average spring temperature of about 60° F. is generally considered minimum. However, even where this condition is met, periods occur in some areas during which the temperature is too low for normal germination and growth. This condition would occur with greater frequency, for example, in the more northerly parts of the Belt and on the higher elevations, such as in the Texas High Plains. While this problem can be partially offset by later planting, delayed maturity and harvesting, and increased insect damage is the price paid. In the humid region, late planting aggravates the boll weevil problem and increases the hazard of crop damage by rain in the late fall. In general, the optimum planting date seems to be about two weeks after the average date of the last killing frost. Delay in planting beyond this point usually results in decreased yield. Frequently even a two-week delay in the humid region causes yield reductions of up to 20 percent. In most of the arid areas, planting can be done over a wider period without appreciable yield reduction. Sufficient time for the crop to mature before frost must be the chief consideration. Furthermore, since water is controlled, planting can be scheduled with certainty, whereas in the humid region it is dependent upon the weather. Sunshine is another factor of importance in cotton culture. Cotton is a sun-loving plant, and areas having as much as 50 percent cloudy weather have too little sunshine for the best growth of cotton. In the western part of the Belt the weather is typically bright and sunny with sunshine more than 90 percent of the time. The figure drops to a general level of 60 to 70 percent in the Southeast.

The total annual rainfall in the Old Cotton Belt of the Southeast ranges from 45 to 55 inches, which would appear at first glance to be adequate for high cotton yields. This is not the case, however. In the first place, considerably less than half the rainfall comes during the growing season. In addition, the high summer temperatures result in high rates of evaporation. These factors, combined with the low-profile moisture holding capacities, result in moisture becoming limiting for crop growth at times during practically every year. On the other hand, when excessive rainfall occurs in the spring, planting is delayed beyond optimum dates, and weed control becomes difficult. During the growing season, periods of wet weather complicate control of insects and favor attacks by disease organisms. Finally, at the end of the season, wet and windy weather, often the backlash of fall hurricanes, delays harvesting and lowers the quality of the crop. So, while the humid areas have an advantage in their near-adequate rainfall, it is at least partially offset by the distinct hazards of excessive and ill-timed moisture.

As a result of its relatively high annual rainfall, the Southeast is a region of many streams and rivers. Subterranean water resources are excellent in some areas. In this respect the Old Cotton Belt as a whole is in a favorable position. Supplemental irrigation of cotton and other crops has expanded rapidly since 1950, especially in the Delta where abundant water lies near the surface and only minor land forming is generally required for furrow irrigation. One important obstacle to full development of the water resources of the South is the lack of up-to-date regulatory legislation. This problem has been widely recognized, especially with the rapidly growing industrial demands for water, and most, if not all of the states, are in the process of correcting it.

In the arid region, in contrast, crop production is totally dependent upon the availability and quality of water for irrigation. Expansion of crop production in these areas is strictly limited, both by the total water supply and by increasing competition for industrial and urban use. For example, it has been shown (9) that in 1958, water was pumped from the ground over a 25,000-square-mile area of the high plains of Texas and New Mexico at a rate 140 times that at which it was being replenished. Further, increasing salt content of underground water often becomes a complicating factor when the supply is overburdened. So, while the possibility of moisture control through irrigation is a distinct advantage in growing cotton, the limited water resources of arid areas impose restrictions on the potential production of these regions.

Soils

Cotton is grown successfully on soils that vary widely in chemical and physical properties from the acid, highly leached soils of the Southeast to the neutral-to-alkaline, m
soils of the arid regions. In fact, it is grown on

the identified, great soil groups in the United States. The bulk of production, however, is on six of these: the Red-Yellow Podsolic soils, the Grumosolic soils, the Alluvial soils, the Reddish Prairie soils and the Reddish-Brown Lateritic soils (2). Within each group, of course, are soils poorly adapted to cotton culture, usually because of unsuitable topography, shallowness, poor internal drainage, extremes of texture or alkalinity and salinity. While native soil fertility was an important influence in the shifting of production to newer soils in earlier times, advances in knowledge of the nutrient requirements of the crop and the development of fertilizer technology have now largely offset this factor.

In general, the soils of the Southeast require lime and complete fertilization for maximum cotton yields, whereas only nitrogen and phosphorus are needed in most of the Southwest and West. Here again, however, the Delta has an advantage over most of the Southeast and is on an equal footing with the West. These Alluvial soils produce high yields with only nitrogen fertilization, although the need for mineral fertilization will undoubtedly increase with time.

Water-holding capacity is an important characteristic that affects production, especially in the humid region. The Red-Yellow Podsolic soils of the Southeast generally have a low capacity, often in the order of only one inch per foot of profile. Moisture stress develops sooner on these soils than, for example, on the Alluvial soils of the Delta during periods of drouth that occur frequently during the summer.

Good internal drainage is a prerequisite for successful cotton culture. Poorly or imperfectly drained soils frequently cannot be planted at the proper time, and weed control is difficult. Poor drainage is the chief reason why the Grumosolic soils of Alabama and Mississippi Black Prairie, which formed an important cotton production center before the advent of the boll weevil, are now primarily devoted to livestock. In Texas, the same soils, but under lower rainfall, are used successfully for cotton. In the Delta, the bulk of the cotton is grown on the medium-textured, better-drained soils, while the finer, more poorly drained members are used for pasture, soybeans and other crops. Similarly, the soils used for cotton culture in the arid and semi-arid regions are generally the intermediate textured and permeable type with good internal drainage.

Topography

The 1958 distribution of cotton production as shown in Figure 7.1, illustrates how the areas of relatively level land gained while in the hill sections production was decreasing. Lack of adaptability to mechanization, and susceptibility to erosion under intensive cotton culture, have placed these traditional producing areas of the Old Cotton Belt at a serious competitive disadvantage with respect to the more nearly level river flood plains of the South and West and the Texas High Plains. It should be mentioned, however, that the extensive areas of gently rolling land in the Lower Coastal Plain of the Carolinas and Georgia are well suited to both mechanization and supplemental irrigation. Drainage is the first requirement for using most of this area.

Insects and Diseases

The boll weevil has been the most important single cause of geographical shifts of cotton production since 1920. As the boll weevil advanced from the Mexican border to the Atlantic seaboard — from 1900 to about 1920 — cotton production dropped in state after state to only a fraction of previous levels, particularly in the southern parts of the Belt. This threatened collapse of the entire economy of the region stimulated movement to areas less affected. It intensified the search for remedial measures that resulted in insecticides development, varietal improvements and increased use of fertilizers and other improved practices. All these tended to offset losses caused by the weevil. The advances began an upward swing in production efficiency that has been maintained. Even so, boll weevils still take a large annual toll of the crop throughout the Old Cotton Belt. In 1950, for example, the estimated loss was 23 percent. These losses, when added to the cost of control measures (which runs up to $30.00 per acre), places the affected areas at a competitive disadvantage with areas where the weevil is not a problem.

The arid region, while free of the boll weevil, does have insect problems, including some insects not common to the humid areas, such as pink boll worms, Lygus bugs and salt marsh caterpillars. Control of these and other insects requires on the average about four applications of insecticides per season at a cost that commonly runs up to $10.00 per acre. Thus, the actual cost of insect control here is considerably less. Furthermore, the effectiveness of control measures is usually considerably greater as a result of climate, which is one of the important reasons for the higher cotton yields in the West.

Diseases have been a serious problem throughout the Cotton Belt and there seems to be little over-all difference in losses among the various sections, as indicated by the 1959 estimates

Table 7.3. Estimated Reduction in Cotton Yield as a Result of Disease Damage, 1959[a]

State	Average estimated yield reduction
	(Percent)
Calif., Ariz., N. Mex.	10.80
Texas, Okla.	13.63
Ark., La., Miss.	10.75
Ala., Ga., Tenn., N.C., S.C.	12.96

[a] Estimates of the Cotton Disease Council.

recorded in Table 7.3. While losses are still serious, they have been reduced markedly through aggressive breeding programs and rapid adoption of improved, resistant varieties as they are developed.

Economic Factors

The general pattern of small, family-operated farms in the Old Cotton Belt was formed after the breakup of the large holdings following the Civil War. The average size of farms in the more recently developed areas of the West and Southwest are larger, of necessity, because of the much larger capital investment required for intensive production under irrigation. This difference is clearly illustrated by the figures of Table 7.4, although data were not yet compiled for the West. Average cotton acreage of farms in the Southeastern Coastal Plain and Piedmont are only 6.1 and 11.6 acres, respectively, with capital investments

Table 7.4. Average Size, Cotton Acreage and Capital Investments of Typical Cotton Farms (5)

	Total acreage	Cotton acreage	Capital investment
Southern Coastal Plain	163	6.1	$ 13,540
Piedmont	183	11.6	18,400
Texas Black Prairie	185	36.3	31,340
Texas High Plains			
Non-irrigated	404	110	53,390
Irrigated	351	146	103,590
Delta			
Small farmers	58	11	13,110
Large farmers	1,000	197	203,350

Table 7.5. Allotted Cotton Acreage and Average Allotment Per Farm in Different Sections of the Cotton Belt, 1960 (6)

Section	Total acreage[a]	Average allotment
		(Acres)
Ala., Ga., S.C.	2,568,761	9.1
Miss., La., Ark.	3,679,047	17.1
Texas, Okla.	8,127,515	32.8
Calif., Ariz., N. Mex.	1,566,940	61.2

[a] Represents 97 percent of the total U.S. cotton acreage.

of only about 14 and 18 thousand dollars. In the irrigated Texas High Plains, by contrast, average cotton acreage per farm is 146 acres, and the capital investment over 100 thousand dollars. While the Delta, which is holding its own easily in cotton, does have a number of small farms, it is typically an area of much larger operating units than the rest of the South.

The average 1960 cotton allotments per farm in different parts of the Cotton Belt are listed in Table 7.5. In the upland areas of the Southeast, the oldest cotton-producing section of the country, it is only 9.1 acres per farm. It is nearly double that in the Delta States. While data are not at hand for the hill counties of these states, their operating units are much smaller than in the Delta counties. The average allotment in Texas and Oklahoma is 32.8 acres, and that of the western states 61.2.

Table 7.6 gives an idea of the size distribution of operating units in representative groups of states in different sections of the Cotton Belt. In the upland areas of the Southeast, 86 percent of the farms had cotton allotments of less than 15 acres, a unit

Table 7.6. Size Distribution of Choice "A" Cotton Allotments in Different Sections of the Cotton Belt, 1959[a] (7)

	Percentage of total allotments			
Section	Less than 15 acres	15 to 50 acres	50 to 100 acres	More than 100 acres
Ala., Ga., S.C.	86.0	11.9	1.5	0.6
Miss., La., Ark.	78.5	15.8	3.2	2.7
Texas, Okla.	54.7	32.0	9.1	4.2
Calif., Ariz., N. Mex.	44.2	31.7	12.5	11.6

[a] Choice "A" allotments represented about 92 percent of the total.

too small to justify conversion from mule to tractor power, considering the cotton alone. It should be mentioned, however, that a large number of these small allotments have not been planted in the past. Under regulations in effect until 1960, allotments turned in were lost, often to the western area. Consequently, small allotments simply have either been held for subsidy payments or rented to larger operators in the vicinity. Under 1960 rules, 75 percent of an allotment must be planted or it must be turned in. But, now, if the allotment is turned in, it is retained in the state, and the individual does not lose the right of reassignment at a later date. This change will go far in stabilizing the production pattern within regions, and will make for more efficient production on larger units. The percentage of small allotments decreases rapidly from East to West with an increasing proportion of farms with allotments of more than 50 acres, where extending mechanization to harvesting becomes an economic possibility. One-fourth of all farms growing cotton in California, Arizona and New Mexico have allotments of more than 50 acres, and half of these are above 100 acres.

The possible gross income from cotton on the bulk of the farms of the Southeast under the present control program is inadequate to support the degree of mechanization required for efficient production. As a result, small operators are forced to seek alternative means of maintaining income. More and more, industry is helping bridge the gap. Those who elect to continue farming are finding the pressure to shift to other farming enterprises increasingly difficult to resist. And here, tradition is an extremely important factor working toward retention of cotton as long as possible. Cotton culture has been practiced for generations, and both the farmer and farm labor are thoroughly familiar with the management of the crop under their particular conditions. Furthermore, markets are established, and private financing is geared to this crop in much of the region. Changing over to a new system requires development of new skills, and, usually, increased capital investment. Many small farmers find these most difficult. Basically, however, the problem is one of finding an alternative cash crop with a ready market and an adequate income potential, but a crop not already under acreage restriction. In spite of these problems, however, change is taking place, as indicated by the figures of Table 7.7. During the two decades 1930 to 1950, the acreages of such crops as soybeans, oats and peanuts have increased markedly in the Southeast. Also, the cattle industry is definitely moving, this time from West to East. Since 1938 the number of cattle in the Southeast has nearly doubled, and quality has improved markedly. And the trend is still upward.

Table 7.7. Changes in Proportion of Land Used for Production of Crops Other Than Cotton in the Seven Principal Cotton Producing States of the Southeast, 1930-50 (8)

Item	Percent change
Oats	+348
Soybeans	+1,402
Peanuts	+84
Hay	+115
Pasture	+54
Tobacco	-18

While cattle production does not solve the small farm operator's problem it does give the larger farm operator an alternative source of income and provides a means of keeping labor busy during the off season for cotton.

These statements should not in any sense be taken to indicate that a complete shift of cotton production from the non-Delta states of the Southeast is inevitable. To the contrary, in many local areas and on many operating units throughout the region, a combination of factors favor successful competition. Under present conditions, however, it appears that production will be concentrated in such areas and on such units to a much greater extent than exists even now.

YIELD POTENTIAL IN DIFFERENT SECTIONS OF THE COTTON BELT

Yield potentials of farming areas cannot be accurately determined but reasonable estimates can be based on the results of field experiments, crop-yield contests and surveys of farmers' yields where intensive production practices are applied. The estimates given here also include the ideas of a number of research and extension workers who were kind enough to give their views.

Considering the irrigated areas of the Southwest and West, yields of short staple cotton of up to 4 bales per acre are possible under the best conditions on individual farms and in field experiments. This is true in practically all of the major producing areas from the Lower Rio Grande to the San Joaquin Valley. Yields of 2 to 3 bales are not uncommon on farms with good management. This is not especially surprising in light of the high average yields in these areas.

What is surprising is that yields of the same order of magnitude can be made in other parts of the Belt, with supplemental irrigation, increased fertilization and intensive insect control. A good example of this is shown in Figure 7.2. This experiment was carried out cooperatively by the ARS and the Alabama Experiment Station, on a typical Coastal Plain soil at Thorsby, Alabama, during 1957-59, inclusive. Although only the data for the first two years are presented, the results have been consistent for the entire period. Top yields have been around 5,000 pounds of seed cotton averaging about 38 percent lint, making just under 4 bales per acre. The experiment included as base treatments mechanical disruption of a plow pan that had formed in the soil prior to the experiment, fumigation for control of nematodes, heavy applications of mineral fertilizer and dusting and spraying, as required, to control insects. In addition to the high yield potential demonstrated, this experiment emphasized several points not previously recognized. Cotton has been generally regarded in the South as a drouth-resistant crop, yet highest yields were made in this experiment with the highest soil moisture level used. Also, nitrogen applications of more than about 120 pounds per acre were generally considered adequate for maximum yields possible in the Southeast, yet there was a strong response up to 240 pounds with the highest moisture level.

These high yields, while indicative of potential, were only

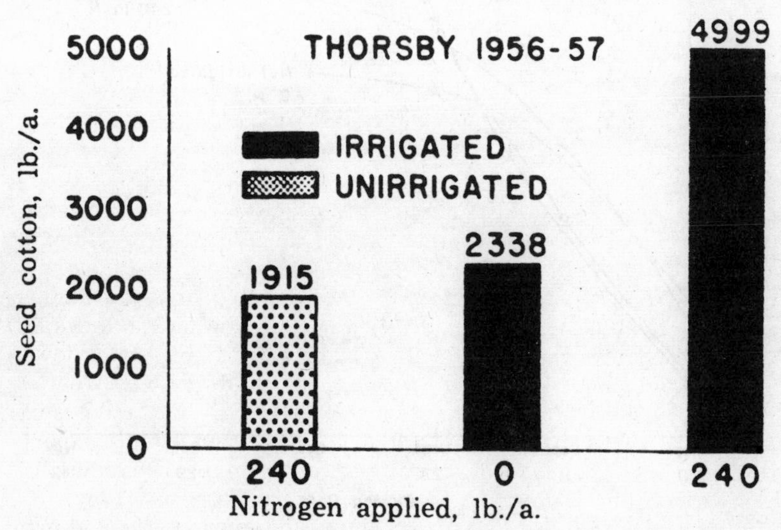

Fig. 7.2. Yields of cotton with high rates of nitrogen and moisture alone and in combination, 1956-57. (3)

obtained at the price of rank vegetative growth and delayed harvest. Also, there was considerable lodging, due primarily to the tremendous weight of fruit set, which aggravated boll rot and harvesting problems. The effect on maturity is illustrated in Figure 7.3, which shows that the gain for both irrigation and increased rates of nitrogen is in fruit that matures during the later part of the growing season. As has been mentioned earlier, the weather hazard increases as the harvest date is advanced into the

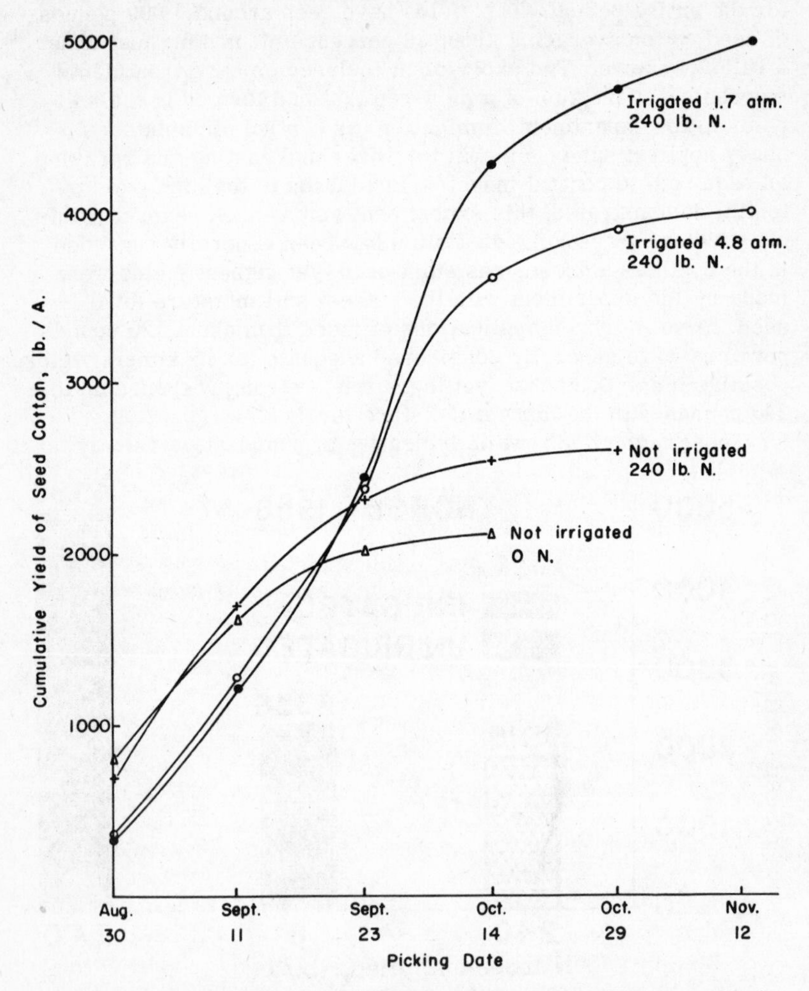

Fig. 7.3. Effect of moisture level at a high rate of nitrogen on yield of cotton. Thorsby, Ala. 1957.

Table 7.8. Top Yields Made in the Mississippi Total Farm Yield Cotton Production Program,[a] 1959 (10)

County	Name	Measured acres	Lbs. lint yield per acre
	0-4.9 Acres size cotton allotment		
Lincoln	Eldon Smith	3.9	1,076.0
	5-14.9 Acres size cotton allotment		
Carroll	J. M. Stanford	12.6	1,183.0
	15-99.9 Acres size cotton allotment		
Sharkey	Maxie Barnett	16.9	1,084.0
	100-499.9 Acres size cotton allotment		
Holmes	H. L. Nichols, Jr.	376.0	1,276.0
	500 Acres up size cotton allotment		
Washington	Marion Stevens	586.0	990.0
Five state highest average lint yield per acre			1,121.8

[a] Each farmer produced the state's highest lint yield per acre within the size cotton acreage allotment.

fall. These data, then, cannot be interpreted as representing present practical possibilities for commercial production in the Southeast. Solution of the several problems raised could, however, give them practical application.

Turning to observations made on farmers' fields, the results given in Table 7.8 should indicate present yield potentials under farmer management in a typical southeastern state. These highest average yields came from both Delta and upland counties. The five highest state yields averaged about 2 1/4 bales per acre, which is very little below the top yields reported on well-managed farms in the West. Turning to a much broader sampling of the same state, Table 7.9 shows average yields of 253 farms entered in the Mississippi Total Farm Yield Cotton Production Program in 1959. Yields on 37 farms in the Lower Delta section approached 2 bales per acre, while those in the southeastern part of the state dropped to a little over 1 bale. The average for the 253 farms was 1 1/2 bales.

These, and similar observations that have been made in other southeastern states, lead to the conclusion that 1 1/2 bales per acre are immediately within the reach of cotton farmers of the region without irrigation, but simply by application of recommended practices. With irrigation, present practical yield potential would probably be about 2 1/2 bales.

Table 7.9. Average Yields of Lint by Sections of the State in the Mississippi Total Farm Yield Cotton Production Program, 1959 (10)

Location in state	No. of farms in contest	Average yield of program growers
		(Lbs. lint per acre)
Upper delta	18	854
North central	22	873
Northeast	50	749
Lower delta	37	904
Central	38	864
East central	33	663
Southwest	10	758
South central	29	610
Southeast	16	690
Weighted average for 253 farms		777
State average		516

The dry-land cotton producing areas of Texas and Oklahoma have a lower yield potential and average yield than the rest of the Belt. The general average yield is somewhat less than 1/2 bale per acre. In exceptionally good years, yields approach a bale, but the estimated maximum obtainable, on the average, by use of all known improved practices would be around 3/4 bale per acre. Thus, present yields in this region are close to the estimated potential. The chief limitations are soil moisture and structure.

PRESENT LEVELS OF APPLICATION OF TECHNOLOGY IN COTTON PRODUCTION

As was noted earlier, cotton yields and efficiency of production began an upward swing as a result of research begun in about 1920, and the trend has been even more marked since about 1950. Average yields increased from 30 to 40 percent during the decade 1947-58 over the previous 10 years (Table 7.10). Also, Figure 7.4 shows how production per man-hour has increased even more rapidly than per-acre yields. Technological advances in a number of fields have combined to make this possible. Further, it is impossible to evaluate fully the impact of improvement in one area of technology alone, since each interacts with the others in determining the potential effect on crop yield. This was illustrated clearly by the interaction of nitrogen fertilization and level of irrigation in the experiment at Thorsby, Alabama.

Table 7.10. Average Yield of Lint Cotton and Yield Trends by Regions, 1938-57 (4)

Region	Average lint yield 1938-47	1948-57	Increase
	(Lb./A)	(Lb./A)	(Percent)
Southeastern	290	379	34
Southwestern	182	238	31
Western	560	785	40

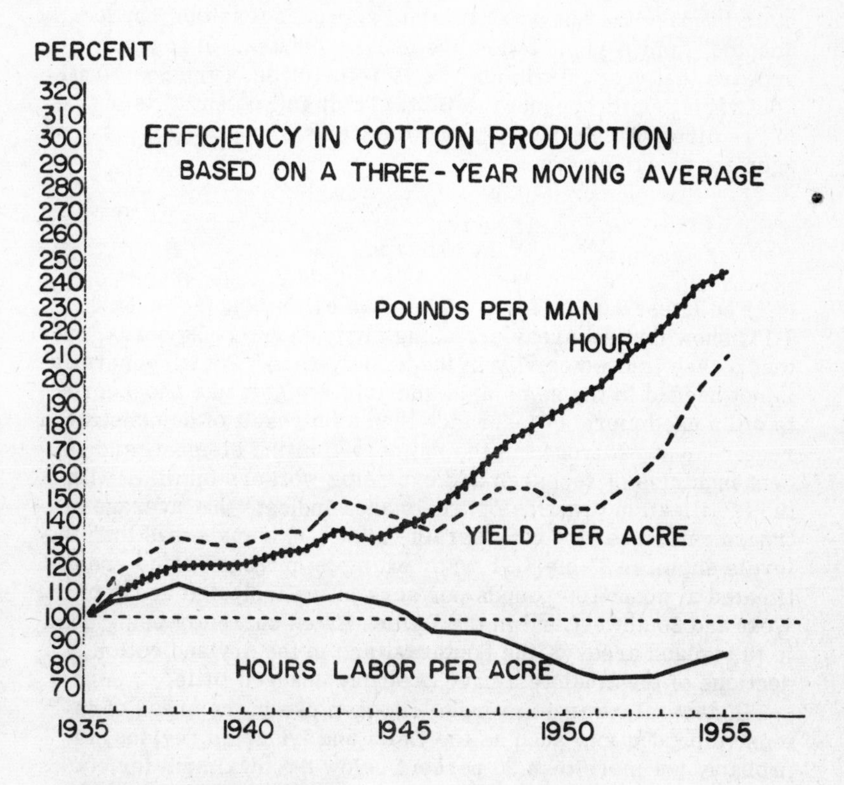

Fig. 7.4. Changes in cotton production efficiency in the United States, 1935-55.

Improved Varieties

The aggressive breeding programs of federal, state and private agencies have developed improved varieties adapted to the various cotton producing areas, and these are used in all commercial cotton plantings. In the West, particularly, variety standardization on a state basis has gone far toward yield and quality improvement. This is recognized in the market, and buying patterns have developed on the basis of the particular lint qualities of each variety. Standardization of varieties has not progressed as far in other parts of the country. In many parts of the Belt, soil and climatic conditions are too variable within a state to make the one-variety-state approach feasible, but locally adapted, improved varieties are usually planted. In general, it appears that near-maximum use is being made of the best available varieties throughout the Belt. Their full potential is not being realized though, because of limitations imposed by other management practices.

Fertilization

The latest data on fertilizer use on cotton, quoted in Table 7.11, show that all areas are using nitrogen and phosphorus, but that potash is used chiefly in the humid areas. Potash generally is not needed in the semi-arid and arid regions, and phosphorus is often used more as insurance than as a result of demonstrated requirement. Nitrogen is the primary limiting element, and recent inquiries of research and extension workers familiar with the fertilization practices of their area indicate that average nitrogen rates are now considerably higher in some areas than the levels shown in Table 7.11. For example, nitrogen rates are estimated at about 100 pounds per acre in the irrigated areas of the West and Southwest and in the Delta. Rates currently being used in the upland areas of the Southeast and in the dryland cotton sections of the Southwest have probably changed little.

In general, present average nitrogen use in the areas of intensive production, such as the Delta and irrigated regions, is probably not more than 20 percent below the maximum for economic return at present level of other practices. Of course, expansion of supplemental irrigation and more effective insect control would widen the gap appreciably. In the upland areas of the Southeast, however, present nitrogen use is only about one-half the recommended level and marked improvement in yields could be made here. Furthermore, fertilization with phosphorus and

Table 7.11. Average Fertilizer Use on Cotton
by Major Producing States, 1954 (1)

State	Rate of application per fertilized acre		
	Lbs. N	Lbs. P_2O_5	Lbs. K_2O
Alabama	37	48	31
Arkansas	39	21	34
California	81	16	1
Georgia	40	45	48
Louisiana	53	18	13
Mississippi	70	20	16
Missouri	40	31	35
New Mexico	43	32	--
North Carolina	33	47	45
Oklahoma	10	19	7
South Carolina	36	45	31
Tennessee	41	35	40
Texas	46	31	7

potassium is essential for satisfactory cotton yields throughout this area, and present average usage is considerably below recommended rates, probably by as much as 50 percent.

In general, then, it appears that there is little opportunity for improved yields from increased rates of fertilization except in the southeastern uplands, without a simultaneous intensification of other production practices, especially insect control.

Insect Control

Some measure of insect control is absolutely essential to economic cotton production throughout the Belt. The problem is, of course, much greater in the humid region than in the West, where control has about reached an economically optimum level, except that some improvement could be made in the timing of applications.

Since absolute control of insects is not possible with present materials and methods, the desirable degree of control becomes a matter of economics. As dusting and spraying frequency is increased, a point is reached beyond which the cost is not compensated by the expected yield increase. In the humid region, and especially in upland areas of small fields where dusting by plane is not feasible, control is considerably below the desired level. In the Delta, control is better because the larger operating units are better equipped and financed for taking advantage of the latest improvements in procedures and insecticides. Even so, it has been estimated that average yields in the Delta could be increased by 100 pounds of lint by strict adherence to recommended insect control measures. In the upland areas the improvement would be perhaps twice as great.

Mechanization

Rising costs of farm labor and the diminishing supply have resulted in the rapid introduction of machines for practically every operation in cotton culture. Machine harvest is the greatest single labor-saving operation. One spindle picker can harvest as much cotton per day as 50 to 70 hand pickers. It does this with an efficiency above 90 percent and very little reduction in grade through the use of defoliants and modern ginning equipment.

Weed control is a very important and difficult problem. Combinations of pre- and post-emergence herbicides, cross plowing and flame cultivation can practically eliminate hand hoeing and get the job done on time. Chemical weed control alone can reduce the hand-hoe labor requirements by up to 90 percent. In the Southeast, particularly, use of herbicides is expanding at a tremendous rate, and is a factor that will hasten complete mechanization in the region. A farm labor force cannot be maintained for picking alone, and itinerant or local seasonal labor cannot be depended upon.

Power stalk shredders and multi-row equipment for land preparation, planting and fertilizing mean planting more acres on time with less labor. Improved ground equipment such as high-pressure mist blowers, and the widespread use of airplanes for insecticide application, permit far better insect control.

To take advantage of these technological advances, however, requires a high gross return and a high capital investment, conditions that can be met only on the larger farms. For example, conversion to tractor power is not economically possible for less than about 15 acres, and purchase of a picker requires around 100 acres. As a result, the Delta Region and the irrigated areas of the Southwest and West are highly mechanized, while the upland areas of the South and Southeast have made much slower progress in this direction. However, smaller, less expensive spindle-type pickers have just appeared on the market. These appear to have real possibilities for farms with cotton allotments in the 50 to 100 acre range. At present, it is estimated that around 60 percent of the cotton produced in the Delta and the irrigated areas is harvested mechanically, but no more than 10 percent of that grown in the rest of the Southeast is mechanically picked. Of course, tractor power has almost completely replaced the mule throughout the Belt, accounting for at least 95 percent of the total production.

Moisture Control

There is room for considerable improvement in moisture control throughout the Cotton Belt. In the irrigated regions, research and extension workers feel improvements can be made in efficiency of water application and in timing of irrigations. In the humid region, practices that decrease runoff and evaporation losses and that encourage deeper plant rooting could add appreciably to the moisture available for crop growth during periods between rains.

In addition, the use of supplemental irrigation offers one of the most promising ways of making real advances in cotton production in those areas where it is practicable. This has been realized and was reflected in the increases in irrigated acreage during the 1950's. A weighted average, calculated from the figures quoted in Table 7.12, shows that about 14 percent of the cotton acreage in Arkansas, Louisiana and Mississippi was irrigated in 1956. Most of this acreage was in the Delta. The figures for Alabama indicate that less than 5 percent is probably irrigated in the rest of the Southeast. Further exploitation of supplemental irrigation, is, like mechanization, dependent upon farm resources and suitability of the land. Continuing expansion can be expected throughout the Delta and on favorably situated individual farms of the uplands, but widespread use of supplemental irrigation in the Southeast does not appear likely.

Table 7.12. Use of Irrigation in the Production of Cotton in Four Southeastern States, 1956

State	Irrigated cotton	
	(Acres)	(Percent)
Alabama	35,300	3.5
Arkansas	230,438	17.0
Louisiana	52,135	9.2
Mississippi	195,721	12.3

Source: Statistics compiled by the National Cotton Council of America.

SUMMARY

Aside from governmental production control programs, the locations of core areas of cotton production in the United States are primarily a result of climatic, topographic and economic factors. These factors have resulted in a marked decline in production on the small farms of the Southeast and those of the dryland areas of the Southwest. This decline has been accompanied by a concentration of production in the Delta and the irrigated areas of Texas and the West, where practically attainable yields with present technology are higher, operating units are larger and production efficiency greater.

Present levels of application of improved practices are higher in these centers of production than are economically possible in much of the remainder of the Cotton Belt. However, marked improvement in yield and production efficiency could be made, especially in the Southeast, through intensified use of present, locally recommended practices.

Potential yields attainable through maximum use of intensive production practices do not appear to be appreciably different among the various cotton producing areas. The practical application of these practices poses problems in the Southeast, however, that are not encountered in the arid region.

Further expansion of cotton production in the arid region will be restricted by the limited amount of water available for irrigation and will be at the expense of other crops. Further shifts will undoubtedly occur within the various areas, however, from the smaller, less efficient units to larger, more favorably situated farms.

LITERATURE CITED

1. ADAMS, J. R., NELSON, L. B., and IBACH, D. B. Crop use patterns of fertilizer in the U.S., Croplife, Aug. 18 – Oct. 13, 1958.
2. BROWN, H. A., and BATES, O. W. Cotton. McGraw-Hill, New York, 1958.
3. PEARSON, R. W., and SCARSBROOK, C. E. Interrelationships of fertilization and irrigation. Com. Fert. and Plant Food Ind., Jan., 1959.
4. USDA. Agricultural Statistics. Washington, D. C. 1920-58.
5. USDA. Farm costs and returns commercial family operated farms by type and location. Info. Bul. 176, 71 pp. Rev. 1959.
6. USDA. Cotton Division, CSS, Mimeograph Release 837-60, Mar. 22, 1960.
7. USDA. Cotton Division, CSS, Unnumbered Mimeograph Release dated June 1, 1959.

8. U.S. Dept. of Commerce, Bureau of Census, Washington, D. C., 1930, 1950.
9. U.S. Senate, Select Committee on National Water Resources. Water Resource Activities in the U.S., Comm. Print. No. 1, 59 pp., Aug., 1959.
10. WALLER, T. M. Total Farm Yield Cotton Production Program. Mississippi Agricultural Extension Service Unnumbered Mimeograph report of 1959.

Chapter 8

L. B. NELSON
Agricultural Research
Service, USDA

Physical Potentials for Crop Production

THERE CAN BE little doubt that a ceiling on total crop production will be reached sometime in the United States. Obviously this will occur when the population pressure is great; when all the land and water resources available to agriculture reach full development; and when natural limitations halt further improvements in technology and management practices. The question is: When will the ceiling be reached and at what level of production?

We can determine, within fair limits, the land and water resources available for expansion during the years between 1960 and 2000. We can also make certain assumptions as to population increases and eating habits, and use these to predict shifts in land use. But even for this brief period, it is exceedingly difficult to predict technological advances and the extent to which they may affect crop-production ceilings.

This chapter brings together published estimates of United States land and water resources available for development over the next few decades. It also points out some of the areas in our present technology that have possibilities for improvement, and some that appear to have approached their potential.

POSSIBILITIES FOR NEW CROPLAND

The total land resource of the United States, exclusive of Alaska and Hawaii, is 1903 million acres. Largely from this we must meet the food, feed and fiber needs of the nation regardless of whether the population is 180 million or 500 million. According to the 1954 U.S. Census of Agriculture, our total land resource is divided as follows: cropland, 460 million acres; open pasture and grazing land, 611 million acres; woodland and forest, 639 million; and all other uses, 193 million. Obviously, additional needs for cropland will have to be met by a shifting from the less intensive land uses.

Possibly as much as 110 million acres of our grassland and 105 million acres of woodland in continental United States are fairly well adapted for use in cropland rotations. Shifts between woodland and cropland are more difficult, time-consuming and expensive than shifts between grassland pasture and cropland.[1]

Of the 110 million acres of grassland suitable for cropland if plowed, drained and otherwise improved, about 12 million acres would make Class I land, 39 million, Class II, and 59 million, Class III (4). In these estimates, about 60 million acres of the grassland are on the Great Plains, 24 million acres in the Corn Belt and Lake States, 7 million in the Mississippi Delta, 5.5 million each in the Northeast and Appalachian areas, 3 million in the Southeast, and 5 million in the Mountain and Pacific States. Not all of these areas are equally suitable and, depending on the need for pastureland, as much as 50 percent might remain in grassland. Probably the most desirable are in the North Central States and the South, and the least desirable are in the Great Plains.

Of the 105 million acres of undeveloped land that could be changed from woodland to cropland as the need arises, about 8 million acres would become Class I land if cleared and properly cultivated. Another 34 million acres would develop into Class II land if simple erosion control and soil fertility practices were followed, and, with special erosion control and soil management practices, 63 million acres could be made into Class III land (4).

About 70 million acres of the undeveloped land lie in the Mississippi River Delta, Southeastern, and Appalachian states. Much of the best land is in the Mississippi River alluvial area of Louisiana, Mississippi, Arkansas and Missouri and requires clearing, draining and often flood control structures. Other undeveloped lands are scattered over much of the Southeast with the greatest concentrations in the Flatwoods, the Everglades and the southern alluvial plains (1, 6). These require clearing, draining, or both, and large amounts of fertilizer and lime. On sloping lands, erosion will be a problem. Tidal marshes, where rice production was once important, probably will be brought into production only as a last resort since they require diking and pump drainage, and many of the soils are of doubtful suitability.

About 12 million acres of cropland in the Northeast could be developed from abandoned farm and woodlands (4). Stone removal, clearing and drainage would be required most frequently.

---

[1] USDA. A 50-Year Look Aheaa at U. S. Agriculture. 20 pp. June, 1959. Processed.

Unfortunately, many of the better tracts are scattered and would be difficult to bring together into farm-size units.

The Lake States and Corn Belt have an estimated 12 million acres of potential cropland now in woods, cut-over areas and wet lands (4). Most of this acreage is in Minnesota, Wisconsin, Michigan and in fringe areas of the Corn Belt, and would require both clearing and draining. Very little suitable land is left for development in the Corn Belt proper.

The Southern Plain States have a potential of 9 million acres (4), about 3 million of which could be reclaimed by draining and breaking the Coastal Prairies of Texas. Most of the remainder could be salvaged by clearing brush, cedar and semi-arid woodland. The Northern Plains have a million-acre potential, and the Mountain States and Pacific States about one million, mostly in the Pacific Northwest. The latter does not include future irrigated lands and would result mostly from the clearing of woodlands and from draining and diking.

The foregoing shifts have been estimated on the physical potential of the land, without thought as to economic feasibility or desirability. The recent report of the Select Committee on National Water Resources, U.S. Senate, cites an estimated need of only 35 million acres of additional land from this source by the year 2000 when projected on the medium population level of 329 million (3).

Alaska now has 20,000 acres of cleared land and 3 million additional acres are thought to be physically suited for cultivation. Practically all of this acreage would have to be cleared and some would require drainage.

About 11 million acres of additional land can be irrigated in the western states (2). The largest development would come in the Upper Missouri River Basin and in the Western Gulf area of Texas. The new irrigation projects would be on lands now used largely for dry farming or grazing.

LOSSES OF CROPLAND

Partially offsetting the possible gains of new croplands are losses of lands to nonagricultural uses and to soil erosion, and the shifting of unsuited cropland to less intensive uses. Urban, industrial, and recreation development, new roads, airports, reservoirs and flood control areas require agricultural lands in ever-increasing amounts. Recently, the average rate of absorption into nonagricultural uses has been about 1.5 million acres per year of which about 25 percent came from cropland and about 15 percent from pasture. Under assumptions of medium population growth from 1960 to 2000, special nonfarm uses are expected to require another 81 million acres of which 20 to 25 percent might come from cropland, and 75 to 80 percent from woodland, pasture and other land (3).

Although the rate of loss of cropland from erosion has been reduced tremendously through application of soil conservation practices, land is still being lost at an estimated rate of 400,000 acres per year. With continuing emphasis on conservation and steady improvement of conservation practices, the rate of loss should decline appreciably in the future. However, about 50 million acres of cultivated land should be shifted either out of cultivation or into less intensive cultivation. Another 50 million acres should be subjected to more effective erosion control practices (3).

EXPANSION OF IRRIGATION

Overcoming all moisture deficits through irrigation is not in the picture. We have definite limitations on the amount of good-quality water available to agriculture. Not all lands are suitable for irrigation, and both available water and suitable land for irrigation are not always found together.

In a normal year, the U.S. averages 30 inches of precipitation. About 21 inches is used in evapotranspiration. The remainder, 9 inches, is returned to streams. About two-thirds of the streamflow occurs during flood periods and less than one-third is available over the majority of the year. By storage and regulation of release, it is thought possible to provide a future constant availability of about 5 inches of the total precipitation. Half of this is required for navigation and waste disposal, leaving about 2.5 inches for irrigation, industrial and domestic uses. Presently we are using about 0.9 inch for all of these, of which about 0.4 inch goes for irrigation. While such average figures are not too meaningful, they do illustrate that definite limitations exist on the amounts of water available for irrigation.

Industrial and domestic use undoubtedly will continue to require more water as the population increases. With industry reaping per-gallon returns for water fifty times that of irrigation, there is little to stop further commercial use of water.

Possibilities for increased irrigation are much greater in the East than in the West. The 17 western states receive about 28 percent of the total water supply (350 billion gallons per day) in the nation. About two-thirds is concentrated in the Pacific

Northwest where a large portion returns to the ocean. This leaves roughly 120 bgd, of which about 85 bgd of the total available are being used. The East, in contrast, has about 225 bgd with a current use of 80 bgd (2).

Not all water is suitable for irrigation. Brackish waters along the tidal inlets of the seacoasts, some western rivers, and many wells, may contain soluble salts in excess of what is safe to apply on the land.

Pollutants from industries, nuclear reactors, drainage ditches and sewage may also render streams unsuitable for irrigation, particularly during periods of low flow. Ground-water supplies may be polluted, also.

Probably less than 15 percent of the potential croplands of the United States are suitable for irrigation. Soils in arid regions having a combination of restricted drainage and high content of soluble salts and alkali are poor irrigation risks. Steep lands cannot be irrigated effectively, and extremely sandy soils retain too little water to justify irrigation except for certain high per-acre-return crops grown in areas of favorable climate. As a rule, only Class I, II or III lands are considered suitable for irrigation.

About 18 million acres of unirrigated land remain in the 17 western states, and about 29 million acres in the East, which conceivably could be irrigated if necessary. Full expansion of irrigation, however, is likely to come slowly and, because of high costs involved, only in response to population pressures. By 1980, assuming a medium potential for irrigation, it has been estimated that an increase of about 4.7 million acres for the West and 2.5 million acres for the East would occur. By the year 2000, using the same assumptions, the increase would be 11.2 million acres for the West and 4.7 million acres for the East (3).

Yield benefits from irrigation vary with the water deficit encountered in the soils during the growing season. In arid regions, practically no crop production can be obtained without irrigation. Crop-production increases that can be attributed to irrigation, decline from West to East as the amount of effective precipitation increases. In humid regions, both yield benefits and acreages irrigated vary more or less directly to the frequency and intensity of droughts and the time of their occurrence. Irrigation of corn, pasture, cotton and tobacco is highest during drought years and drought cycles, and declines considerably during years of ample or near-ample rainfall. Irrigation of rice remains constant from year to year and that of vegetables and speciality crops remains fairly constant.

LAND IMPROVEMENT THROUGH DRAINAGE

Removal of excess water from croplands and prevention of overland flow markedly affect crop production potentials. About one-fifth of our present cropland either has been brought into production or has been greatly improved through drainage. Drainage also goes hand-in-hand with development of successful irrigation projects in the West. The full potential to be realized from drainage, however, has not been reached on existing croplands, and many of the new croplands of the future will require extensive drainage.

In 1950, 102,688,000 acres were in organized public drainage enterprises in 40 states, of which four-fifths, or 82 million acres, were improved. Some 15 million acres in enterprises were still too wet for cultivation, and crop losses were frequent on an additional 10 million acres. In addition to the organized enterprises, an estimated 50 million acres have been drained by individuals (5).

Improvements in present cropland drainage can be brought about largely through rehabilitation of existing drainage systems at comparatively low costs. Improved yield potentials and more efficient operation can be achieved through such things as combinations of surface and subsurface drainage systems; more effective spacing and depth placement of tiles or moles, and improvement of outlets and lateral systems; drying out of potholes; adjustments of rates of water removal to crop and soil needs; improved maintenance and functioning of installed drains and drainage channels; adjustment of water tables to prevent subsidence on peat and muck soils; and removal of unneeded field ditches and spoil banks. Also, greater efficiency would result from coordination of piecemeal drainage systems and incorporation of larger acreages into community drainage enterprises.

No accurate data exists on the exact amount of undeveloped wetlands that can or should be drained in the United States. According to Wooten (5), there are some 50 million acres of wet and overflow lands which would be suitable for agricultural development if adequate drainage were provided. Of the 50 million acres of inadequately drained land, 60 percent is in organized drainage enterprises. Approximately 30 million acres are in partial cultivation and 20 million are undeveloped. The recent estimates and projections made for the Select Committee show that 10.1 million acres of grassland, and 24.7 million acres in forest which might eventually be shifted to cropland, would require drainage (3).

There seems to be little question that drainage will be a

major factor in increasing our agricultural potential. Undoubtedly drainage improvements on present croplands will be continued. In response to increasing population pressures, new or improved drainage systems will expand first into grasslands and gradually into the better forest lands. Other wetlands, such as the inland and coastal marshes and swamps, which are also important wildlife habitats, will probably receive drainage only as a last resort. In western irrigation projects on new lands, however, drainage is a necessary complement to the successful application of water.

Real possibilities exist for reducing costs of drainage and for improving the design and effectiveness of drainage systems. Plastic-lined mole drains equipped with grade-control devices are now in advanced stages of development and offer considerable promise for greatly reducing the cost of internal drainage. Improvements are being made in design of surface removal of water. Use of electrical resistance networks, combined with better understanding of soil properties as related to water movement into and through the soil, promise to take much of the guesswork out of designing drainage systems. Much research, however, still remains to be done.

CONSERVATION AND EFFICIENT USE OF WATER

As was indicated earlier, water is a major limiting factor in crop production, and there are definite limitations on the amount available to agriculture. The only alternative to moisture shortages is moisture conservation. Fortunately, there are tremendous possibilities for moisture conservation. They fall into three main categories: (1) conserving runoff water for irrigation, (2) getting more water into the soil moisture reservoir and (3) obtaining more efficient utilization of the available moisture stored in the soil.

Water conservation for irrigation can be achieved through increased use of dams and regulated release, increasing underground storage by artificial means, reduction of conveyance losses through canal lining systems, control of phreatophytes, increased re-use or recycling of waste waters, improved management of watersheds to regulate water yield, reduction of pollutants, prevention of salt intrusion, reduction of siltation of reservoirs and the like. Full exploitation of these measures can go far in increasing the water supplies available to agriculture, particularly in the western states.

There are possibilities, although seemingly remote, for

supplementing water supplies through artificial induction of precipitation, processing of sea or brackish waters, and control of evaporation from free water surfaces by chemical means.

Replenishment of the soil moisture reservoir through encouraging water intake and reducing runoff offers more potential in subhumid and humid regions than does irrigation. Replenishment can be achieved mainly through adoption or improvement of known practices. These include surface mulches, cropping systems designed to increase the intake rate, contour cultivation to hold the water on the land longer, strip cropping, graded terraces and water spreading. The effectiveness of these practices will vary with soil and climatic conditions and with the character of the individual rainstorms. However, they often improve the soil moisture situation materially.

Certainly the inefficient moisture-conserving practice of summer fallow in dry farming areas will be displaced by other more efficient practices. Usually only one-quarter of the rainfall that falls during the fallow season is stored in the soil for future use. Since there are about 25 million acres of cultivated summer fallow, this would add considerably to our land resources.

Exciting possibilities exist for more efficient use of soil moisture. It has been variously demonstrated that 40 percent or more of the water used in crop production is evaporated from the soil surface, which is much higher than originally thought. Although evaporation can be suppressed in experiments by covering the soil surface with a thin layer of plastic, practical field measures present many problems. Since heat from the sun converts liquid water into vapor in the evaporation process, evaporation suppression becomes largely a matter of diverting the heat from the evaporation process. Possibilities for reducing surface evaporation thus rest primarily in providing more thorough shading of the soil surface by the growing plants and in arranging the row directions and the geometry of the plants so there is a minimum of solar energy to be dissipated in evaporation at the soil surface. Evaporation suppression probably will be practical only on soils having a sufficiently high water holding capacity to store sizeable amounts of moisture. Also, sufficient precipitation is required to fill or nearly fill the soil reservoir. The Midwest would most closely meet these criteria.

Possibilities also may exist for reducing water losses from transpiration by spraying plants with wax-like chemicals. However, since evaporation is a major means of cooling the atmosphere around the growing plant, transpiration control would encourage heat build-up which in turn might increase respiration and tend to offset over-all yield gains. On the other hand, dissipating heat through air turbulence brought about by controlling the arrangement of crop plants in the field, or by limiting this treatment to crops that make their major growth during the cooler portions of the growing season, might offer real promise.

Anything that increases the dry matter production of a crop increases its water efficiency. Fertilizers are particularly effective in this respect. In fact, the efficiency of water use may be doubled. Increasing plant populations, utilizing more of the growing season through early planting and later maturity, encouraging rapid initial growth and substituting high yielding for low yielding crop varieties will all improve efficiency.

Weeds are extravagant users of water and greatly reduce the amount of water available for crop growth. Ragweed, for example, takes three times as much water as corn to produce an equal amount of dry matter. With the rapidly advancing technology of weed control through herbicides in combination with weed-free seed and cultivation, adequate control measures should be no problem in the long-term future.

INCREASED USE OF FERTILIZERS AND LIME

Fertilizers and lime play a very great role in the maintenance and improvement of the productive potential of agricultural lands. Before the advent of fertilizers and lime, our early agriculture was marked with abandonment of exhausted land. About 20 percent of the increase in farm output since 1940 has been attributed to fertilizers. We are now applying 7.4 million tons of primary plant nutrients of which 2.6 million tons are nitrogen, 2.6 are available phosphate and 2.2 are potash.

Considerable evidence indicates that we have not yet exploited the full potentials of fertilizers as a crop producing factor. Fertilizer use on most agricultural lands in the United States is modest in comparison with other progressive countries having highly developed or intensive agricultures. This is brought out in Table 8.1. As pressures on our agricultural lands approach those of western Europe, there is good reason to believe that fertilizer use on our better croplands where moisture is not a critical factor will also approximate that of western Europe. However, on drylands and lands of lower productive potentials, fertilizer use will stabilize at lower levels.

Although we are short on utilizing the full potential of fertilizers in over-all crop production, this situation does not apply equally for all crops or for all areas of the country. As shown in Table 8.2, the high cash-return crops approach or exceed the

Table 8.1. Average Rates of Fertilizer Application ($N + P_2O_5 + K_2O$) Per Acre of Agricultural Land[a] in 1957 for Selected Countries

Country or region	Lbs. per acre
Japan	190
Belgium	182
Netherlands	177
Formosa	129
Norway	126
West Germany	122
Denmark	107
United Kingdom	47
France	46
U.S.A.	12.5
Central America	6.5
South America	1.0
Africa	0.7

[a] Agricultural land includes arable, tree crops, permanent meadows and pastures.

Source: H. J. Page, "Trends in fertilizer consumption in relation to world food supply." Outlook in Agriculture, 2(5):203-12. 1959.

average fertilizer use reported for the leading fertilizer using countries. Also, we are closer to meeting the potentials of fertilizer use in the Southeast and Northeast than in other humid or irrigated areas of the country.

Considerable potential still remains for increased fertilizer use on the grain crops and hay and cropland pasture. Also, there would appear little question that the entire cropland acreage, except possibly in the more arid dry-farming areas, will eventually receive fertilizer. Fertilizer use probably will not increase equally for all three of the major nutrients. Greater quantities of nitrogen are needed by crops on most soils, and its use should increase accordingly.

While fertilizer use has increased greatly in the United States in recent years, the same does not apply for lime. Acid soils remain notoriously underlimed, and this situation must be corrected before we can realize full potentials of crop production.

Current use of lime in the United States averages about 20 million tons annually. This level of lime consumption is sufficient only to offset lime depletions through leaching and crop removal. For example, assuming a 250 pound per acre annual loss from an estimated 170 million acres of harvested cropland in the humid regions, this would amount to about 21 million tons. In addition to normal losses, many farm soils have accumulated

Table 8.2. Estimated Use of Principal Plant Nutrients by Crops and Regions, 1954

Crop or region	Acreage fertilized	Av. rate of $N + P_2O_5 + K_2O$ per fertilized acre
	(Percent)	(Pounds)
Tobacco	97	298
Potatoes	78	277
Vegetables	63	209
Fruits	58	151
Sugar crops	91	118
Cotton	58	105
Corn	60	80
Wheat	28	64
Oats and barley	30	65
Hay and cropland pasture	10	81
ALL CROPS		
Northeast	43	126
Lake States	29	73
Corn Belt	39	82
Appalachian	44	119
Southeast	69	112
Mississippi Delta	48	79
Southern Plains	13	59
Northern Plains	11	41
Mountain	13	70
Pacific	34	57
U.S.	30	79

Source: Fertilizer Used on Crops and Pastures in the United States — 1954 Estimates. Stat. Bul. 216. USDA, ARS, Aug., 1957.

residual acidity as a result of inadequate liming in the past, and others, particularly those in permanent pasture, have never been limed. A 1950 U.S. Department of Agriculture survey of conservation needs indicated that annual use should approach 80 million tons and that some 556 million tons would be required to reduce acidity to a level conducive to good crop production.

New lands and grasslands shifted to croplands will require large initial applications of fertilizer and lime. Soils of many of these lands, particularly in the East, are inherently very acid, and low in phosphorus and potassium.

Recovery of fertilizer nutrients by plants is alarmingly inefficient. Seldom over half of the nitrogen, 10 percent of the phosphorus and half of the potassium applied is recovered by crops. Certainly more efficient ways will be found someday to provide crops with the nutrients they require. Marked improvements in the efficient use of fertilizers, however, do not seem to be forthcoming in the immediate future.

MORE PRODUCTIVE CROPS

Crop breeding has been one of the more important and fastest moving ways to increase the productive potential of crops. Costs to the farmer are small, largely in the price of the seed, and adoption of improved varieties is rapid and widespread.[2] Increased yield and greater stability of production has resulted for many crops when improved varieties are combined with good practices. Crop breeding also has permitted establishment of disease and insect resistance, expansion of the area of adaptation of certain crops, adaption to mechanization and improvement of quality.

Commercial use of first generation hybrids has been successfully applied to corn, sorghum and a number of vegetable crops. First usage of commercial hybrids usually accounts for an initial yield increase of 20 to 25 percent over open pollinated varieties. Improvements and refinements over a period of years, as in the case of corn, further increase the yield potential about 15 percent. Hybrid grain sorghums are expected to follow the same pattern of improvement as corn. Present yield improvements for hybrid sorghum are reported to range from 20 to 30 percent and about 75 percent of grain sorghum is now hybrid.

Utilization of commercial hybrids may be realized in other crops. Hybrid alfalfa is a possibility, although present hybrids outyield open pollinated varieties by only 10 percent. In the South, hybrid cattail millet has come on the market within the last year (1959), and hybrid Pensacola Bahiagrass should be on the market within a few years, followed by a hybrid Starr millet and hybrid Sudan grass. One by one, cross-pollinated crops appear to be yielding to hybridization although many problems face the plant breeder. Hybrid cotton, for example, has failed so far because of the difficulty of producing hybrid seeds on a commercial scale.

Potentialities seem more limited for improvement in yields of self-pollinated crops that have already been tested intensively, such as small grains. The dwarf wheats, however, seem to be establishing a higher yield plateau in the Northwest. Shorter straw in crops such as dwarf wheat, dwarf sorghum and dwarf internode castors makes them adaptable to higher rates of nitrogen fertilizer application.

---

[2] Material reported here was obtained largely through discussions with Dr. Martin G. Weiss, Crops Research Division, ARS, USDA.

Progress in forage crop breeding, with few exceptions, has lagged behind accomplishments with several other crops. As research effort is increased, however, considerable advance in yield potentials of forage crops appears likely.

Breeding for disease resistance does much to maintain yields, although higher yield potentials usually are not established. Oat breeders have successfully evaded serious onslaughts of different races of crown and stem rust through a continuing program of developing new disease-resistant strains. There is hope, too, of introducing a broad-type of disease resistance into oat varieties that now exist in the wild species, _Avena strigosa_. Bacterial wilt, which virtually eliminated alfalfa from long rotations, was conquered by the resistant varieties such as Ranger, Buffalo and Vernal. Continuing success in the general area of disease resistance is expected.

Real advances have been made, and are likely to continue, in adapting crops to different climatic areas. There has been development of varieties of soybeans, for example, which permit the crop to be grown successfully in Minnesota and other northern areas. Grain sorghum breeding for earliness and laxness of head (to evade molding) is progressing. This will aid adaptation to more northern conditions.

IMPROVEMENTS IN FARM MECHANIZATION

Farm mechanization also must be considered in any evaluation of future potentials of crop production. We have all seen the effects of mechanization upon our agricultural economy. Replacement of animal power alone released an estimated 82 million acres of land which was used almost exclusively to produce feed for horses and mules. While such a far-reaching revolution in agriculture is unlikely to occur again, there are nevertheless continuing improvements and inventions which affect crop production.

Mechanization improvements[3] can be expected largely through perfection of machines that will permit more timely tilling of the soil and harvesting of crops, better and more effective methods for applying pesticide chemicals, less loss of crops during the harvest operation, manipulation of the soil in a manner to improve the soil environment for crop production and improved mechanical means for reducing erosion and water runoff.

Looking at the future on a crop basis, there seems to be little opportunity for much further improvement in the mechanization

[3] Material reported here was obtained largely through discussions with Dr. Walter M. Carleton, Agricultural Engineering Research Division, ARS, USDA.

of grain crops. Man-hours required for their harvest already have reached a low level beyond which further advances can only be small. Greatest and most far-reaching possibilities lie in the mechanization of forage-crop harvesting and processing. We now have high yielding, coarse grasses which will produce 8 to 10 tons of dry matter per acre if properly fertilized. Such grasses are difficult to harvest and preserve in a palatable state. As machines are developed to harvest coarse vegetation, cure and process into pellet or wafer form, the forage processing will become simplified, the crop will be more palatable to livestock and the actual amount of useable animal food per acre will be high. High yielding forages effectively processed can result in drastic changes in the grassland economy, particularly in warmer climates, and higher per-acre returns can be expected on lands that are not suitable for cropland because of their erosion hazard.

OTHER ASPECTS

My discussion has been limited to only a few of the factors that contribute to the crop production potential. Many others contribute mightily, for example, insect control, soil microorganisms, nematocides, plant disease control and utilization of crops by livestock.

In any case, however, the truly major advances in the agricultural technology of the future are likely to result from new scientific breakthroughs rather than from a slow accumulation of minor improvements. There is ample evidence to support this thesis. Hybrid vigor in plants, the farm tractor that made possible replacement of animal power, selective chemical herbicides and the organic insecticides — all resulted from major breakthroughs. None of these could have been predicted in advance.

That additional major discoveries will be made, and at an accelerated rate, seems without question. Science is the new frontier which we have hardly started to exploit. Rapid basic discoveries in physics and other fields open the way to discoveries in the biological fields. Scientists are becoming better trained, the organized research approach is replacing the lone worker and greater effort is being placed on fundamental lines of research that will produce major advances.

Furthermore, it must be recognized that the strength of our present agriculture lies in our ability to combine practices and technological improvements and thereby achieve production levels that would be otherwise impossible.

LITERATURE CITED

1. ANDERSON, J. R. Land Use and Development, Southeastern Coastal Plain. USDA Info. Bul. 154, 1956.
2. SMITH, GUY-HAROLD, Editor, Conservation of Natural Resources, John Wiley & Sons, Inc., New York, 1958.
3. U.S. Senate, Select Committee on National Water Resources. Water Resource Activities in the U.S. Comm. Print. No. 12, 1959.
4. WOOTEN, H. H., and ANDERSON, J. R. Agricultural Land Resources in the United States. USDA Info. Bul. 140, 1955.
5. WOOTEN, H. H., and JONES, LEWIS A. A History of Our Drainage Enterprises. Water. USDA Yearbook, pp. 478-91, 1955.
6. WOOTEN, H. H., and PURCELL, MARGARET R. Farm Land Development: Present and Future by Clearing, Drainage, Irrigation. USDA Circ. 825, 1949.

Chapter 9

D. B. IBACH
Agricultural Research
Service, USDA

Economic Potentials of Agricultural Production

FACTORS AFFECTING physical potentials of crop production were indicated by Dr. Nelson and others. These physical potentials have related both to land now used for crops and to additional land that could be brought into use if needed. For crops, this chapter is confined to the question of economic potentials associated with improvements in technology on land now in use. On the value of product side, the same potentials per-unit area of land may well apply to much of the new land that could be brought into production. On the cost side there would, of course, be an annual charge on the capital investment needed to bring new land into production through drainage, clearing, land forming or other necessary operations. Some factors influencing livestock potentials are included also.

CHANGING TECHNOLOGY AND ECONOMIC POTENTIALS

Apparently, economic potentials of land now used for some crops will be adequate to meet projected needs from approximately 1960 to 1990. The magnitude of some of our surpluses would seem to indicate that this is true. For other crops, it may not be true. Some crops respond more than others to changes in technology. For example, our technical experts expect less gain in yields per acre of soybeans than has occurred for many crops, as a result of adoption of current or envisioned technology. In contrast, we have seen what has happened to the size of the corn crop, mainly through plant-breeding efforts and application of fertilizers. The big breakthrough associated with the shift from animal to mechanical power and the substantial continuing improvement in mechanization have made major contributions to increased output of all crops. Mechanization has made it possible for more of the specific technological opportunities to be realized by a higher proportion of commercial farm operators on more acres.

Perhaps we will see even greater gains from application of new technology to forage production than has been the case for corn. These gains will be in realized yields per acre, whether harvested or pastured, and in still further improvements in methods of handling forages to increase vastly the quantity that the labor of one man can transform into edible product. The tremendous yields of coastal bermuda grass in the Southeast and the high protein content of the crop attained through use of nitrogen fertilizer suggest possibilities in filling the gap between current production and projected needs for forage in areas where it is adapted. Harvesting and utilization of the phenomenal yields attainable, however, present some problems.

If we have some crops that do not respond to technological improvements, substitutes are likely to take their place. Plant forms that cannot respond to new technological opportunities are likely to give way to alternatives. Some of these alternatives will be of natural origin, that is, other crops. Others may be synthetic.

OTHER FACTORS AFFECTING ECONOMIC POTENTIALS

Economic potentials in crop production are in large measure a function of technological change. They are also functions of managerial competence, available capital, adequate supplies of needed inputs and, of course, factor product price relationships. We could, of course, go further and say that these potentials are a function of the demand for farm relative to nonfarm products. In the long run, at least, mobility of human resources permits an adjustment to changes in this relationship, and this affects the quantity of output that is economically feasible to obtain from farm sources. In this book we are dealing partly, at least, in long-time terms. I mention the possibility of this substitution of nonfarm for farm products because it is difficult for our projectors of future needs to make quantitative allowance for significant shifts that might occur in this direction. As with our potentials estimators, our needs projectors may sometime become uncomfortable in the presence of their thought progenies. The remedy for this is to have frequent reappraisals as new factors appear and to improve projection techniques through better understanding of physical-economic relationships. So I do not rule out the possibility that relative change in demand for farm and nonfarm products, which might come about partly through synthetic substitutes for some items currently farm-produced, may render obsolete any list of quantities of items that we might now say describe our economic potentials. The matter of estimating the rate of population growth far into the future may be even more hazardous than that of estimating future crop yields.

NORMATIVE AND PREDICTIVE ECONOMIC POTENTIALS

Economic potentials have different time dimensions. We can estimate them in terms of the present, and some projected future technological setting. We choose a factor-product price level and relationship that we think appropriate, and set up the assumption that there will be adequate supplies of inputs and of available capital. Then, if our appraisal of economic potential is to be predictive in aggregative terms, we must take into account the item of managerial competence.

This means that we must not only find the economic potential per acre at different points on a surface that has been widened to include envisioned technology; we must predict the rate of adoption, which will be conditioned in part by the number of farmers operating at different managerial levels at specified points in time. I use the term "managerial level" rather than "managerial competence" because there will always be some farmers who for one reason or another choose to operate at both a level and a scale that is below their competence. We have all heard of the farmer who resisted a new idea suggested by the county agent by saying: "I don't farm now as well as I know how."

At any particular time, present or future, there is a wide range between output per acre and total output among different sizes and economic classes of farms. So we need to estimate future trends in importance of different components of the farm plant, each of which has its own physical and economic potential. This type of forward estimating is as important as projecting future yields per acre, if we are to predict economic potentials. With reference to physical yield potentials as they influence economic potentials, we seem to be in a flowtide of improving technology, so that 20 years hence (by 1980), operations may be cast on a plane as much higher than the present as the present is above the level of the early forties. This process of technological change is not reversible. Barring some major catastrophe that would destroy modern civilization, and assuming the kind of price-cost relationships usually used in making long-range projections, there is no ebb tide.

Past trends reveal a major increase in size of farm. This has been accompanied by unprecedented technological developments. Although extrapolation of past trends could not be expected to describe the degree of future development, there is little doubt that there will be further substantial increases in size of farm. The apparent potential for further advances in technology offers a solid basis for such a conclusion.

I have taken a quick look at trends in cropland harvested from farms of different sizes — those having less than 100 acres of cropland, those with 100 to 259 acres, those with 260 to 999 acres, and those having 1,000 acres. For the smaller of these groups, the declining trend since 1935 has been drastic. Slightly less than 78 million acres of cropland were harvested on these farms in 1935. By 1955, this had declined to about 40 million acres, a reduction of 38 million acres. In the group harvesting from 100 to 259 acres of cropland, the decline amounted to about 16 million acres. These two groups combined represent a total decline by 1955 of about 54 million acres from the 1935 level of about 199 million acres harvested from these farms.

In contrast, the gain in total cropland harvested during this period, from farms of 260 to 999 acres, was about 52 million, and the gain for farms having 1,000 acres or more of cropland was 39 million acres. Thus, the total gain in cropland harvested from farms of the two larger size groups was 91 million acres. This compares with a total decline of 54 million acres for the smaller farms. Thus, the net gain was 37 million acres, which brought the total to about 333 million acres of cropland harvested in 1955.

A simple extrapolation of trends in cropland harvested for the farms in the two larger size groups (260 to 999 and 1,000 acres or more) would indicate about 237 million acres by 1980. The rest of the cropland acreage to be harvested would then be from farms with less than 260 acres. The 1955 census shows a total of 333 million acres. If this were taken as the base, the extrapolated acreage for the two larger size groups of farms would account for about 70 percent of the cropland harvested. In 1935 these two groups accounted for approximately a third of the acreage harvested then.

The trend in numbers of commercial farms by economic class has been documented.[1] I have arranged them into three major income groups with value of sales at 1954 prices of (1) $250 to $2,499, (2) $2,500 to $9,999 and (3) $10,000 and over. The number of farms in the lowest income groups declined from about 2.4 million to less than 1 million from 1939 to 1954, a drop of

[1] Jackson V. McElveen, "Family farms in a changing economy," USDA, Agr. Info. Bul. 171, March, 1957.

57 percent. Numbers in the second group declined by 82,000 farms, or about 5 percent. But the number of farms having value of sales of $10,000 or more rose from 312,000 to 583,000, an increase of about 87 percent.

In looking to the future, Bachman projects that by 1975 the average volume of sales per farm, in 1954 dollars, could be expected to rise to nearly $17,000 per farm. This would be an increase of about 124 percent over 1954 sales per commercial farm as reported by the census.[2]

In constant dollars, and assuming continuation of current trends in numbers of farms, average investment per farm in land, buildings, livestock and machinery is projected to rise from $34,000 in 1954 to $68,000 by 1975. The number of commercial farms is projected to 2 million by 1975.

These projections are not intended as predictions, but they are undoubtedly in the direction of what will occur. As such, they have a bearing on the economic potential in crop production. As the number of farms and the harvested cropland in farms, large in both acreage and income, will no doubt rise substantially, while the smaller farm component is likely to decline, we can expect a more rapid rate of adoption of improved technology in the future than in the past. Improved management and more capital associated with larger farms should increase this rate, and as a result a higher proportion of the total farm output will probably utilize improved technology in the future. On this basis, future yields per acre will be higher than would be projected if no change in the relative importance of different components of the farm plant were assumed. In areas in which more technology can substitute profitably for land, operators with sufficient capital and managerial ability would tend to use their capital to adopt yield-increasing technologies, as well as to enlarge units, in an effort to achieve the optimum balance for maximum total returns.

From work now being undertaken, it is hoped to develop in a few areas some estimates of the acreage of each major crop to which different projected yield levels could be assumed to apply. This is in conjunction with development of an estimated technological yield surface, from which appropriate yield estimates can be drawn. As the "package" making up each point selected will be known, corresponding return-cost ratios can be established. Also, a "normative" solution can be developed for the characteristics of a farm for each of specified income levels

---

[2] Kenneth L. Bachman, "Prospective changes in structure of farming," presented at the 36th Annual National Outlook Conference, Nov. 18, 1958, Washington 25, D. C.

based on technical coefficients reflecting return-cost ratios for enterprises adapted to the area. This will involve use of coefficients appropriate to the production situations applicable to different scales of operation. The "predictive" part then becomes a matter of estimating expectancy as to number of farms and number of acres to be operated at different technological levels. This type of approach by relevant areas needs looking into in any thoroughgoing forward-looking appraisal of economic potentials in agricultural production. It should contribute to increased consideration of the economics of changing technology, its impacts where adopted and some predictions of its rate of adoption, so that an appreciable amount of quantifying that will reflect this aspect of the problem can be done.

SOME QUANTITATIVE ESTIMATES OF ECONOMIC POTENTIALS

I assume that in using the term "economic potential," all of us think of what would be economic to individual firms, considering the problems of risk, uncertainty, capital position and managerial level. This, of course, is a lower potential than might be economic to society as a whole in case of a national emergency. In an emergency situation, the public need might dictate use of general powers to effect allocation of more resources to certain lines of agricultural production than would be allocated by unaided individual firms. But the estimates of economic potentials presented here reflect decisions that would be profitable to farmers under other than emergency situations.

Economic potentials are largely determined by opportunities for increase in yield per acre. Different estimates of yield potentials have been developed. None of us who are associated with any of them is particularly satisfied with them. As researchers approach the job area by area and utilize the best local information available they should be able to improve them substantially.

An estimate of economic potential has greater meaning if measured against economic need. Here again, there are different levels. The one used here relates to the medium level population projection of 244 million by 1980, as indicated in a recent committee report.[3] The projected requirements assuming this population level, divided by the yields in Table 9.1, would suggest the acreage needed. The projected yields indicated in Table 9.1

[3] USDA, "Land and water potentials and future requirements." A report to the Senate Select Committee on National Water Resources, Washington, D. C., Dec., 1959.

Table 9.1. Projected U.S. Average Crop Yields With Acreage Requirements for Medium-Level Needs for 1980, With 1957-59 Average Yields and Acreage

Crop	Unit	1957-59 average yields	Projected yields per harvested acre[a]	Acreage: Needed at projected yields	Acreage: 1957-59 average
				(1,000 acres)	
Corn	Bushel	50.2	57	81,456	76,843
Cotton	Lbs. lint	440	539	19,812	13,522
Tobacco	Pound	1,552	1,453	1,882	1,118
Sugarcane	Ton	23.5	---	300	289
Soybeans	Bushel	23.8	27	19,704	22,382
Dry beans	Pound	1,187	1,377	1,637	1,489
Peanuts	Pound	1,092	1,451	1,688	1,488
Potatoes and sweetpotatoes	Bushel	264	369	1,394	1,688
Vegetables	Ton	4.8	6.1[b]	2,932	3,624
Fruit	Ton	2.5	3.1[b]	8,696	4,210[c]
Grain sorghum	Bushel	33.9	37	10,297	17,244
Wheat	Bushel	23.6	25	51,480	50,073
Oats	Bushel	39.9	44	38,250	31,656
Barley	Bushel	29.6	37	20,784	14,994
Rye	Bushel	16.6	20	1,500	1,624
Rice	Pound	3,235	4,300	1,535	1,447
Hay	Ton	1.65	1.90	78,421	71,939
Total crops		---	---	342,585	316,162
Pasture		---	---	111,835[c]	111,835[d]
Total		---	---	453,603	427,105

[a] Projected yields, 1980 – USDA, "Land and water potentials and future requirements." A report to the Senate Select Committee. Washington, D.C., 1959.
[b] Average of estimated yields of selected vegetables and fruits.
[c] Average requirements same as 1954 average based on yield projections for 1980.
[d] 1954 pasture acreage includes cropland pasture in all regions and permanent open pasture in humid regions.

were prepared in collaboration with a committee of scientists in the Agricultural Research Service. They indicate yields considered probable by 1980, with continued adoption of presently known technology under a set of assumed economic conditions.

However, in discussing economic potentials, considerations previously indicated, plus some others I shall present, suggest a basis for somewhat higher yields than those mentioned. For some crops, my estimates of economic potential yields based on certain assumptions as to changes in extent and intensity of improved technology, are similar to the published projected yields.

But there are some differences, most important of which are concerned with three crops — corn, wheat and hay — which account for rather large acreages.

I offer four reasons for yield estimates which in the main are somewhat higher than those heretofore projected: (1) The trend to larger farms will mean a higher rate of adoption of new technology in the future; (2) generalized estimates of yield response to fertilizer, with some improvement in other technology, would seem to justify somewhat higher yield estimates; (3) the probability of new developments now unknown or in the earliest experimental stages that would provide some addition to estimates based on the first two reasons; and (4) anticipated further geographic shifts in production of some crops. For example, some further shift of acreage of grain sorghums to the Corn Belt fringe might be expected.

Part of the basis for estimating somewhat higher-level yields may be found in previously published material relating to the economics of fertilizer use.[4] So far as fertilizer use is concerned, an estimate of the economic potential by 1980 requires an assumption as to the proportion of the acreage to be fertilized. In 1954, 30 percent of the acreage of all crops including permanent pasture in the humid areas was fertilized. In my estimates of the economic potential yield level for crops generally, the corresponding figure projected to 1980 is 52 percent. Greatest increases projected compared with 1954 are from 60 to 90 percent for corn, from approximately 30 percent to 40 to 50 percent for small grains, and from 10 to 40 percent for hay. These projected changes account for most of the difference in proportion of the acreage fertilized assumed, compared with 1954.

Corn is the dominant crop as to both acreage and fertilizer use. A yield of about 25.5 bushels without fertilizer was estimated. With 90 percent of the crop fertilized, generalized estimates of response indicate about 64.5 bushels per acre harvested. This would mean a yield of 68.8 bushels per acre fertilized. Using the generalized average yield function for corn based on a level of other technology that is probably lower than that now followed by the more progressive farmers, this yield would be associated with a marginal return to fertilizer of about $2. This estimate is based on a price level somewhat lower than that used in calculating volume of production per acre in the report to the Select Committee. At the rate of application associated with this yield, a ton of plant nutrients would substitute for about 5.1 acres.

[4] D. B. Ibach and R. C. Lindberg, "The economic position of fertilizer use in the U.S.," USDA Agr. Info. Bul. 202, Washington, D. C., Nov., 1958.

The cost of a ton of plant nutrients was calculated at about $240. Thus, the variable cost per acre at which the marginal return to fertilizer would equal average return on all costs would be $47.06 ($240/5.1). But $20 of this would be cost of fertilizer, leaving $27 for other costs. United States average variable costs per acre other than those for fertilizer are currently estimated at $23. Some items of other costs may be expected to rise during the 1960's and 1970's; of course, the effect of larger scale operations may reduce costs of land preparation, tillage and harvesting. But new technology that would include some of the items mentioned in other chapters will bring about added costs. Other things being equal, a rise in total discrete variable costs would require more fertilizer and higher yields to maximize average returns.

If allowance is made for the effect of a reasonable improvement in technology during the 1960-80 period on fertilizer-yield relationships, it is clear that the corn yield projected would be reached at a lower rate of fertilizer than would be needed to maximize average return on all variable costs. Farmers without serious capital limitations, of course, could well afford to fertilize for still higher yields.

Hay is one of the crops for which yields are expected to gain substantially from improved technology. Assuming that 40 percent of the hay will be fertilized by 1980, a yield of 2.4 tons per harvested acre seems not unlikely as an economic potential. This would mean a yield of 4 tons per fertilized acre. With other technology at present levels comparable to that for corn, the rate of fertilizer associated with a yield of 4 tons would result in a marginal return to fertilizer of about $2.25. A ton of plant nutrients would substitute for about 7.9 acres. A ton of plant nutrients used on hay was calculated to cost about $218. Thus, the variable cost per acre at which the marginal return to fertilizer would equal average return on all costs would be about $27.60 ($218/7.9). Of this amount, $16 would be for fertilizer, leaving $11.60 per acre for other variable costs. This means that even today, farmers on the average would fertilize for a 4-ton yield to maximize average return unless their variable costs other than fertilizer were $11.60 per acre or below. The estimated 1960 United States average variable cost other than fertilizer for a 4-ton yield of unirrigated alfalfa is estimated to fall within a range of $22 to $30 per acre, depending on the method of harvesting.

The average yield of vegetables per harvested acre in 1954 was 4.2 tons. But the yield of 5.9 tons on the acreage fertilized represented a marginal return of about $6 to fertilizer. To obtain a yield of 8.4 tons per harvested acre would require a yield of 9 tons per fertilized acre (80 percent of the crop fertilized) at which the marginal return to fertilizer would be about $2.65, assuming about present average management. The rate of fertilizer required for this would equalize marginal return on all costs, if other costs were about $70 per acre. No United States average data are available on variable costs per acre of vegetables generally. However, some 1957 data from the Northeast indicate that for processing tomatoes yielding 13.5 tons, variable costs per acre other than fertilizer would amount to about $225 per acre. The return per dollar of these costs would be about $2.20: The expenditure per acre for fertilizer was about $43.

These examples suggest that if we have appreciable gains in technology other than use of higher rates of fertilizer, economically potential yields may be materially higher than the projected yields included in Table 9.1. I have developed estimates of economically potential yields for each crop included in Table 9.1. In addition to the crops mentioned, I suggest that a yield of 45 bushels for grain sorghums may not seem too high as an economic potential. Probably the potential gains from existing hybrids have not yet been fully reflected in harvested yields. Also, as mentioned earlier, further shift of this crop to the Corn Belt fringe should result in an increase in average yield. Response of grain sorghums to fertilizer in the nondry areas is similar to that for corn. Additional moisture-conserving practices may be expected to result in increased yields of grain sorghums and wheat in the dry-farming areas where grown. These considerations, together with comparison of 1957-59 average yields with those projected (Table 9.1) and a look at yield trends for some crops, may lead some economists and some natural scientists to consider the latter a bit on the conservative side.

I have indicated, in the main, the crops with economically potential yields that I estimate to be appreciably higher than projected yields. Without going into further detail, acreage requirements for the medium-level output requirements for 1980, assuming such yields, would be about 392 million acres of cropland (including cropland pasture in all regions), plus permanent open pasture in the humid regions. This compares with the 454 million acres needed at projected yields and the 1957-59 average of 427 million acres shown in Table 9.1.

On the conservative side, it should be pointed out that constant war must be waged on the "protective" research front. New diseases and pests and development of immunities of present ones to some of the newer control measures present problems for plant breeders, agronomists, soil scientists and chemists. But there seems little reason to doubt that protective research can safeguard the gains made and maintain the base for further advances.

EFFECT OF NEW COMBINATIONS OF TECHNOLOGY

In the examples given, it was pointed out that the economic position of fertilizer use on a crop would be strengthened as other yield-increasing improvements in technology were adopted. An illustration of the effect of such adoption may be helpful. The illustration used is drawn from one stage of a joint effort on macro-analysis of soil and crop technology, between the Farm Economics Research and Soil and Water Conservation Research Divisions of the Agricultural Research Service and the Georgia Agricultural Experiment Station. The illustration relates to the effect of supplemental irrigation on corn yield response to fertilizer in the Georgia Piedmont area. The corn is grown in a rotation with coastal bermuda grass. The effects indicated in this illustration should be considered as preliminary and subject to revision after further review of yield response estimates by technical specialists.

Table 9.2. Corn: Expenditure for Fertilizer to Equalize Returns on Variable Costs (Class II Land, Georgia-Piedmont)[a]

Unirrigated		Irrigated	
Expenditure per acre for fertilizer	Variable costs/Acre (excl. fertilizer)	Expenditure per acre for fertilizer	Variable costs/Acre (excl. fertilizer)
(Dollars)		(Dollars)	
6.92	5.11	7.47	1.64
9.98	6.61	10.51	1.71
13.07	9.33	13.60	2.45
16.22	13.71	16.74	4.03
19.42	20.26	19.92	6.66
22.45	28.57	23.13	10.60
25.91	42.57	26.37	16.17
29.19	60.21	29.67	23.72
31.78	78.35	32.92	33.84
		36.22	47.01
		39.53	63.97
		43.11	85.37

[a] Preliminary — subject to further review.

The lower curve of Figure 9.1 is based on estimates of yield response, assuming the level of technology practiced now by the more progressive farmers. Reading along the abscissa, if varible costs per acre excluding fertilizer are $20, an expenditure of a little less than $20 per acre for fertilizer would be required to

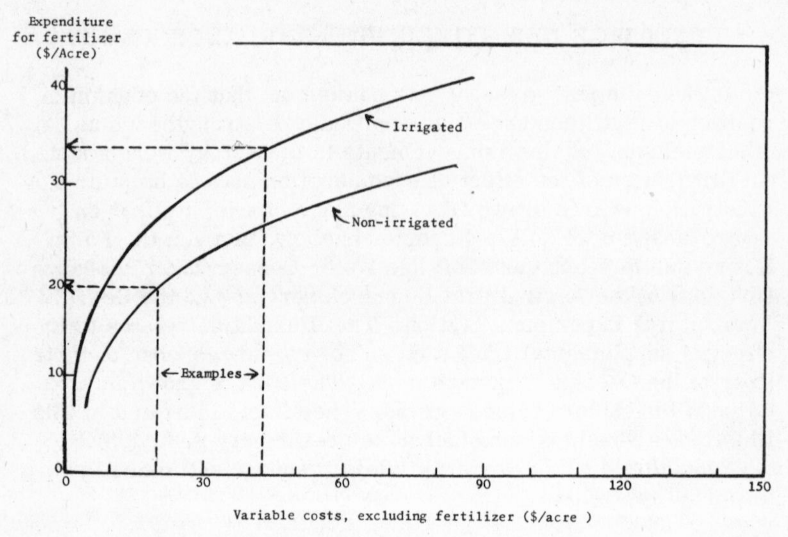

Fig. 9.1. Corn: Expenditure for fertilizer to equalize returns on variable costs (Class II land, Georgia-Piedmont).*

* Preliminary — subject to further review

maximize average return on total variable costs. Most profit will be made on a given investment for producing the crop at that expenditure per acre for fertilizer. This expenditure per acre would represent a minimum, even for farmers with limited funds. At this expenditure, the marginal return to fertilizer ($2.30) is the same as the average return on the other variable costs.

As improved technology is adopted, represented by the top curve in Figure 9.1, the minimum expenditure for fertilizer is increased for two reasons. First, there is a complementary effect from use of irrigation with fertilizer. This fact alone would increase the expenditure needed to maximize average returns. Second, there is an added cost for most practices that substantially increase yields; certainly this is true in the case of irrigation. As other variable costs rise, greater expenditure for fertilizer is needed to maximize the average return. In this illustration, other costs would be increased to about $43 per acre, and this would establish an expenditure of about $34 per acre for fertilizer for maximum profit on the investment made in producing the crop.

As farmers become more aware of optimum combinations of new technology for limited as well as unlimited capital situations, we can expect rates of adoption to be stepped up and hence an acceleration in the trend toward higher yields. This trend will likely be augmented by another trend — that toward larger operating units with more capital at the disposal of their operators.

SOME OTHER POTENTIALS

I shall not discuss potentials in the livestock sector in any quantitative sense. Generally, progress in the feed-livestock input-output relationship has been less pronounced than has been the case with respect to crop yields. Improvements in rations and some improvement in selection of animals for feed conversion efficiency have been made, and there seems to be some prospect for further gains. Specialists in the Agricultural Research Service indicate that feed conversion efficiency for livestock in general may rise from 10 to 13 percent during the 1960-80 period. More widespread use of artificial insemination in livestock generally could accelerate the process of better animal selection and perhaps make present estimates of feed conversion efficiency seem conservative.

The arrangement referred to as vertical integration has been a means of facilitating combinations of capital and management to make spectacular gains in the volume of product one man can turn out. Various predictions have been made as to future developments along this line. When it can greatly increase factor returns, as it has in the case of broilers, this type of arrangement will no doubt be extended.

Perhaps the most spectacular gains by innovators (aside from vertical integration) has been in the handling of materials and products on the farm. These new methods permit great savings in labor and, in many instances, marked reductions in the capital investment in facilities needed per unit of output. In dairy production, savings in both capital investment and labor, made possible by use of new designs of building and milking facilities, represent one of the truly major gains. The loose-housing barn and the herringbone design of milking arrangement, where adopted, have reduced building and equipment cost per cow by more than 50 percent. Compared with stanchion barn systems found on farms, they have also reduced the number of man-minutes required per cow by 30 percent.[5] If these potential gains are more widely adopted, they will contribute to still further increases in the trend toward greater agricultural output per

[5]Morris M. Lindsey, "Investment costs and efficiency of one-man dairy systems," U.S. Agr. Res. Serv. Farm Cost Situation, ARS43-102, May, 1959.

worker in agriculture. Such new developments in roughage handling as wafering and pelleting are still in the experimental stage. But as they are perfected and become feasible for general adoption, they offer possibilities for further substitution of capital for labor and for increasing the farm output potential.

I have attempted to outline some of the factors by which we might project economic potentials in agriculture. For crop production, I have ventured some quantitative evaluation in relation to projected needs for 1980. By 1965, or perhaps sooner, I may want to alter the picture as presented for purposes of this discussion. American agriculture has the economic potential to meet such forseeable needs as have thus far been projected. I have attempted to sharpen this statement a bit by suggesting that through improved technology and probable changes in scale of operations by individual farmers, needs in 1980 might conceivably be reached with no increase in the acreage used for crops and pasture.

IMPLICATIONS FOR RESEARCH

If this conclusion were regarded as substantially correct, different implications might be drawn from it. One implication that to me would be unwarranted would be that we could afford to slow down on research designed to advance the technological front and allow consumption to catch up with the potential we now have in relation to current needs. There are several reasons why this course would be not only unwarranted, but dangerous. First, research results do not come off the assembly line in a steady stream. A continuous flow of resources must go in to insure progress that comes only as discrete bundles. Results cannot be forecast; usually, they come as more or less unpredictable breakthroughs which have back of them a great deal of hard, routine work. Furthermore, in the long run, only research results can insure the kind, the quantity and the quality of output needed by growing populations in modern society.

But most important for the present and in the short run, we need continued research to enable us to assess potentials and determine resource combinations to meet needs most economically in the less remote future. There is no conflict between technological research and economic research in this regard. There is, however, need for a team approach in a look to the future that will best utilize existing research results and guide future research in both subject matter and geographic areas so that it can make a more direct contribution in meeting the larger economic problems.

No one questions the place of research in long-time terms or in times of high-level need. But technological research results are needed in times of surplus, for use in finding present and potential lower cost resource combinations for levels of output that would clear the market at prices remunerative to farmers. This point has not yet received adequate attention with respect to both development and use of research results or in "selling" research as a need, irrespective of the current economic situation.

Chapter 10

FREDERICK S. HOPKINS, JR.
Iowa State University

Potential Supply of Forest Products

THE TOPIC of this chapter, taken in its broadest sense, would represent a task of formidable proportions. Rather than discuss the potential supply of all forest goods and services, I propose to comment on the prospects for the recreational services of the forest rather briefly and on the potential supply of timber products at some length.

Such a restriction of the subject is not altogether without justification. Generally speaking, and looking at the country as a whole for the last few decades of the 1900's, timber production at levels approaching a social optimum could be expected to enhance production of such forest goods and services as watershed benefits, fish and game and aesthetic values. With the exception of areas where problems are particularly acute, it seems fairly reasonable to assume that the products in question are, in large degree, joint with timber. It should be admitted, too, that both the methodology and the data essential to an analytical consideration of these classes of forest value are still far from adequate.

FOREST RECREATION

In thinking of forest recreation it is perhaps helpful to consider two categories of land. The first of these would include areas which are necessarily devoted exclusively to intensive recreational use. Campsites, picnic areas and points of outstanding scenic interest fall into this class. Such use is incompatible with timber production and would presumably represent a more productive use of the land. Expansion of the land area devoted to intensive recreational use will be accomplished by withdrawals from the timber-producing areas of the country and from lands in non-forest use.

The second category is comprised of forest land on which extensive recreational use, with only moderate restriction, is

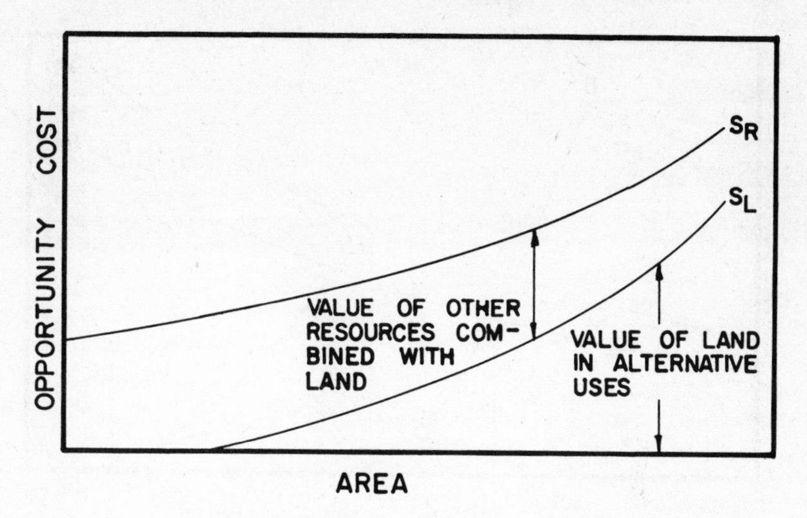

Fig. 10.1. Supply of intensive forest recreation services.

compatible with timber production. This would characterize the great bulk of land now described as commercial forest area. Timber production often facilitates recreational use and, over the course of a rotation, need not detract appreciably from recreational values.

The supply of forest recreation services in the "intensive use" category might be roughly conceived as consisting of two elements as shown in Figure 10.1. As far as land is concerned, such a supply function (S_L) would express the value of successive units of land area in alternative uses, i.e., the opportunity cost of land in recreational use. Since a portion of such land may have no alternative use, the lower part of a supply curve (S_L) would coincide with the abscissa. To this must be added the value of other resources which are combined with land in providing recreational services. The sum of these two elements, indicated by S_R, is perhaps as close as one could get to a concept of the aggregate supply of forest recreation.

Looking into the future, then, the shifts in supply to be anticipated will be governed largely by changes in the value or opportunity cost of land and other resources employed in providing forest recreation. In view of growing population pressures, such values may tend to become greater. Thus, the supply of forest recreation would tend to diminish as indicated by the shift from S_R to S_R' in Figure 10.2.

Demand for forest recreation is increasing and promises to continue to increase at a rate far in excess of the rate of

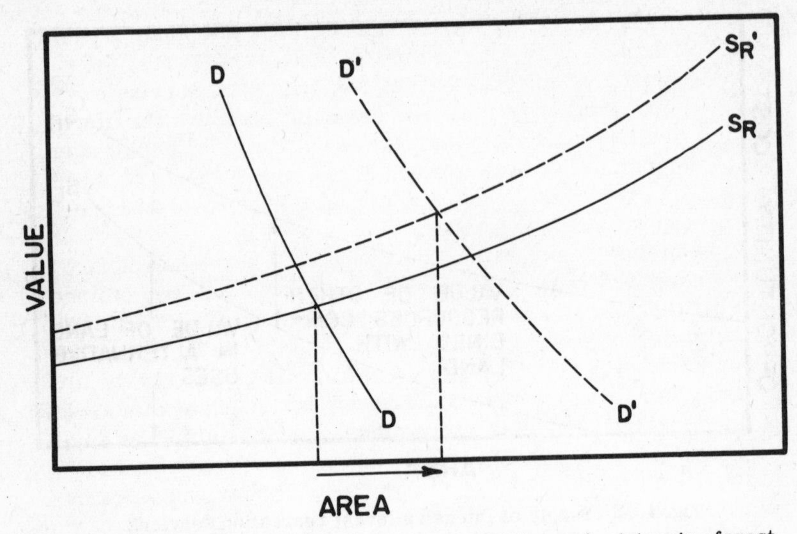

Fig. 10.2. Prospective changes in supply and demand — intensive forest recreation.

population growth. This is attributed to increasing productivity in the economy-at-large, with consequent rising incomes and more extended periods of leisure time. There is also evidence of strengthening preference for this kind of recreation and growing skill in its consumption. The result of these tendencies is that the significance of forest areas for their recreation values is rising more steeply than for timber production. The Forest Service (1959) anticipates a ninefold increase in the number of recreation visits to the National Forests between 1958 and the year 2000. Despite diminishing supply, the prospect for rising demand for forest recreation is such that substantial increases in the land area so utilized, as indicated in Figure 10.2, will come about in the next few decades. It has been estimated that the increase may amount to as much as 20 million acres by the year 2000.[1]

While exceptions are becoming more prevalent, forest recreation is not generally subject to the pricing mechanism. This would be explained partly on an institutional basis. It is also due to the fact that such recreational services, by their very nature, do not lend themselves to the degree of control essential to pricing on the basis of cost and utility relationships. Thus, the

[1] R. E. McArdle. "The sixties — decade of decision," address before the 83rd Annual Convention of the American Paper Association, New York, Feb. 25, 1960.

provision of facilities for forest recreation is primarily a public function. Expansion occurs, as in the case of the Forest Service's "Operation Outdoors" and the National Park Service's "Mission 66," largely in response to public pressure for more adequate facilities. It remains the responsibility of public agencies to determine the extent to which resources should be so allocated, i.e., the point at which marginal social costs and benefits would be approximately equated.

Even in view of the expansion anticipated in the use of land for intensive forest recreation, such use would still be confined to a relatively small portion of the existing and potential forest land area of the country. Actually, the bulk of the land area used for forest recreation will also be used for the production of timber and other forest goods and services. On much of this area, the extra cost of providing recreational services would be small or negligible. A policy of multiple use will have the effect of greatly increasing the supply of extensive recreational services. This would be true because a large part of the opportunity cost of providing for recreation exclusively is eliminated when recreation is combined with other kinds of forest production. Multiple-use of forest land must, however, be better understood and appreciated by the public and by those responsible for the management of forest land.

It should be borne in mind throughout this chapter that the value of land in forest production may stem from potential recreational use, timber production or the production of other forest goods and services, alone or in combination. In bypassing the latter category, it is not my intent to suggest that the values involved are of little significance. On the contrary, such benefits often warrant major consideration in the appraisal of land for forest use, particularly if the social viewpoint is adopted.

FOREST SERVICE PROJECTIONS OF POTENTIAL TIMBER DEMAND AND GROWTH IN THE YEAR 2000

The obvious jumping off place for a discussion of potential timber supply is Timber Resources for America's Future,[2] the report on the latest and most intensive of a series of timber resource analyses conducted by the U. S. Forest Service. In this study, the Forest Service made very detailed projections of "potential demand" for timber products. Potential demand here is

---

[2] Forest Service, USDA. Forest Resource Report No. 14. U. S. Government Printing Office, Washington, D. C., 1958.

Table 10.1. Summary of Basic Assumptions Underlying Three Estimates of Potential Timber Demand in the Year 2000

Projection level	Population	GNP	Real price of timber products
	(Millions)	(Billion dollars)	(Trend)
Lower	275	1,200	rising
Medium	275	1,200	constant
Upper	360	1,450	constant

an estimate of the quantity of timber products which would be demanded under the conditions assumed, i.e., a point on a future demand function. Unfortunately, the Forest Service did not analyze potential supply except in terms of the prospect for physical inventory of growing timber and growth.

For the year 2000, three projections of potential demand for timber products were developed on the basis of three different combinations of assumptions as to the future development of the economy-at-large and real price trends for timber products. These underlying assumptions are summarized in Table 10.1.

It should be emphasized that the assumption of constant real prices underlying the medium and upper level projections relates strictly to estimates of potential consumption. Sufficient growth to provide for timber products consumption at projected levels would not, in itself, assure constant real prices. It would also be necessary that productivity in harvesting and conversion advance at about the same rate as productivity in the rest of the economy increases. It is evident, however, that constant real prices would be impossible in the presence of declining timber supply at the levels of demand anticipated.

Also basic to forecasts of timber growth are assumptions that forest management practices and technology in harvesting, conversion and distribution will continue to improve. Another pertinent assumption concerns the extent of the commercial forest land area of the country. Since 1910, commercial forest area has tended to increase, but it is anticipated that this trend will be reversed over the period in question.

The supply problem as visualized by the Forest Service is the prospective gap between the volume of growth required to provide for the potential consumption of timber products and projected growth. These forecasts, under the assumptions of the lower and medium level projections of potential demand are summarized in Table 10.2.

The medium level projections indicate that we may, in the year 2000, be growing just a little over half of the timber

Table 10.2. Required and Projected Timber Growth for the Year 2000[a]

	Level of potential demand	
	Lower	Medium
Total growing stock:[b]		
Required growth - (Bil. cu. ft.)	18.0	22.0
Projected growth - (Bil. cu. ft.)	19.1	12.2
Projected growth as percent of required growth	106	55
Sawtimber:[c]		
Required growth - (Bil. bd. ft.)	79.3	105.4
Projected growth - (Bil. bd. ft.)	66.7	25.2
Projected growth as percent of required growth	84	24

[a] *Timber Resources for America's Future*, p. 488.
[b] Total growing stock. Volume of all merchantable trees over five inches, d.b.h. to a four inch top inside bark.
[c] Sawtimber. Volume of all trees suitable for lumber or comparable use. Minimum d.b.h.: E. softwood, 9 inches; hardwood and western softwood, 11 inches.

required to meet demand at 1952 real prices. In the case of sawtimber, more than four times the growth projected would be required to provide for potential demand. With rising real prices the lower level projections indicate that total timber growth would be sufficient but sawtimber growth would fall short by 16 percent.

Aggregate projections such as these fail to disclose more drastic deficiencies which can be anticipated with respect to particular species, sizes and qualities of timber. The prospect of growth insufficient to provide for projected volumes of consumption is largely a reflection of inadequate inventories of growing stock by the year 2000.

With respect to timber products, the outlook for the future presented by the Forest Service is not bright. If demand increases to the extent anticipated due to growth in population and income, timber deficits will become more pronounced. Continued upward trends in real prices will be accompanied by restricted consumption and forced substitution. Barring substantial non-price substitution, such tendencies can be avoided only by measures to increase timber supply and to advance technology in the conversion industries well beyond those anticipated by the Forest Service. Will it be in the best interest of society to accept the conditions which are imminent? Or would the position of society be improved by diverting more resources to the end of increasing the supply of timber products?

AN INTERPRETATION OF POTENTIAL DEMAND ESTIMATES

The projections made by the Forest Service in the Timber Resource Review are expressed entirely in terms of potential demand under assumed conditions and corresponding growth. A reasonable interpretation seems possible, however, in terms of the changes in demand and supply which such estimates of consumption would represent should they materialize in the year 2000. In taking such liberties with the projections made, it is assumed that the three estimates of timber products demand are points at which supply and demand would be equal under corresponding sets of conditions. Since price changes are projected more concretely for lumber than for other products, sawtimber (for lumber production) will be used to illustrate the supply and demand relationships which seem evident. This interpretation is shown in Figure 10.3.

Turning first to the changes in demand which are implied, demand in 1952 is approximated by DD. With growing population and rising gross national product as assumed in connection with the lower and medium projections, demand would increase to the

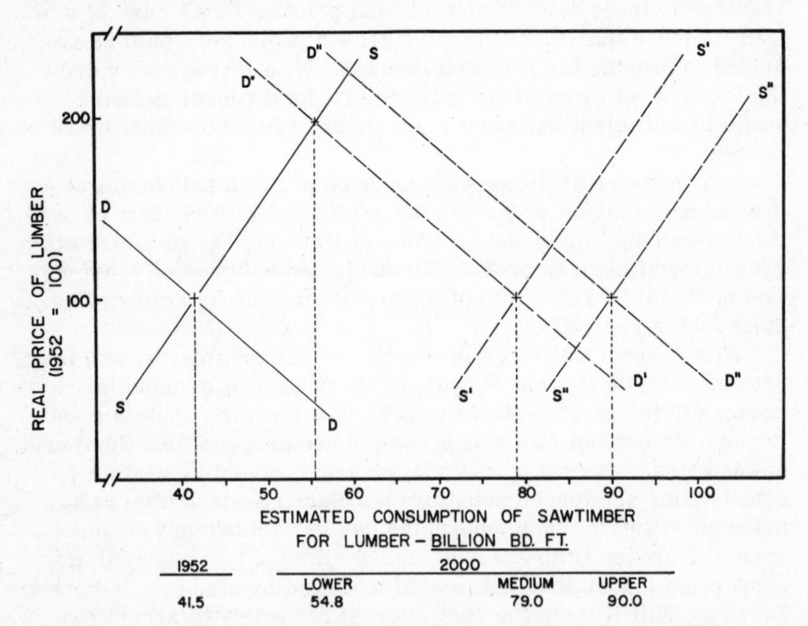

Fig. 10.3. Increases in sawtimber supply required to meet demand projections for the year 2000.

level indicated by D′D′. If, as the Forest Service anticipates in developing its lower estimate of potential timber demand, real price rises 97 percent[3] between 1952 and 2000, the quantity of sawtimber demanded would increase from 41.5 to 54.8 billion board feet. On the other hand, using the same population and income assumptions, if 1952 real prices were somehow sustained, then demand at 79 billion board feet is anticipated for the year 2000.[4] The upper level projection, based on larger estimates of population and gross national product in 2000 (though slightly lower GNP per capita), suggests still greater demand as indicated by D″D″.

Turning to the implications as to the supply of sawtimber for lumber production, one is apt to get the impression that supply is regarded as being perfectly elastic. This is particularly true in looking at the medium and upper level projections in which constant real prices at the 1952 level are assumed. However, the idea that any quantity of timber demanded would be made available at the price level indicated is untenable. In fact, the price elasticity of timber supply in any short period tends to be very low.

For the purpose of this illustration, let it be assumed that the lower level projection represents no change in supply relative to 1952. With a 97 percent increase in real price over 1952 levels, the amount supplied in 2000 is estimated at 54.8 billion board feet, a 32 percent increase over 1952. This supply function is indicated by SS in Figure 10.3. The lower projection might be regarded as an estimate of what will most likely happen by the year 2000 in the absence of extraordinary measures designed to favorably alter timber supply.

If the price elasticity of timber supply is not infinite, then the medium and upper level projections based on the assumption of constant real prices could come about only with very substantial increases in the supply of sawtimber for lumber production. These increases, indicated by S′S′ and S″S″ respectively in Figure 10.3 amount to 90 percent and 117 percent at the 1952 price level.

The prospect of such increases in sawtimber supply as have

[3] Annual rate of real price increase is 1.4 percent or about half of the 2.8 percent annual rate reported for the period 1926 to 1950.

[4] The two points described are shown in Figure 10.3 to be lying on the same demand curve (D′D′). To the extent that the lower level estimate, essentially a projection of past experience, includes non-price substitution, that point would fall on a lower and less elastic demand function. No non-price substitution is assumed in the development of the medium and upper level projections. The point remains, however, that the Forest Service anticipates a substantial increase in the aggregate derived demand for sawtimber. Price is regarded as the major factor underlying substitution.

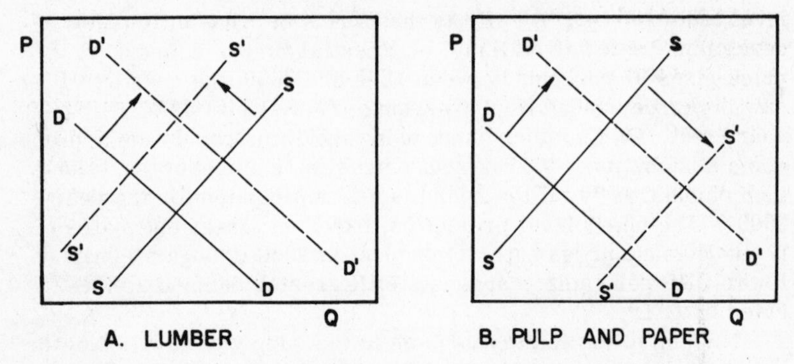

Fig. 10.4. Apparent changes in supply and demand; 1900-50.

just been described would represent a drastic reversal of the direction of shifts in supply experienced in this country over the past century. Zaremba reported that the long-term trend of real lumber prices had been rising at the rate of 2 percent per year between 1860 and 1955.[5] He explained this trend on the basis of failure of productivity in the lumber industry to advance while productivity in the economy-at-large was rising at about 2 percent per year. Technological improvements in the industry were just about able to compensate for the disadvantages of less accessible timber, smaller sizes and poorer quality. Declining supply, however, was offset by increasing demand. Between 1900 and 1950, the real price of lumber rose about 185 percent while consumption, though fluctuating over the period, was practically the same in 1950 as in 1900. The changes apparent are indicated in Figure 10.4-A.[6] While this describes the behavior of lumber supply, the tendency toward diminishing supply is even more pronounced as far as sawtimber is concerned.

In the pulp and paper industry the changes have been quite different. From 1900 to 1950, the long-term trend of real prices has been about level. While real prices have remained about constant, consumption of paper products has increased tremendously. Both demand and supply have increased as suggested in Figure 10.4-B. In this case, however, the increases in supply have come about through technological improvements in conversion and adaptation to the changing character of timber inventories. Productivity has risen along with the rest of the economy. Unfortunately, the downward shift in supply which has characterized the lumber industry has been more typical of the timber

[5] J. Zaremba. "The trend of lumber prices," Jour. For. 56:179, 1958.

[6] W. A. Duerr. Fundamentals of Forestry Economics. McGraw-Hill, New York, 1960.

products industries as a whole than has the behavior of supply in the pulp and paper industry.

It is evident that if the medium level projection were to be regarded as a timber production goal, then the direction in which timber and timber products supply functions have been moving must be reversed. As the Forest Service insists, timber supply must be increased appreciably. A significant upward adjustment of supply would require measures to this end well beyond those now in effect.

Unfortunately, we do not, at present, have estimates with regard to the cost side of the basic input-output relationship for forest production. Without the necessary cost estimates, a suitable goal for purpose of public planning cannot be established. Ideally, such a goal should be an estimate of an optimum level of timber production as seen from the viewpoint of society — a level which represents an equation of marginal costs and benefits.[7] Currently, we seem to be relying upon the conviction that reallocation of resources in favor of timber production is in the public interest, but we have yet to determine how far such reallocation should go.

SOME ECONOMIC FACTORS AFFECTING TIMBER SUPPLY

Two characteristics of timber bear special consideration in any attempt to project timber supply. The first is the familiar fact that production periods are relatively long, up to 100 years or more, depending upon the economic circumstances of the owner, the site, the species and the product. The second is the fact that timber can be regarded either as a means of production or as product at the discretion of the owner.

The price elasticity of the timber supply functions shown in Figure 10.3 for the year 2000 is low. This is characteristic of timber supply in any short-term (stock or market supply) period. There is relatively little that a timber producer can do to increase the amount supplied in response to a positive price change. He (or society) might reach out to harvest stands, trees or parts of trees which are geographically or technically more remote. That is, the margins of availability may be extended. Basically, however, any supply response he exhibits is a stock response. The quantity of timber made available rests largely upon his forecasts of the advantages of holding growing stock relative to the opportunity cost of carrying inventories of timber.

---

[7] Ibid.

He weighs the prospect of growth in volume, improvement in quality and a favorable change in timber prices against the return he sees possible through alternative uses of the capital tied up in timber. Thus, the cost of capital, the interest rate, or, as it applies to a particular timber producing firm, the alternative rate of return is of overwhelming significance with respect to supply responses made from timber inventories. If the price rises, the value of growth increases, but the production (capital) cost also increases to the same extent, and no supply response is to be anticipated.

While the quantity of timber which would be made available from growing stock is inelastic with respect to price, the amount supplied is very responsive to changes in the opportunity cost of capital. The more productive alternative opportunities to use capital appear to be, the more pressing the demands for current consumption, or the greater the apparent risks in timber production, the more an owner would be inclined to liquidate timber capital. The stock supply of timber is positively correlated with the alternative rate of return.

It must also be recognized that a positive stock supply response, or reduction of growing stock, in one period means that less timber will be available in future periods. In the longer term, then, timber supply is negatively correlated with the alternative rate.

In looking ahead to the year 2000, or to any other future target date, any projection of timber supply must reflect the stock supply responses which will be made in intervening short-term periods. If substantial increases in supply are to be effected by the year 2000, it would be largely due to conditions over the intervening period which are consistently favorable to the accumulation of growing stock on a substantial portion of the commercial forest land of the nation. This is a large part of what the Forest Service implies in assuming a continued trend of improvement in forest management practices.

The treatment of timber supply to this point is appropriate to existing commercial forest lands, and particularly to those lands which are stocked with timber to some extent. But what about forest land which is, at present, unstocked or seriously understocked? And what are the circumstances under which some lands now used for other kinds of production might be shifted to forest production? Here we are concerned with long-run timber supply responses.

In the long run, timber supply may be somewhat more elastic in relation to prospective price (or cost other than capital) than is stock supply. The prospect of price levels sustained at high levels or of low establishment and administration costs would tend to elicit a positive long-run supply response. Such response would be manifest in the seeding or planting of understocked or barren forest lands, or possibly in the diversion of non-forest lands to timber production. In view of the long production periods entailed, however, the interest rate is still highly significant. Presumably the condition essential to such action is that the estimated present net worth of the land (soil expectation value) under such a management program exceeds that under alternative uses. Planning of this order must, of course, anticipate decisions concerning the disposition of growing stock as the stand matures. The lower the alternative rate, other things held constant, the greater the extent to which positive long-run timber supply responses can be expected. This is the sort of response implied by the Forest Service in referring to the 52 million acres or nearly 25 percent of the commercial forest land area of the United States in need of planting. Some restocking of such lands occurs naturally, of course, usually by default rather than by positive decision. Though trees planted or otherwise established in the 1960's may not reach maturity by the year 2000, such action would substantially increase the allowable cut from older stands by that time.

The Timber Resource Review outlined in broad terms the measures which would reduce the gap between anticipated timber production and consumption at 1952 prices. Basically, these measures all have the effect of expanding the capital plant for timber production, i.e., increasing the volume of growing stock. In addition to the planting indicated, protection against fire, insects and disease must be improved. Growing stock levels on existing forest areas should be increased. Technology in conversion must be improved to increase product recovery from timber harvested and to permit utilization of a wider range of species. Such developments would also have the effect of increasing growing stock.

As in the earlier Reappraisal Report,[8] the forest management practices of small forest owners are described as falling short of socially desirable standards most drastically. According to Timber Resources for America's Future, forest management practices on the part of some 4 million small owners who control about half of the commercial forest land of the country must be greatly intensified if timber production is to be substantially increased. One might wonder if it's not suggested here that small

[8] Forest Service, USDA. Forests and National Prosperity. Misc. Publ. No. 668, U.S. Government Printing Office, Washington, D. C., 1948.

producers subsidize society. Forest Service proposals for specific action to reduce problems identified are to be published in the near future.

The economic factors that bear most directly on future timber supply are those that relate to the timber producers' decisions concerning the level of growing stock. Growing stock, or timber capital, is the basic and predominant ingredient of timber production. By and large, the output of timber can be increased only by increasing growing stock, the timber producing machinery.

SOME IMPLICATIONS FOR LAND-USE PLANNING AND POLICY

Turning now to the possibility of shifts in land use, the Forest Service's assumption with respect to prospective changes in the extent of the commercial forest land area of the country is of particular interest. In Timber Resources for America's Future, mild concern was expressed for an expected downward trend between 1960 and 2000. More recently, however, the Forest Service has come to view such prospects with much greater alarm (McArdle, 1960). The chief of the Forest Service cited the possibility that our present 484 million acres of commercial forest land might, through pressure of alternative uses, be reduced by 25 percent over the next 40 years. This could reduce timber growing capacity by as much as one-third.

In view of the central issue which is the concern of this book, however, it seems conceivable that additions of submarginal cropland to the commercial forest area may continue to more than compensate for such inroads as are being made by urban and industrial developments, highways, reservoirs and intensive recreational requirements. As long as the rate at which increases in productivity in agriculture exceeds the rate at which demand increases, a normal tendency toward falling prices and rising output may be expected. In the absence of public measures to control price and production, the value of agricultural lands on which technological improvements cannot be applied would tend to fall. Under competition, crop production would yield to forest production where conditions are favorable to the latter.

There is nothing particularly mysterious about the economic principles underlying changes in the use of land. When more can be paid for the use of land in one kind of production than in another, that use would tend to predominate. Two considerations seem to be critical with regard to any comparisons between forest production and marginal agricultural production. The first has to do with the circumstances under which shifts to forest production might represent a desirable re-allocation of resources. The second consideration, closely related to the first, bears upon institutional problems that inevitably arise in the process of accomplishing such adjustments.

It was mentioned earlier that capital is the principal ingredient in forest production, and that the opportunity cost of capital is the critical determinant of the intensity of forest management. If the cost of capital to a landowner is high, forest production may be economically impossible. The value (present net worth) of land is low or negative. Productivity is low and the potential contribution to supply is small. These circumstances lie at the heart of the so-called small forest owner problem in the United States and other nations. They lie behind the present unproductive condition of extensive areas of land on which crop production has been abandoned and forest production, largely involuntary, has taken its place in the Northeast and other parts of the country. A shift to forest production exclusively on an existing marginal farm could not be expected to improve the lot of the owner and his family.

If forest production is to compete with even marginal agricultural production, then, the first essential condition is that ownership be transferred to firms characterized by a relatively low alternative rate of return. Generally speaking, this means public ownership or ownership by large, vertically integrated corporations among the wood-using industries. A second condition essential to high productivity is the aggregation of substantial areas of land in the ownership of a single firm. In timber production, the economics of scale to be realized with increasing size of forest holding are appreciable up to several thousand acres. In the absence of public subsidy to forest production on the part of present landowners, or of drastic public regulation, changes in ownership are indicated along with shifts in the kind of production to which land is devoted.

As to the relative merits of public ownership versus ownership by the larger, vertically integrated wood-using concerns, trends suggest that the most intensive management and greatest productivity in timber production can be anticipated on the part of the latter. This is to be explained, in part, on the basis of the advantages of integration, particularly the opportunity to realize the values inherent in high productivity more fully.

From the social viewpoint, however, non-monetary elements may carry great weight in the appraisal of land. In some areas, the value of land based on timber production alone may not be sufficient to be competitive, but when recognition of other forest benefits is taken into account, forest production would represent the most desirable use. The issue between public and industrial ownership rests, to a large extent, upon the possibility of additional non-monetary net benefits under public management.

At the risk of over-simplification, the changes which appear to be taking place in the value productivity of land for farm crops relative to that for land in forest production may be shown by means of a ceiling rent model as in Figure 10.5. Ceiling rent, the highest price per acre per year which could be paid for the use of land in alternative kinds of production, is shown in relation to land areas arrayed in order of diminishing value productivity. In the absence of public support programs the ceiling rent gradient for much of agricultural production would appear to become more steep. Where productivity is relatively low, land tends to become worth less. Where technological advances can be applied to greatest advantage, the value of land would tend to rise.

In the case of forest production, the relatively low and flat ceiling rent gradient appears to be rising. The combined effect of these two tendencies would be to shift the extensive margin for agricultural production (the intensive margin for forest production) to the left to some extent. Some land which has been most

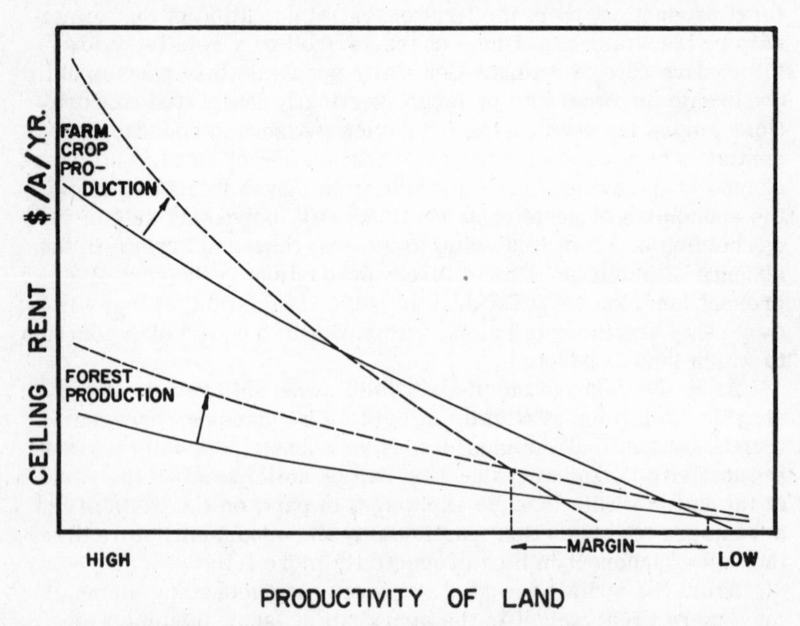

Fig. 10.5. Apparent shifts in hypothetical ceiling rent gradients for farm crops and forest production.

productive in agricultural use may now be more productive in forest use.

The institutional problems entailed in such an adjustment in land use are apparent. What's to become of the people now gaining, with the aid of various public programs, a meager livelihood from these farms? Alternative employment opportunities for these people are apt to be limited. Often, they simply don't want to leave the land and their accustomed way of life. An acceptable adjustment policy must give primary regard to facilitating the changes implied on the part of the families and communities involved. To some extent, simply the fact that a public agency or private firm stood ready to purchase the land at a fair price based on its most productive use would meet the problem. In other instances, it might be desirable to provide that families could remain on the land, as tenants or otherwise, after purchase. The conversion process could be expected to provide some opportunity for gainful employment. While they are great, the institutional problems do not appear to be insurmountable.

The degree to which shifts in land use from agricultural production to forest production appear to hold favorable prospects varies considerably among the geographic regions of the country. In terms of the three major problem areas considered here, the cotton area of the Southeast is, without question, the one in which forest production would hold the greatest promise as an alternative use of marginal farm land. Physical conditions are favorable to forest production. Wood-using industries, particularly the pulp and paper industry, are well established in the South. The intensification of forest management, especially on private holdings, has generally proceeded more rapidly than in other regions of the country. It is with regard to the eastern softwood species that the most critical shortages of timber have been anticipated by the Forest Service. The Southeast is the area in which supplies in this species group can be enhanced to the greatest degree.

In the Corn Belt the areas on which forest production could compete with the production of farm crops are perhaps more limited than in the South. There are, however, rather substantial areas of near marginal farm land on which productivity in forest use would be high. In parts of the region, recreation would be a relatively important factor in contemplating an expansion of the forest area. Shelterbelts and roadside strips present significant opportunities for productive alternative use of croplands.

The Wheat Belt offers the least promising prospects for forestry as an alternative to the production of farm crops. By and large, precipitation is inadequate for forest growth except in the river bottoms. In this region, limited forest areas would have their greatest value in recreational use and as shelterbelts. It is unlikely, however, that the productivity of the region can be enhanced by attempts to shift from wheat to forest production on an appreciable scale at assumed and lower levels of consumption. The most drastic shortage anticipated by the Forest Service is in the eastern softwoods. If consumption proceeded as assumed in connection with the medium level projections, the inventory of eastern softwood growing stock would be practically exhausted by the year 2000. Some shift in land use in favor of softwood timber production in the cotton area, and to a lesser extent in the Corn Belt, would help to alleviate this condition. Adjustments in land use and intensification of forest management in other parts of the East would also tend to increase supply.

SUMMARY AND CONCLUSIONS

In contrast with substantial portions of the agricultural sector, the prospects for timber production are characterized by deficit conditions. Without more aggressive measures than are contemplated at present, rising real prices and restricted consumption of timber products can be anticipated. The relative significance of forest recreation and of other forest goods and services is rising rapidly. There is strong evidence that more intensive management of forest resources may be in the best interest of society. The productivity of some land now in agricultural use may be enhanced by shifts to forest production in public or corporate ownership.

There are significant opportunities for increasing the marginal efficiency of capital in timber production. Greatly expanded research efforts, in timber growing and in the technology of utilizing timber products, would contribute substantially to this end. Measures designed to increase timber supply, however, must also focus upon means of reducing the opportunity cost of capital required in timber production. Among the important approaches in this direction which would tend to favor expansion of the timber supply would be:

1. Reduction of risks in timber growing.
    a. Increased protection against fire, insects and disease.
    b. Expanded availability of insurance on growing stock.
2. Low-cost credit.
3. Continuance of favorable income tax provisions.
    a. Capital gains treatment of income from timber.
    b. Expansion of costs incurred in cultural practices.

4. Measures to favor transfer of ownership from small, low income owners to public agencies and large wood-using firms characterized by low capital cost.

These measures and others, including programs now in effect, would tend to alleviate the timber supply problem anticipated, and to enhance the production of other forest goods and services. Furthermore, such measures would tend to increase the productivity of land in forest use, and to improve the competition position of forest production for land which is near marginal in agriculture.

It seems possible that, by subsidizing forest production to a relatively small extent, society has the opportunity to de-subsidize agriculture substantially. The institutional problems incident to such adjustment do not appear to be beyond solution. There is reasonable prospect that social benefits arising from expanded production of forest goods and services would exceed the extra costs entailed. The public interest requires that forest production be considered as a possible alternative use of land of low value in the production of farm crops.

Chapter 11

ALVIN C. EGBERT
Agricultural Research Service, USDA
LLOYD C. DUMENIL
Iowa State University

Nature, Magnitude and Physical Areas of Potential Supply-Demand Imbalance[1]

THE TOPICS to be covered by this and the following chapter by Professor Bottum are: (1) An evaluation of surplus problems as an over-input of land and labor, (2) the (possible) effects of technological prospects on a relative supply of land and agriculture's capacity to produce, (3) the relative overcapacity of farming from 1960 to 1985 and (4) the acreages not needed in agriculture and where located. Obviously, this is a large order if one is to take the assignment literally. But the purpose of this book is: (1) To bring into analysis and technical discussion facts and ideas relevant for providing answers and (2) to suggest areas of further study necessary to an adequate understanding and amelioration of these problems. Hence, we take our cue from this statement and present what we believe to be some of the more relevant ideas for analysis of farm surplus problems, together with some partial facts — partial because they deal with only a part of the surplus problem. Scattered within these ideas and facts will be found a number of suggestions for more exhaustive research.

The plan of this chapter is to consider the topics mentioned in the order given. We consider first the surplus problems of agriculture as an over-input of land and labor.

SURPLUS OUTPUT AND SURPLUS RESOURCES IN AGGREGATE

We believe the majority opinion to be that there is surplus capacity in agriculture. There seems also to be greater

[1]The opinions expressed in this chapter are those of the authors and do not necessarily represent those of the Farm Economics Research Division, ARS, or the United States Department of Agriculture. The writers wish to acknowledge helpful comments received from Arnold Paulsen. Naturally, he is not responsible for any errors or omissions.

agreement that the surplus capacity and corollary-income problems are caused chiefly by excess labor in agriculture. Only recently has the magnitude of the land input become suspect. Yet while there is agreement among many that there is surplus capacity in agriculture and that surplus capacity is in terms of land and labor, there are those who remain unconvinced. Why is this so? First, some persons believe that potential demand has not been fully exploited. "Just give low-income families adequate incomes or promote farm products at home and abroad and farm surpluses will disappear," they say. This reason is in the minds of a majority of the dissenters. Second, others believe that more efficiently organized farms would permit farmers to cover all costs with total output marketed at lower prices.

The hope expressed by the first reason given by the "unconverted" has been adequately repudiated elsewhere.[2] Attention to the problem of what would happen to surplus production if farm organization were changed has been less adequate. A priori evidence, however, appears strong on this question, and we would now like to present what seems to us to be this a priori evidence. To do this, we shall first present our definition of surplus production, then relate this definition to the specification of surplus factors in agriculture.

We begin by considering national agriculture in the aggregate. To further simplify the analysis, we first use static concepts. Later, the analysis is modified to include some dynamic aspects of production and consumption and more than one product.

In aggregate, surplus production can be simply and perhaps adequately defined in this way: Given that all factors are priced at opportunity cost, agriculture is producing surplus output if the cost of producing a marginal unit exceeds its competitive market price. (Because crop yields vary so greatly, this definition implies that marginal output is based on expected or average response.) A simple diagram may help to explain this definition of surplus production. In Figure 11.1, aggregate demand and supply curves for the agricultural sector are shown for a single period of production.

The aggregate supply curve in Figure 11.1 is based on marginal unit costs as defined above and the aggregate demand curve is for a unit of time, say one year, and includes export as well as domestic demand. According to the definition, all units represented by oq_2 - oq_1 are "surplus" because for each of these units a price would be less than the unit cost. For the moment, let's

[2] See, for example, "Demand for farm products." CAA Report 2. The Center for Agricultural and Economic Adjustment, Iowa State University, Ames.

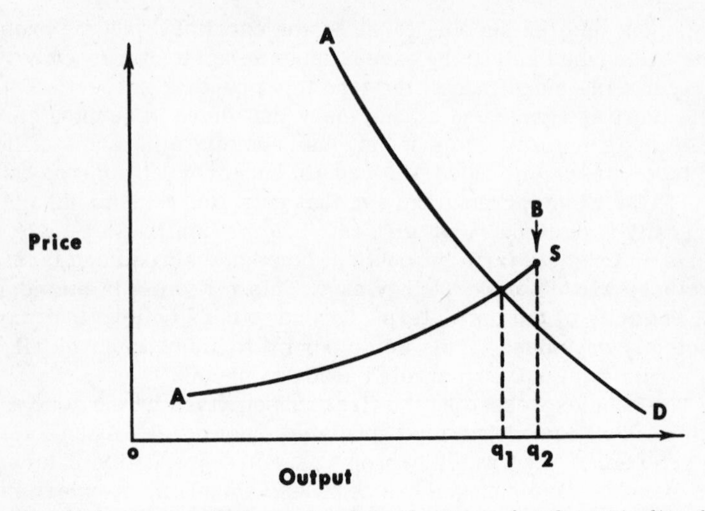

Fig. 11.1. Aggregate demand and supply curves for the agricultural sector for a single period of production.

call this quantity a "tentative" surplus. Only for the q_1-th unit does the price equal cost. Hence, the quantity oq_1 is the equilibrium output and represents nonsurplus production. Furthermore, given that the quantity $oq_2 - oq_1$ represents surplus production, then all factors used to produce these units are themselves surplus.

This statement can be illustrated by referring to the aggregate production function underlying the supply curve shown in Figure 11.1. This production function is shown in Figure 11.2.

In Figure 11.2, land — in acres or some other convenient unit — is plotted on the horizontal axis and is represented by the symbol x. Associated with each of these land units is the customary "bundle" of other resources including labor, machinery, operating capital and so on.

In Figure 11.2, the equilibrium quantity of factors is represented by ox_1. At this level of factor use, the factor/product price ratio represented by line bb′ is equal to the transformation ratio, $\frac{dq}{dx}$. At input level, ox_2, the factor/product price ratio represented by line cc′ is greater than $\frac{dq}{dx}$. (The slope of the factor price-product price line changes as output increases because we are dealing with aggregate demand and higher levels of production can be marketed only at lower prices.) Hence, all factors represented by $ox_2 - ox_1$ are surplus and these are the factors associated with output $oq_2 - oq_1$ in Figure 11.1.

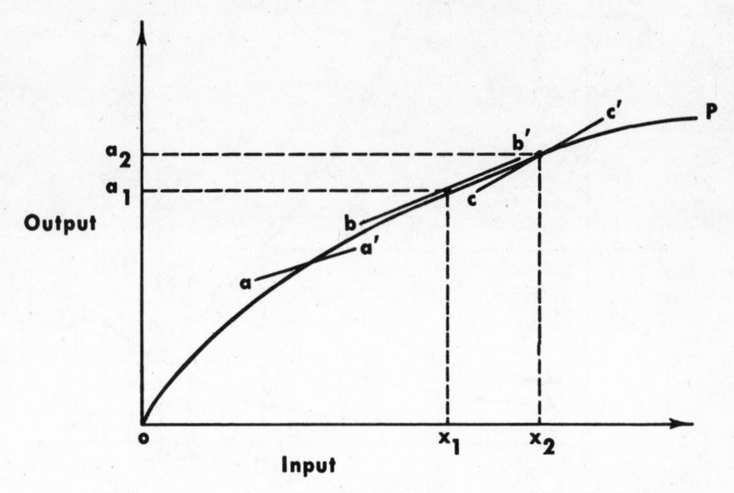

Fig. 11.2. Aggregate production function underlying the supply curve shown in Figure 11.1.

Figure 11.1 portrays total agriculture about as it exists today with a surplus output somewhere between 6 and 10 percent, depending on the "estimator."

Can anything be done to "remove" this so-called surplus? Conceptually, a number of possible alternatives are open.

The most desirable alternative seems to be that of increasing the demand for farm products, which would mean a shift of demand curve AD (Figure 11.1) to the right. This shift would need to be great enough so that demand curve AD would pass through point B (Figure 11.1). As noted earlier, results of research indicate that a shift of such magnitude is highly unlikely.

If we are willing to admit that demand expansion cannot take up the slack in agriculture, another alternative is to "remove" the surplus resources. Thus, with a given state of technology, if resources, ox_2 - ox_1 (Figure 11.2), were to be withdrawn from the agricultural sector, surplus output, oq_2 - oq_1 (Figure 11.1), would not be produced. Such a withdrawal implies not only a removal of land and labor from agriculture but also other resources including machinery, farm improvements and operating capital.

Apparently some persons believe that a third alternative that will bring supply into balance with demand is open to agriculture. This alternative is evidenced by the statement, "What farmers need to do is reduce cost of production." It is not quite clear just what this statement implies. Consequently, it opens up two possibilities. The statement can mean that farmers need either

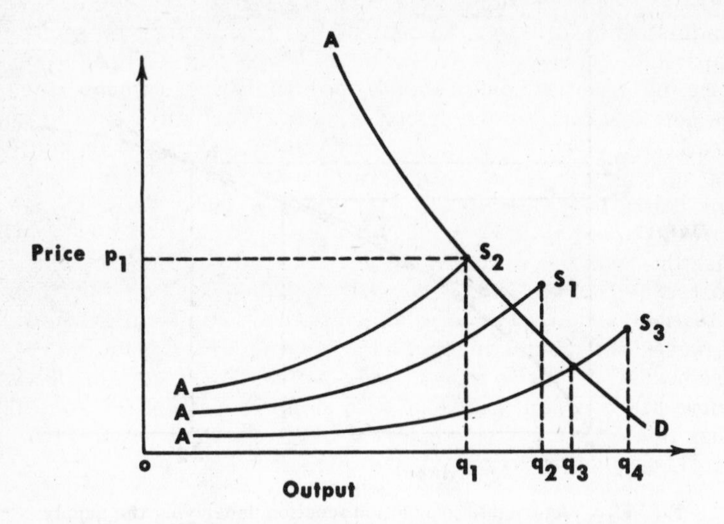

Fig. 11.3. Showing relationship of how drastic reduction in inputs could contract output to such a degree that supply and demand would be in balance.

(1) to reduce total production costs or (2) to reduce unit production costs. If farmers would reduce total production costs, this would mean that they probably would contract their expenditures for such things as fertilizer, hybrid seed, insecticides and other variable inputs. These are unit-cost-decreasing expenditures. Hence, if such action were taken, unit production costs would increase and, consequently, supply costs would increase. But if such a reduction in inputs were drastic enough, it might be possible to contract output to such a degree that supply and demand would be in balance. This relationship is depicted in Figure 11.3.

In this figure, curve AS_1 represents the supply curve as it presently exists, and AS_2 represents the supply curve that would result if farm expenditures were reduced. Given this adjustment, total capacity (oq_1) could be marketed and farm resources would receive opportunity cost returns. It seems obvious that such an equilibrium position would be highly unstable. This would be true because each farmer could improve his profit position (given the price level p_1, Figure 11.3) by increasing the variable expenses just contracted.

The other possibility – that of reducing unit costs – implies that expenditures for fertilizer, insecticides, hybrid seed, improved machinery and so on would be increased. Such changes would result in a shifting of the aggregate supply curve of agriculture. This shift could be represented by curve AS_3 (Figure 11.3).

As this curve is drawn, an output (oq_3) greater than present total capacity (oq_2) could be marketed and the resources used to produce this quantity could receive opportunity cost returns. (Again we note that factors are priced at their opportunity costs in Figure 11.3.) However, because resources would have been added to the agricultural "plant" (capital in the form of fertilizer and so on), output capacity exceeds equilibrium output. We have excess capacity equal to $oq_4 - oq_3$. This excess capacity may be greater than that existing before resource adjustments to reduce unit costs were made. Of course, Figure 11.3 shows only hypothetical situations and should not be interpreted as empirical evidence. However, such adjustments as that characterized by curve AS_3 are now occurring in agriculture. At the same time, the demand curve has been shifting along with shifts in supply. We shall discuss this dynamic aspect later, but first we shall relate Figure 11.3 to the aggregate production functions.

In Figure 11.4, oP_1 represents the aggregate production function of agriculture as it now is. The acreage of land and other resources in the agricultural "plant" is represented by ox_2. Output capacity, therefore, is oq_3 and the resources that produce this output are represented by ox_1. Production function oP_2 is the one underlying curve AS_2 (Figure 11.3). But ox_2 represents fewer total resources when associated with oP_2 than when associated with oP_1 because each acre of land is farmed less "intensively"; that is, less fertilizer, insecticides, livestock or other resources

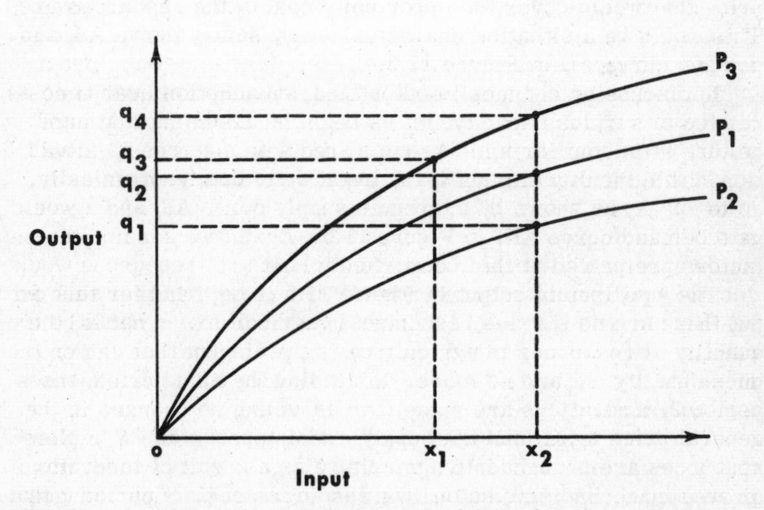

Fig. 11.4. Relationship of agricultural production functions to resources in the agricultural "plant" and output capacity.

are used per unit of land. Conversely, production function oP_3, which underlies curve AS_3, represents greater total resources for each level of output. Also, oP_2 represents less efficiently organized resources and oP_3 more efficiently organized resources as compared to oP_1 because unit production costs are higher and lower, respectively.

For production function oP_3, ox_2 - ox_3 represents the level of "surplus" land, that is, land not needed for the production of wheat and feed grains. But, as already noted, each acre of this land has a larger quantity of other resources "tied up with it" than does surplus land (see Figure 11.2) associated with function oP_1 because of intensive production practices. No surplus land and other resources are associated with function oP_2, as oq_1 is the equilibrium output.

A final note as to surplus output and resources should be added before we turn to some of the dynamic aspects of surplus production. Suppose that agriculture were organized to achieve absolute efficiency; that is, that total production costs were a minimum for each level of output. We could then ask the question, "Would there be surplus resources in agriculture?" The answer would be "yes." This answer would follow because, for efficient least-cost output, more labor would be available than could be efficiently employed on the available land. But also, with complete efficiency and assuming no change in the land base, very likely the total output forthcoming from this land could not be sold at a price that would cover the opportunity cost of the resources used. This would be a situation characterized by supply curve AS_3 and demand curve AD in Figure 11.3.

In discussing changes in output and consumption over time as related to surplus capacity, let us begin by assuming that agriculture is in equilibrium. As compared with the present situation, the agricultural plant is "brought up to date economically," so to speak, as shown by aggregate supply curve AS_1 and aggregate demand curve AD_1 in Figure 11.5. Again, we assume that factors are priced at their opportunity cost.

The equilibrium output in Figure 11.5 is oq_1, and for this output there are no surplus resources in agriculture. That is, the quantity of resources in agriculture is the amount that can produce quantity oq_1 and no more. In a following time period, time period 2, innovations are made (and assuming no changes in the general price level) and the supply curve appears as AS_2. New resources are brought into agriculture as a result of innovations or adopted technology, but all the resources of time period 1 that have not worn out are retained. (We assume that there is a normal shrinking of the agricultural labor force.) Consequently, the

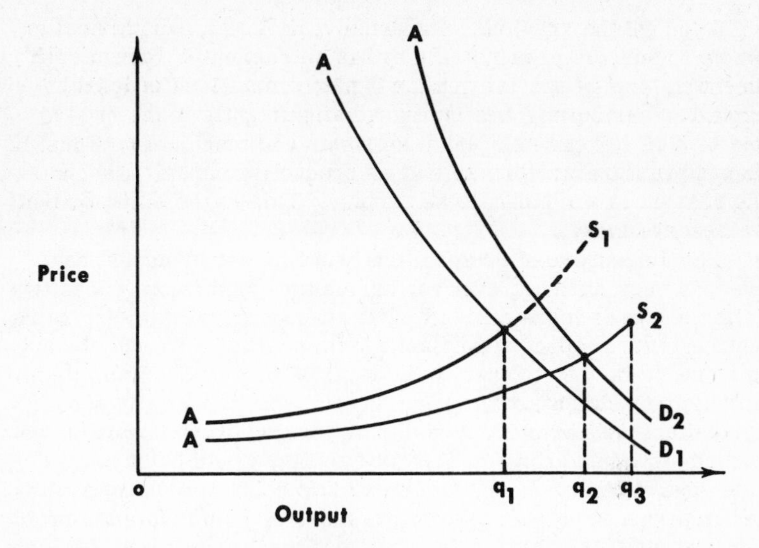

Fig. 11.5. Changes in agricultural output as shown by shifts in aggregate supply and demand.

maximum output of agriculture is oq_3, as shown in Figure 11.5. Although change in the aggregate supply of agriculture occurs over time, changes in aggregate demand occur also. The aggregate demand curve shifts, therefore, as is shown by curve AD_2 in Figure 11.5. Even though both aggregate demand and supply have shifted, relatively, the shift in supply is greater. Equilibrium output, consequently, is less than the capacity output. That is, oq_2 is less than oq_3 (Figure 11.5).

All the previous examples are hypothetical characterizations of the nature of surplus production in agriculture. The general conclusion was that surplus production implied a surplus of some or all factors used to produce agricultural commodities, not land and labor alone. But if the goal is that of production efficiency within agriculture, for any given point in time, some resources may not be surplus even though excess output exists. This may be the case for certain capital inputs, such as fertilizer. All the fertilizer used on "surplus" farm units could be shifted to non-surplus units and production efficiency would be increased; that is, each level of output would be produced at a lower total cost. But it is possible that this reallocation of fertilizer would increase the surplus of other factors above and beyond that existing in the absence of such reallocation. This might be true, even though all other surplus resources were removed from agriculture prior to the redistribution of fertilizer, because output would be greater than demand, as we have defined this condition.

Although the previous discussion dealt with a hypothetical example of surplus production, there is an element of fact in such an example and especially in the dynamic model. The level of capital in agriculture has increased significantly in the 1940's and 1950's, for example, plant nutrients and machinery. Thus, if demand is not expanding as fast as productive capacity, some of the resources are bound to be surplus. This is the situation that we observe today.

The measurement or specification of these surpluses, however, is very difficult, even for agriculture as a whole. Specification becomes more difficult if we attempt to delimit surplus resources with respect to particular commodities. We may be able in some crude way to specify the level of resources committed to production of wheat, corn or cotton, but what can we say about agriculture as a whole? Would it be possible to shift surplus resources to other crops or livestock so they would be earning a rate equal to their opportunity cost? No doubt some such shifts are possible. But such possibilities further complicate the problem.

Although the measurement of the current level of surplus resources in agriculture is a significant problem, it is doubly difficult to make such specification for some future period in time. The more important variables involved in such a projection are changes in technology, population, income and export demand and geographical shifts in population.

We have seen that resources are usually added to agriculture as a result of changes in technology. These additional resources are substitutes for resources already in agriculture and primarily those arising in agriculture – land and labor. If the demand for agricultural products does not expand rapidly enough to absorb the additional output forthcoming from these additional resources, there will be additional excess resources. But just what will happen in the area of future technological innovations is difficult to predict. The rapidity by which presently available technology will be adopted is also difficult to predict. Probable increases in population and income also represent a knotty problem for the prognosticator. Thus, the only conclusion that one can come to is that the prediction of surplus production and, therefore, of surplus factors in agriculture can only be crude, even for agriculture as a whole.

REGIONAL SURPLUSES

If we want to "pin down" surplus output and resources to particular areas or regions, the problem is further complicated. If we want to move in the direction of greater production efficiency, the result could be that regions would be contracting at different rates or that some might be expanding while others would start contracting. For example, data in Table 11.1 show that there have been great differences in the increase in output among regions. The greatest expansion in output has been in the Northern Plains and Mountain States where the increases have been 64 and 57 percent, respectively. In contrast, the increases in output have been only 25 and 24 percent, respectively, in the Southern Plains and Delta States, the areas with the smallest increases in the nation.[3] Other data in Table 11.1 partly explain the differences in output changes. Cropland used for crops increased in the Northern Plains and Mountain States by 9 and 38 percent, respectively, while the acreages of cropland used in the Southern Plains and Delta States declined by 19 and 25 percent, respectively. The increased output in the face of reduced acreages is explained mainly by the use of additional commercial fertilizer. For example, as acreages declined from 25 percent in the Delta States from 1939 to 1958, fertilizer use increased 292 percent. Similar examples are shown in Table 11.1 for other regions. The data in this table imply that fertilizer was substituted for cropland during the period shown in a number of areas. Even in the areas where cropland has increased, this substitution is evident in a relative sense.

Table 11.1. Percentage Change in Total Farm Output and Use of Specified Resources, by Regions, 1939-58

Region	Total output	Cropland used for crops	Plant nutrients	Man-hours of labor
	(Increase or decrease - in percent)			
Northeast	34[a]	-20	115	-46
Lake States	40	-3	1,178	-43
Corn Belt	44	9	957	-42
Northern Plains	64	9	5,318	-38
Appalachian	29	-25	132	-46
Southeast	44	-34	136	-57
Delta	24	-25	292	-60
Southern Plains	25	-19	1,371	-51
Mountain	57	38	1,500	-35
Pacific	59	15	656	-33

[a] Based on averages for the periods 1939-41 and 1956-58.

Source: USDA Stat. Bul. No. 233. Revised Sept., 1959.

[3] The tacit assumption here, of course, is that these changes are the result of competitive pressures that augment resource efficiency.

Table 11.2. Percentage Change in Specified Farm Commodities, by Regions, 1939-58[a]

Product	Region									
	Northeast	Lake States	Corn Belt	Northern Plains	Appa-lachian	Southeast	Delta States	Southern Plains	Mountain	Pacific
All livestock and products	45	29	30	33	54	142	69	14	27	57
Meat animals	11	14	33	51	36	91	55	29	41	35
Dairy products	24	33	13	-15	35	34	12	-22	8	37
Poultry and eggs	99	66	42	17	120	432	194	40	25	139
All crops	7	31	39	61	7	8	-4	15	62	58
Feed grains	31	43	30	75	13	52	-20	40	112	164
Hay and forage	7	13	15	67	14	7	-11	-30	30	22
Food grains	-14	16	20	38	-15	53	91	45	71	42
Vegetables	17	6	-38	-9	-32	30	-30	8	54	84
Fruits and nuts	-13	15	-47	-76	-33	87	-38	-46	-13	14
Sugar crops	-33	16	-46	25	-63	-44	-4	-84	17	80
Cotton	--	--	-31	--	-33	-41	-19	14	246	231
Tobacco	-14	-41	-22	--	25	41	--	--	--	--
Oil crops	776	134	277	448	83	10	1,450	38	-44	-50

[a]Data derived from Supplement 1 to "Changes in farm production and efficiency, a summary report" USDA Stat. Bul. 233. Based on averages for the periods 1939-41 and 1956-58.

Data in Table 11.1 show further that while the number of man-hours of labor has declined in all areas, the decline is greatest in the area where the increase in output is lowest. For example, the Appalachian, Delta, and Southern Plains regions show the smallest increase in output and the largest decline in use of labor. Comparable data on machinery and equipment on farms in each of these regions would show large increases in number and value of machinery and equipment used. Unfortunately, these data are not available by regions. It seems evident then that machinery has provided a significant replacement for farm labor.

Obscured by these aggregate data are the changes occurring in the output of many products of agriculture, region by region. Even though the over-all output of agriculture in each of these 10 regions is expanding, this is not true of individual commodities. This fact is brought out by the data in Table 11.2. These data show that while certain regions are expanding output of some product sectors, others are being contracted. Furthermore, within each region, the rates of expansion or contraction are not the same for any commodity group. For example, in the Delta States, the over-all agricultural output increased by 24 percent. But the output of all crops decreased by 4 percent. Furthermore, while the output of all crops decreased in this region, output of food grains and of oil crops increased by 91 and 1,450 percent, respectively. In the main, the data in Table 11.2 point to increased regional specialization, which for the most part has been due to improved technology in both production and marketing. But these regional changes in production also result from population shifts. This influence is probably indicated by the relatively great increases in production of poultry and feed grains and vegetables in the Mountain and Pacific regions.

It should be remembered, however, that the data in Table 11.2 are based on aggregates, in terms of both commodities and land area. A more detailed disaggregation may reveal "islands" of a trend counter to that shown in Table 11.2. For example, the great increase in poultry and egg production in the Southeast is due chiefly to the great increase in broiler production in northern Georgia and South Carolina. Increased regional specialization is evidence of changes in comparative advantage. Technological advancement, population growths, income changes and shifts in population and consumer taste have great impact on the changes in the comparative advantages enjoyed by regions over time. The development of the combine assisted in the shift of comparative advantage in wheat production from the East to the Great Plains. Currently, development of the cottonpicker seems to have given the Southwest and West, where the topography and climate is more favorable to its use than in other regions, a comparative advantage in cotton production.

The important point here is that prospective regional changes in specialization and production patterns need to be taken into account if the level of resources required in agriculture at some point in the future is to be estimated with any degree of accuracy.

All of the factors mentioned will influence the quantities, kinds and location of resources that will be needed in agriculture during the next quarter century of 1960 to 1985. These things we know. What we do not know is the magnitude of these influences. Simple projections will not provide the answers. We need to take into account the complex of influences that operate in the economy, with the individual influences taken into account simultaneously. Otherwise, the estimates are likely to be greatly in error.

The preceding paragraphs may lead the reader to believe that we have given up on our assigned task because of the grossness of the admonitions. This is not the case, as we hope the rest of this chapter will reveal.

In a following section are shown the results of a method of analysis that seemed relevant for estimating the regional changes in resource use that will need to take place if one sector of agriculture — wheat and feed grains — is to keep in step with the demand. But first we would like to speculate about underlying factors, the probable direction of change in aggregate resource use and the prospective overcapacity in the wheat and feed grain sector in the next 25 years.

PROSPECTIVE OVERCAPACITY IN THE WHEAT AND FEED GRAIN SECTOR OF AGRICULTURE FROM 1960-85

The chief reason for the excess production of feed grains, wheat and other crops over demand has been the rapidly rising output since about 1940 — because of adoption of combinations of improved technology and management which have greatly increased output per acre.

In programming future adjustments in agriculture needed to balance the supply of and the demand for agricultural products, we need to estimate the rates of change in the years ahead. In this section, we attempt to estimate the aggregate production of feed grains and food wheat for the next 25 years, using available information.

POTENTIAL CHANGES IN PRODUCTION OF FEED GRAINS

Total production of the four feed grains – corn, oats, barley and grain sorghum – has increased greatly in the last few years mainly because of higher yields per acre and an expanded corn acreage in 1959. Regression of feed grain production by years for 1940-58 indicates that it increased at the rate of about 1.86 million tons per year during this time.[4] As corn represented 67.5 percent of the feed grains produced in 1958 and an estimated 74.2 percent in 1959,[5] major emphasis will be placed on potential changes in corn production.

Changes in Product Mix

Production of feed grains (particularly corn and oats) is on the threshold of another technical revolution because of changes in rotations. In areas where high corn yields can be maintained in a continuous corn[6] or corn-soybean rotation and where erosion is not a problem, corn and soybeans are likely to replace much of the acreage now in oats and forage.

When acreage allotments for corn were discontinued in 1959, total harvested acreage increased from 73 million in 1958 to 84 million in 1959; but the total acreage of feed grains increased by only 7 million as the acreage of oats decreased by 3 million.[7] The national estimates for 1960 plantings are for a slight increase in corn acreage, a 6-percent increase in soybean acreage, and a 5-percent decrease in acreage of oats.[8]

For each acre of oats or hay shifted to corn, there will be an increase in feed production. Using feed unit conversions[9] and 1960 projected yields,[10] each acre of oats and hay shifted to corn will produce, on the average, 160 and 40 percent more feed units,

---

[4] L. M. Thompson, I. J. Johnson, J. T. Pesek, and R. H. Shaw. "Some causes of recent high yields of feed grains." Proceedings of the Iowa State Feed-Livestock Workshop, Ames, Feb. 16-18, 1959. Special Report 24.

[5] R. P. Christensen, S. E. Johnson, and R. V. Baumann. "Production prospects for wheat, feed and livestock, 1960-65. U.S. Agr. Res. Serv., ARS, 43-115. Dec., 1959.

[6] W. D. Shrader, J. Pesek, and W. D. Moldenhauer. "What about continuous corn?" Iowa Farm Sci. March, 1960.

[7] Christensen _et al., op. cit._

[8] "Federal-state crop and livestock reporting service." Report on a survey of prospective crop plantings in the U.S. Des Moines Register. Mar. 19, 1960.

[9] E. O. Heady, R. McAlexander, and W. D. Shrader. "Combinations of rotations and fertilization to maximize crop profits on farms in North-Central Iowa." Iowa Agr. Exp. Sta. Res. Bul. 439. 1956.

[10] Christensen _et al., op. cit._

respectively. The comparative value of corn over oats is likely to increase in the future since the rate of yield increase per year has been about three times higher for corn than for oats.[11]

Shrader and Riecken[12] in their chapter state that soils, climate and present status of technology favor increased production of corn on extensive areas in the Midland Feed Region. They estimate that continuous corn or row-crop rotations could be used on about 86 million acres of classes A and B land in this region. In the three sub-regions (Central Prairie, Eastern Forest and Southern Prairie-Forest) where the climate is most favorable and yields are highest, about 49 million acres could be planted to continuous corn or a corn-soybean rotation. The potential corn production in these sub-regions, using estimated acreages of classes A and B land and attainable corn yields estimated for different soil and land-capability situations, could approach about 3.3 billion bushels, they estimate. If present soybean acreage is maintained, the potential corn production then would be about 2.6 billion bushels. In contrast, corn production in 1955 was 1.4 billion bushels in these three sub-regions.

The substitution of soybean acreage for acreages of oats and forage will occur also in the above-mentioned areas. Soybean acreage will depend partly upon the relative prices of corn and soybeans. Soybeans will also be grown with corn to decrease weather risks and income variations.

With the reduction of wheat acreage in 1954, when acreage allotments went into effect, much of this land was diverted to feed grains. The two Plains regions and the Mountain Region had the largest diversion of wheatland to feed grains. Grain sorghum was substituted for wheat and forage sorghums in the Great Plains. Barley has been planted on some of the diverted wheat acreage in the Mountain Region and Pacific Region.

Changes in Capital Inputs

Fertilizer. The three most important factors that have affected yield increases of corn since 1940 have been (1) adoption of hybrid corn, (2) use of more fertilizer (particularly nitrogen) and (3) concentration of corn on more favorable soils in a more favorable climate. Of the estimated 17.5-bushel increase in yield from 1940 to 1958, about 6 bushels have been attributed to fertilizers, with most of the influence of nitrogen occurring since

---

[11] Thompson et al., op. cit.

[12] W. D. Shrader and F. F. Riecken. "Potentials for increasing production in the Corn Belt," Chapter 5, this volume.

1950.[13] Increased fertilizer usage will be the dominant factor in further increases in yields of corn.

The tonnage of fertilizer for all crops has increased linearly with time since 1940. The annual increase was 1.032 million tons; if this trend is projected to 1965, the estimated tonnage will be 34 million tons.[14] The tonnage of plant nutrients (N, P_2O_5 and K_2O) has increased at an average rate of 257,000 tons per year. A projection of the 1940-57 trend estimates that 8.2 million tons will be used in 1965; the tonnage of N, P_2O_5 and K_2O will be about 3.0, 2.6 and 2.5 million tons, respectively, in 1965.[15] The more rapid increase in nitrogen usage than of P and K usage is likely to continue beyond 1965, particularly if corn is grown more intensively on increased acreages and if prices of corn remain high in relation to N fertilizer.

Since World War II, fertilizer use has been increasing throughout the country, with a larger percentage of total nutrients (25 percent) and nitrogen (19 percent) applied in the Corn Belt than in any other region. A report shows that 35.3 percent of the nitrogen used in 1954 was applied to corn and 7.1 percent to oats and barley.[16] The study showed also that 60 percent of the corn and 30 percent of the acreages of oats and barley were fertilized in 1954.

The percentage of the corn fertilized and the rates of nutrients applied vary widely among the states in the Midland Feed Region.[17] Generally, a higher percentage of the corn is fertilized in states east of the Mississippi River than in those west of the river. Higher rates of P and K fertilizer generally are used in the eastern part of the area, but the patterns of nitrogen usage are less distinct. The rates of N fertilizer in the various states are affected by soils, rotations, manure applications, precipitation and irrigation. Fertilizer usage also varies widely among soil association areas within a state. In Iowa, for example, the percentage of fields fertilized and average rates of the nutrients vary widely among the soil association areas.[18] It is obvious, however, that corn yields in Iowa can be increased considerably as more farmers fertilize corn, as rates are increased and as other associated high-level management practices are adopted.

About 8.4 percent of the total nutrients were applied to oats and barley in 1954, with 31 percent of the acreage fertilized;

[13] Thompson _et al._, _op. cit._

[14] _Ibid._

[15] _Ibid._

[16] J. R. Adams, L. B. Nelson, and D. B. Ibach. "Crop use patterns of fertilizer in the United States." _Croplife_. Aug. 18 to Oct. 13, 1958.

[17] _Ibid._

[18] _Ibid._

average nutrient application was estimated at 15, 31 and 24 pounds of N, P_2O_5 and K_2O, respectively, per fertilized acre.[19] The percentage of the total fertilizer used on oats and barley will decrease in the future.

Fertilizers have accounted for very little of the increase in sorghum production, although, under adequate moisture, sorghum responds to fertilizers much the same as does corn. Since much of the grain sorghum acreage is in the Great Plains area of uncertain and variable rainfall, fertilizer usage for sorghums is not likely to increase rapidly.

Other management practices. A large increase in corn yields occurred from 1940 to 1950 with the development and adoption of hybrid corn. Hybrids have increased corn yields an estimated 25 percent over open-pollinated corn; about 7 of the 17.5-bushel increase from 1940 to 1958 has been estimated to be due to corn improvement.[20] In recent years, yields have been increased about 1 percent per year because of improved hybrid varieties.[21] A somewhat lower rate of increase is expected to continue in the future with adoption of the best present varieties and development of varieties resistant to corn borer and diseases, varieties better adapted to high stand and fertility levels and varieties that can utilize moisture more efficiently.

Variety improvements in oats and barley from 1940-60 have been made largely to overcome potential yield losses from new races of rust and from new diseases. No appreciable gains in yields per acre from variety improvement are expected in the future.

Sorghum yields increased slightly from 1940 to 1956 but the marked upward trend in 1957 and 1958 reflects the initial use of hybrid sorghums and favorable weather. The new hybrids yield about 25 to 30 percent more than the older varieties. About two-thirds of the grain sorghum in 1958 was planted to hybrids. Yields are expected to increase in future years because of improvements in hybrid varieties.

Increased use of insecticides to control soil insects will be particularly important as the intensity of corn in the rotation increases. At present, the level of adoption of soil insecticide treatment is very low to moderate among different counties in Iowa.[22] Insecticides for control of corn borer have not been

---

[19] Ibid.

[20] Thompson et al., op. cit.

[21] Ibid.

[22] Unpublished data, Project 1377, CAEE and Iowa Agr. Exp. Sta., Iowa State University.

widely used, although research has shown that application at the proper time often is profitable.

The use of herbicides for weed control in row crops may be both a cost-decreasing and a yield-increasing practice. Application of 2,4-D for controlling broadleaf weeds in corn has been widely accepted in Iowa, although its use has not reduced noticeably the number of cultivations. The use of pre-emergence herbicides to control grassy weeds, now in the trial stage by a few farmers, is expected to increase. Tillage operations and production costs can be reduced with the pre-emergence herbicides, and farmers will depend less on timely cultivations or rotary hoeing for effective weed control in the row crops.

One of the dominant factors limiting corn yields in Iowa has been inadequate stand levels.[23]

Although stand levels may be nearer the optima in the eastern part of the Corn Belt than in Iowa, increased stand levels will contribute to higher average corn yields in the future and will allow fertilizers and other practices to be used more efficiently.

Improved and larger machinery has been an important factor in increased production of feed grains. Increased mechanization has given the areas with large, level to gently sloping fields an increased comparative advantage in crop production over areas with small, irregular-shaped fields and those with the steeper slopes on which conservation practices should be used. Further improvements in mechanization will decrease production costs and increase harvested yields somewhat.

The effects on feed grain yields of the management practices discussed here, as well as others, such as irrigation, drainage, soil conservation and conservation and efficient use of water are discussed in more detail by Nelson.[24]

Projected Yields to 1985

Corn. Christensen et al.[25] reported corn-yield projections from 1960 to 1965 (Table 11.3) made by a committee of ARS scientists who assumed 1959 acres for harvest and continued adoption of known practices that result in yield increases. The predicted annual rate of increase (0.4 bushel per year) is lower for this period than the rate of increase that occurred from 1940 to 1959.

---

[23] Ibid.

[24] L. B. Nelson. "Physical potentials for crop production," Chapter 8, this volume.

[25] Christensen et al., op. cit.

Table 11.3. Projected Average Corn Yields Per Acre Based on Various Sources, United States

Year	ARS	1940-58 trend[a]
	(Bushels per acre)	
1960	49.0[b]	48.3
1965	51.0[b]	53.2
1970	52.0[c]	58.0
1975	53.0[d]	62.9
1980	57.0[e]	67.7
1985	60.8[c]	72.6
2000	72.0[e]	----

[a] Thompson *et al., op. cit.*
[b] Christensen *et al., op. cit.*
[c] Interpolated from linear trend.
[d] R. O. Rogers and G. T. Barton. Unpublished data. FERD, ARS, USDA.
[e] USDA. "Land and water potentials and future requirements." Report to the Senate Select Committee on National Water Resources. 1959.

Christensen et al.[26] stated that the continuation of the 1940-58 yield trend to 1965 is possible. They cited Ibach and Lindberg,[27] who estimated that if fertilizer applications on corn were increased to give a marginal return of $2 at present prices and 75 percent of the corn acreage were fertilized at this rate, the national average yield might be about 59 bushels in 1965. Required rates of plant nutrients per acre fertilized were estimated to be 60, 50 and 60 pounds of N, P_2O_5 and K_2O, respectively. It is unlikely, however, that these average rates will be reached by 1965, although 75 percent of the corn acreage is likely to be fertilized by them. In 1958, 65 percent of the corn acreage was fertilized, but only 32 pounds of nitrogen was applied to each fertilized acre.[28]

An economic, attainable average corn yield for 1975 has been projected by Rogers and Barton[29] (Table 11.3). This projected yield appears to be lower than ARS projections for earlier or later years. The ARS corn yield projections for 1980 and 2000[30] (Table 11.3) indicate an upturn in the average rate of yield

[26] Ibid.
[27] D. B. Ibach and R. C. Lindberg. "The economic position of fertilizer use in the U.S. USDA Info. Bul. 202. 1958.
[28] Christensen et al., loc. cit.
[29] Rogers and Barton, op. cit.
[30] USDA. Land and Water Potentials and Future Requirements, op. cit.

increase. For these projections, the major assumptions were: (1) There would be a greater use of technology presently known by research workers; (2) future rate of adoption by farmers of improved practices would be consistent with current educational efforts and technical assistance; (3) price-cost relationships for farm products would be consistent with a high-employment economy; and (4) average weather would prevail in the projected period. It was emphasized in the report that the yield projections are based chiefly on past rates of research and rates of adoption of technology by farmers.

Thompson et al.[31] assumed that the regression of corn yields per acre on years from 1940 to 1958 was the best estimate of the yield trend during this period. They pointed out that the effect of fertilizer was greatest since 1950, but that of crop breeding was greatest before 1950. The major deviations from the regression line probably were due to weather.

Many consider that the slope of the 1940-58 yield trend line is not a good estimator for projected corn yields in the future. The yield trend during this period does include three technical developments in corn production — mechanization, hybrid varieties and markedly increased fertilization. The adoption of the first two is nearly 100 percent, but the most efficient use of the last one is still in the future. Another technical development in corn production — continuous corn — is beginning with the probable concentration of corn production in the areas where soils and climate are most favorable for higher yields. If a major breakthrough occurs in moisture utilization, which has tremendous and exciting possibilities in the Midwest according to Nelson,[32] corn yields may be increased markedly. These scientific advances and others are expected to keep increasing average corn yields.

Some also have thought that the slope of the 1940-58 yield trend line is biased upward by the higher yields in 1956 to 1958, particularly in 1958 owing to favorable weather. However, they seem to ignore the 1950, 1951 and 1953-55 yields, which, mainly because of unfavorable weather, were lower than the trend line. The best evidence that the yields are increasing at about the rate given by the trend line is that the line fitted through the points for corn yields in 1942, 1948 and 1958 (excellent growing seasons for corn in most of the major producing areas) is almost straight and closely parallels the regression fitted to the yields of all years.

The regression equation[33] for the 1940-58 yield trend line is:

---

[31] Thompson et al., op. cit.
[32] Nelson, op. cit.
[33] Thompson et al., op. cit.

$\hat{Y} = 27.92 + 0.971X$, where X is years (1940=1). The projected corn yields up to 1985 from this regression are given in Table 11.3. Although these projections may be closer to economic maximum yields than to economic attainable yields, they may be reasonable under the following assumptions: (1) fertilizer, particularly nitrogen, usage increases at the rate indicated by recent trends; (2) rapid technological advances in corn growing continue to be made; (3) rate of adoption of new technology increases more rapidly in the future than it has in the past because of better prediction of the production functions for specific conditions; (4) corn acreage shifts are accelerated into the higher-yielding areas that Shrader and Riecken[34] indicated; and (5) there are no institutional restraints on the shifts in the corn acreage to the areas which have the greatest comparative advantages.

Of more importance than the projections for the average U.S. corn yields are the projected yields for the economic areas or broad regions of similar soils, states and soil association areas within the states. From these projections, a more precise analysis can be made of the future corn production, where shifts in acreages can be made for most efficient production, how many acres need to be taken out of feed-grain production and where these acreages would be located.[35]

Oats and barley. Yield projections for oats and barley were made by the ARS scientists, previously cited, for the years 1960 to 1965, 1975, 1980 and 2000 (Table 11.4). The projected yields from the 1940-58 trend lines are also given in Table 11.4. The regression equations[36] are: $\hat{Y} = 31.08 + 0.34X$ for oats and $\hat{Y} = 22.53 + 0.386X$ for barley, where X is years (1940=1).

There is little difference between the two estimates of projected oats and barley yields. Barley production can be estimated with more confidence than oat production, as barley acreage is expected to remain fairly constant, but the rate of decrease of oat acreage in the future is difficult to estimate.

Grain sorghum. The ARS scientists have projected grain sorghum yields of 30, 32, 35, 37 and 46 bushels per acre for the years of 1960, 1965, 1975, 1980 and 2000, respectively. The interpolated yield for 1985 is about 39.2 bushels per acre. Acreage is expected to be about 14.5 million acres in the next several years unless the Conservation Reserve is expanded more rapidly.

---

[34] Shrader and Riecken, *op. cit.*

[35] E. O. Heady and A. C. Egbert. "Programming regional adjustments in grain production to eliminate surpluses." Jour. Farm Econ. 41:718-33. Nov., 1959.

[36] Thompson *et al.*, *op. cit.*

Table 11.4. Projected Average Yields of Oats and Barley, United States

	Oats		Barley	
Year	ARS[a]	1940-58 trend[b]	ARS[a]	1940-58 trend[b]
	(Bushels)		(Bushels)	
1960	37.5	38.2	30.0	30.6
1965	39.0	39.9	32.0	32.6
1970	40.5[c]	41.6	33.5[c]	34.5
1975	42.0	43.3	35.0	36.4
1980	44.0	45.0	37.0	38.4
1985	46.0[c]	46.7	38.8[c]	40.3
2000	52.0	----	44.0	----

[a] 1960, 1965 – Christensen *et al., op. cit.*
1975 – Rogers and Barton, *op. cit.*
1980, 2000 – USDA, "Land and water potentials and future requirements," *op. cit.*
[b] Thompson *et al., op. cit.*
[c] Interpolated from linear trend.

The 1940-58 regression line of grain sorghum yields on years is not a good estimate of future yields.[37] High yields in 1957 and 1958 resulting from introduction of hybrid varieties and favorable weather have increased the slope of the regression higher than would be expected for the long-term trend.

Feed grains. Projections of feed-grain production from 1960 to 1985 based on constant harvested acreages of corn, barley and grain sorghum, a decreasing harvested acreage of oats, and ARS-yield projections are given in Table 11.5.

The regression of total feed-grain production on the years 1940-58 does not appear to be a good estimate of future feed-grain production because of (1) the large increase in corn acreage in 1959 and expected acreage equally as high in the near future and (2) the decrease in oat acreage in recent years. The projected production based on the 1940-58 trend line,[38] $\hat{Y}$ (million tons) = 102.2 + 1.86X, where X is years (1940=1), appears to underestimate future production, particularly during the 1960's and 1970's.

Projections of feed-grain production are considerably higher (Table 11.5) if they are based on yields of corn, oats and barley projected from the 1940-58 trend lines rather than on ARS yield

[37] Ibid.
[38] Thompson et al., loc. cit.

Table 11.5. Projected Feed Grain Production, United States, 1960-85

Year	ARS[a]	1940-58 trend[b]	Based on 1960 acreages and 1940-58 yield trends[c]
		(Million tons)	
1960	154.4	141.3	153.3
1965	160.0	150.6	165.8
1970	162.8	159.9	177.7
1975	165.5	169.2	189.6
1980	175.7	178.5	201.7
1985	185.3	187.8	213.8

[a] Assumptions: (1) Constant harvested corn, barley and grain sorghum acreages of 84.0, 14.8 and 14.5 million acres, respectively, and a harvested oat acreage of 27.1 million acres in 1960 but decreasing 0.4 million acres per year thereafter and (2) yields based on ARS yield projections.

[b] Thompson *et al.*, *op. cit.*

[c] Assumptions: (1) Same acreages as given in footnote a and (2) projected yields of corn, oats and barley based on the 1940-58 trend lines of Thompson *et al.*, and projected yields of grain sorghum based on ARS estimates.

projections. For these projections, we assumed constant harvested acreages for corn, barley and sorghum grain of 84.0, 14.8 and 14.5 million acres, respectively, in 1960 and a harvested oat acreage of 27.1 million acres, which would decrease about 0.4 million acres per year thereafter. It is expected that soybeans will replace much of the acreage in oats.

POTENTIAL CHANGES IN PRODUCTION OF WHEAT

Changes in Product Mix

The number of harvested acres of wheat decreased from 71 million in 1952 to 53 million in 1959 because of the acreage allotment and marketing-quota programs that were put into effect in 1954 and still continued. Wheat is still concentrated in the Great Plains, Mountain and Pacific regions. These regions harvest 80 percent of the total wheat acreage. If acreage restrictions were removed, wheat acreage likely would increase in these regions; the increases would depend upon price and program relationships between wheat and feed grains.

Changes in Capital Inputs

The upward trends in wheat yields have been due to new varieties and increased use of fertilizer, chiefly nitrogen. The percentage of the wheat acreage fertilized in the United States increased from 18 percent in 1947 to 28 percent in 1954; the largest increase occurred in the Pacific Region and increases were moderate in the Northern Plains Region and Mountain Region.[39] From 1947 to 1954, the average rate of nitrogen per fertilized acre in the United States increased about 3.5 times; the average rate of P_2O_5 and K_2O increased in the Corn Belt and Lake States but in no region west of these.[40]

From the percentages of the acreages fertilized and the average rates of nutrient applications in the important wheat-producing states, it seems that more fertilizer can be used and that it will be an important factor in increased wheat yields in the future. Since the risk of drouth is high in most of the wheat-producing regions, fertilizer usage will be moderate. However, more efficient use of nitrogen is now being obtained by adjusting the rate to the amount of available moisture in the soil in the early spring.

In the regions that produce most of the wheat, production is highly mechanized; little gain in average yields is expected from increased mechanization.

Projected Yields to 1985

Projected wheat yields from 1960 to 2000 by ARS scientists are given in Table 11.6. The long-term upward yield trend from 1940-59 has been at the rate of 0.3 bushel per acre per year;[41] yield projections from the linear trend (Table 11.6) are somewhat higher than the ARS projections. With the increasing yields and a constant acreage, the production of wheat (Table 11.6) will continue to exceed market outlets.

POTENTIAL CHANGES IN UTILIZATION OF FEED GRAINS BY LIVESTOCK

Although in production of livestock products many advances, such as improved feeding methods, better equipment and trends

---

[39] Adams *et al.*, *op. cit.*

[40] Adams *et al.*, *loc. cit.*

[41] Christensen *et al.*, *op. cit.*

Table 11.6. Projected Average Wheat Yields and Total Production, United States, 1960-2000

Year	Projected yields per acre		Projected production[c]	
	ARS[a]	1940-59 trend[b]	ARS	1940-59 trend
	(Bushels/acre)		(Million bushels)	
1960	21.0	22.0	1,108	1,160
1965	23.0	23.5	1,213	1,240
1970	23.5[d]	25.0	1,240	1,319
1975	24.0	26.5	1,266	1,398
1980	25.0	28.0	1,319	1,477
1985	26.5[d]	29.5	1,398	1,556
2000	31.0	34.0	1,635	1,793

[a] 1960, 1965 – Christensen *et al.*, *op. cit.*
1975 – Rogers and Barton, *op. cit.*
1980, 2000 – USDA, "Land and water potentials and future requirements," *op. cit.*
[b] Christensen *et al.*, *op. cit.*
[c] Assuming a constant harvested acreage of 52.745 million acres.
[d] Interpolated from linear trend.

trends toward more efficient breeds, have been made, the average amounts of livestock products produced per pound of concentrates have not changed greatly in recent years with the striking exception of broilers and turkeys. The trend has shown a higher amount of concentrates fed per unit of livestock product in all instances except those mentioned.[42] However, projections by the USDA have assumed a 10 percent increase in feeding efficiency by 1975.

The aggregate figures for the feeding efficiency of feed grains may be confounded with other factors. With lower prices for feed grains, probably there has been substitution of these for protein feeds in the rations. In addition, with the substitution of feed grains for forage, there has been more drylot feeding of hogs, and a trend toward substituting more feed grains for pasture and roughage for fattening beef cattle is evident.

POTENTIAL EXCESS ACREAGE IN WHEAT AND FEED GRAINS, 1985

Time did not permit detailed projections of wheat and feed-grain demand for 1985. However, linear extrapolation of

[42] Agricultural Marketing Service, ARS, USDA. Agricultural Outlook Charts, 1959. Nov., 1958.

available projected demands indicates that 182.4 million tons of feed grains and 1,120 million bushels of wheat will be required by that year.[43]

What do these projected outputs and requirements imply in terms of excess acreages? To answer this question, first we shall give acreage estimates based on ARS yield projections, then we shall give similar estimates based on 1960 acreages and 1940-58 yield trends. All these data are shown in Tables 11.5 and 11.6.

Taking the ARS projections given in these tables and the demand projections given above, the potential excess acreage for 1985 is 10.5 million acres of wheat and 2.1 million acres of feed grains. Because these estimates are based on harvested acreage, about 1.3 million acres need to be added to these figures to account for average abandonment. Finally, if the 17.0 million acres of wheat and feed-grain land currently in the Conservation Reserve Program were replanted to grains in 1985, the total excess acreage in wheat and feed grains would amount to 30.9 million acres.

Similar estimates of potential surplus acreages using 1940-59 yield trends and 1960 base acreages are 14.8 million acres of wheat and 19.1 million acres of feed grains. Adding the Conservation Reserve acreage and 2.2 million acres for average abandonment gives an estimated total excess of 53.1 million acres.

These two estimates of potential surplus acreages point out the range in estimates that occur under different sets of assumptions. We don't know which set of assumptions is more realistic, only time will answer that question. Too, a different set of assumptions for estimating requirements would change the surplus picture. These potential surpluses are subject to considerable error. Unfortunately, we are unable to set any confidence limits.

Finally, the estimates made are based on national averages. Analysis of the surplus land picture in terms of regional comparative advantage and adjustments in land use consistent with

[43] These values represent liberal extrapolations based on the work of: Rex Daly. "The long-run demand for farm products." Agr. Econ. Res. 8:73-91. 1956; and Statistical Data and Notes on the Long-run Demand for Farm Products. U.S. Agr. Market. Serv., Mimeographed. July, 1956. For example, if a population of 179 million and 230 million for 1960 and 1975 is assumed, and this implied linear rate of increase is extrapolated to 1985 (i.e., 257.2 million) and the trend in per capita consumption of wheat likewise is extrapolated, the indicated requirements of wheat for 1985 are 1,138 million bushels, or just 18 million bushels more than the estimate given above. A population of 230 million for 1975 is the upper limit of current population estimates. If Daly's highest rate of increase in feed grain requirements for 1975 is extrapolated linearly to 1985, the increase in feed grain consumption from 1952-53 to 1985 is 53 percent, whereas the 182.4 million tons of feed grains given above are 159 percent of the 1952-53 disappearance.

comparative advantage needed to balance production with consumption will give a different estimate of the surplus land potential. This is true because of the variation in yields from region to region. If comparative advantage dictated that acreages be withdrawn from corn production in areas outside the Corn Belt, the potential surplus acreage would be greater than if Corn Belt acreages were to be taken out.

We now proceed to an analysis that attempts to identify region by region the potential excess wheat and feed grain acreages when "restricted" comparative advantage, as measured by relative cost of production, is taken into account.

REGIONAL SURPLUS LAND AND OTHER RESOURCES IN THE WHEAT AND FEED-GRAIN INDUSTRY[44]

The analysis of regional surpluses in the wheat and feed industry presented here parallels many of the concepts outlined in the introductory part of this chapter. Because of the limited space, much of the procedure and supporting data cannot be presented here but they are available elsewhere.[45]

For this analysis, 104 programming regions in the United States were demarcated. These regions are shown in Figure 11.6. At attempt was made to include in each region areas that were homogeneous with respect to grain production. As may be seen in Figure 11.6, certain parts (the blank areas) of the United States were not included in these 104 programming regions. The reason for not including these areas was that less than 25 percent of the total cropland here was usually planted to wheat and feed grains. Hence, grains are of minor importance and as such represent supplementary enterprises that would be continued at present levels despite drastic changes in grain prices. Actually, on the average, these omitted areas produced less than 10 percent of all wheat and feed grains produced in the United States.

The 104 programming regions provided the basis for two linear programming analyses, one of an *ex post*[46] and the other of an *ex ante* nature. These might be called "backward-looking" and "forward-looking" models, respectively. The programming

---

[44]The data presented in this section are from results of cooperative research by A. C. Egbert, and E. O. Heady, Iowa Agr. Exp. Sta. and the Center for Agricultural and Economic Adjustment.

[45]Alvin C. Egbert. Programming Regional Adjustments in Resource Use for Grain Production. 1958. [Unpublished Ph.D. thesis. Iowa State University Library, Ames.] Heady and Egbert, *op. cit.*

[46]This is model C presented in Heady and Egbert, *op. cit.* It is presented here again for purposes of comparison.

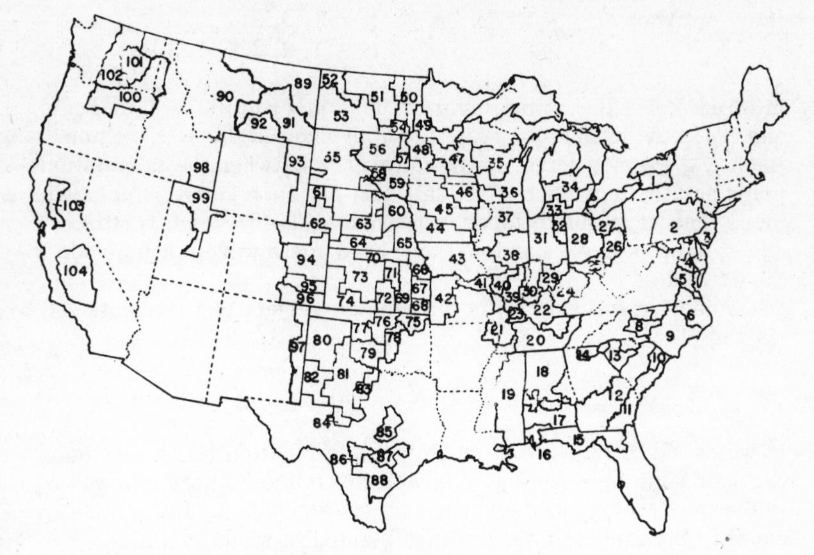

Fig. 11.6. Production regions.

activities considered for the programming regions were food wheat, feed wheat and a feed grain composite. The four feed grains — corn, oats, barley and grain sorghum — were weighted by the average relative acreage of each planted in 1952-54 in the particular region to form this composite. This feed-grain activity was constructed because of production problems of labor use and crop complementarity existing on farms.

Restrictions or restraints on production included the maximum acreages of these crops, plus two absolute constraints representing (1) the total United States food-wheat and feed-grain requirements and (2) net exports of each. The programming analysis used considered the least-cost comparative advantage of different regions in producing food and feed grains under the assumption of linear or constant input-output coefficients. A spatial production pattern and resource use thus determined differs from that which would be obtained by adding up "low per unit cost" regions until output of wheat and feed grain was balanced with requirements.

Programming Models

Ex post model. The formal or linear programming structure of the ex post model is as follows:

(1) $$\text{Max. } f(r) = \sum_i \sum_j x_{ij} r_{ij} \qquad \begin{matrix} (j = 1, 2, 3) \\ (i = 1, 2, 3, \ldots, 104) \end{matrix}$$

in which x_{ij} is the output level of the j-th crop in the i-th region and r_{ij} is the net return from the j-th crop in the i-th region. Each r_{ij}, the net price, is the difference between the normal unit price and the unit cost. The unit cost for each activity included those that were due to labor, power, machinery, feed, fertilizer and related inputs. Land and overhead costs were not included in the estimates of unit costs.[47]

Objective function (1) is maximized subject to restraints (2), (3) and (4),

(2) $$\sum_j x_{ij} a_{ij} \leq A_i$$

in which x_{ij} has the same meaning as in function (1), a_{ij} is the per unit land input for the j-th activity in the i-th region and A_i is the maximum grain acreage in the i-th region. Each A_i is equal to the largest total acreage planted to wheat and feed grains. There were 104 inequalities of type (2) in the model. In addition, there were these two national-demand constraints:

(3) $$\sum_i \sum_{j=2}^{j=3} x_{ij} \geq D_1$$

(4) $$\sum_i X_{i1} \geq D_2$$

In each of these national-demand constraints, the coefficients of the x_{ij} are (1) because outputs are in terms of a bushel of wheat or of feed grain in corn equivalent. Likewise, the demand constraint for feed grain is in corn equivalent.

Ex ante model. The programming structure of this model is the same as that specified by functions (1) through (4) for the ex post model. Changes are made, however, in the activity net return, r_{ij}, the land-input coefficient, a_{ij} and the demand constraints, D_i. These changes result from these assumptions or

[47] A preferred objective function is one in which total costs are minimized rather than net returns maximized. In this case, transport costs to the regions of demand as well as production costs would be included in total unit cost. In the maximum net return formulation used here, it is assumed that net prices account for transport costs to the consuming regions. In effect, it is assumed that prices in each region are equal to those in a central market (or a series of interrelated markets) less the cost of transportation from the region. If this is the case and if markets absorb the programmed quantities at the implied prices, then solutions under either formulation will be the same.

modifications: (1) An optimum amount of fertilizer is applied on each crop; optimum fertilizer use is defined as the level beyond which net income could decline.[48] In other words, fertilizer is applied up to the point at which added cost is equal to added return.[49] (2) Mechanized production methods only are used. (3) Demand requirements are those projected for 1985.

The above changes that were made in formulating the ex ante model represent just a few of the possible changes pointed out earlier that probably will take place in the wheat and feed-grain industry, mainly on the supply side, between 1960 and 1985. These changes, however, are related to the factors that almost certainly will have some of the greatest impacts on the output potential of this industry in the future.

Before presenting the results of these models, we shall attempt to summarize the objectives visualized in formulating them and some of their more critical limitations. The answers to be obtained from the ex post model are these: Given the conditions (a) that production and consumption are in balance, (b) production occurs only in the region with the highest comparative cost advantage and (c) production relationships, prices and requirements are those of 1954: (1) What would be the production pattern of wheat and feed grain? (2) What would be the acreages of grainland left idle? (3) What are the levels of labor and other resources usually associated with these idled acreages? Stated another way, what would have been the structure of the wheat and feed-grain industry in 1954 if there had been no surplus production and if it had been organized on a least-cost basis?

The answers to be obtained from the ex ante model are the same as those for the ex post model when we suppose that the changes outlined above were to take place; that is, the changes in fertilizer application rates, production methods and demand requirements. We further suppose that price relationships and acreages and associated resources were similar to those existing in 1954. In essence, we are asking this question: What would be the surplus situation if certain variable inputs were increased with only small adjustments in the level of fixed resources and if the industry were organized on a least-cost basis?

Actually, the ex ante model does not surround the whole

[48]Formally, we find f_i such that $\frac{dy}{df} = \frac{p_f}{p_y}$ in which $\frac{dy}{df}$ is the derivative of crop output with respect to fertilizer inputs and p_f is the price of fertilizer and p_y is the price of the grain.

[49]The optimum fertilizer rates used were based on data presented in the USDA Handbook 68. The assistance of Professor John Pesek, Department of Agronomy, Iowa State University, in interpreting the data in the publication and working out the procedure for calculating the optimum fertilizer application is acknowledged.

Table 11.7. Estimated Wheat and Feed-Grain Requirements and Selected Data Derived by the Programming Models

Model	Requirements[a]		Acreage needed to produce requirements[b]	Grain acreage unused	Labor associated with unused acreage	Value of other resources associated with unused acreage
	Food wheat	Feed grains				
	(1 million bushels)		(1,000 acres)		(1,000 man-hours)	(1,000 dollars)
Ex post	757	3,887	202,254	28,855	290,397	481,548
Ex ante	880	5,888	190,554	40,555	171,337	838,088

[a] In addition to the quantities needed for seed, silage, and other forages.
[b] Includes acreage used for summer fallow.

problem of surplus production potential in the wheat and feed-grain industry, not only because it does not take into account the interrelationships of all agricultural commodities, as is also true of the ex post model, but also because it does not consider all the factors that are expected to influence this industry in the future: changes in technology other than those assumed, such as shifts to continuous corn; income changes; geographical shifts and growth in population; changes in export markets; and various institutional factors. Although the consideration of wheat and feed grains as the only crop alternatives may not represent a severe limitation in many regions, this may not be true in regions in which cotton and soybeans are important. For these reasons, the results are conditioned accordingly.

Programming Results

Surplus resources. Results of the two models are represented in Table 11.7. The ex post model provides for production of 755 million bushels of food wheat and 3,887 million bushels of corn equivalent. For the ex ante model, the quantities provided are 880 million bushels of food wheat and 5,888 million bushels of corn equivalent.[50]

As shown in Table 11.7, the 1954 wheat and feed-grain requirements could have been met while leaving 28.9 million acres idle. (This acreage includes summer fallow.) Associated with these acres in 1954 were 290.4 million man-hours of labor. In addition, the value of other inputs and services is calculated at $481.5 million. These inputs and services include those of machinery, fertilizer, lime, insecticides, irrigation water and others. These surplus levels are premised on the condition that the total 230 million acres of land had remained in grain production in 1954, as they probably would have done had production controls not been in effect.

For the ex ante model (Table 11.7), 40.6 million acres (including summer fallow) of the 1953 base acreage would have been unused despite increased requirements of 16 percent in food wheat and 51 percent in feed grains. The 171 million hours of labor associated with the 40.6 million acres is less than that of

[50]The requirements for the ex post model are at the 1954 level but are adjusted for normal livestock production, exports and given food uses. The ex ante requirements are the national estimates previously cited less residual production, seed and silage (see footnote 44). The residual production — that produced in the "plain" areas (Figure 11.1) — and silage are exogenous to the model. Seed is accounted for within the model by using net yields.

the ex post model. The reason, as suggested before, is that fewer man-hours are associated with each acre when mechanized production methods are used, as was assumed for this model. The value of other inputs and services associated with this unused acreage amounts to $838.1 million, which is much greater than for the ex post model.

The reader should recognize that these results imply that the acreage planted in grain would remain at the level of 1953, but that fertilizer rates would increase to the "optimum" level and a complete shift to mechanization would occur. This model was deliberately structured in this way to show how persistent surplus grain production could be without acreage adjustments, and also to show how the above-mentioned interfirm adjustments could affect regional production patterns in the future if production and consumption were in balance.

Regional-production patterns. The regional-production patterns resulting from the two models are shown in Figures 11.7 and 11.8. The cross-hatched areas in Figure 11.7 show the regions in which wheat and feed grains would have been produced if the average production had been equal to requirements and if

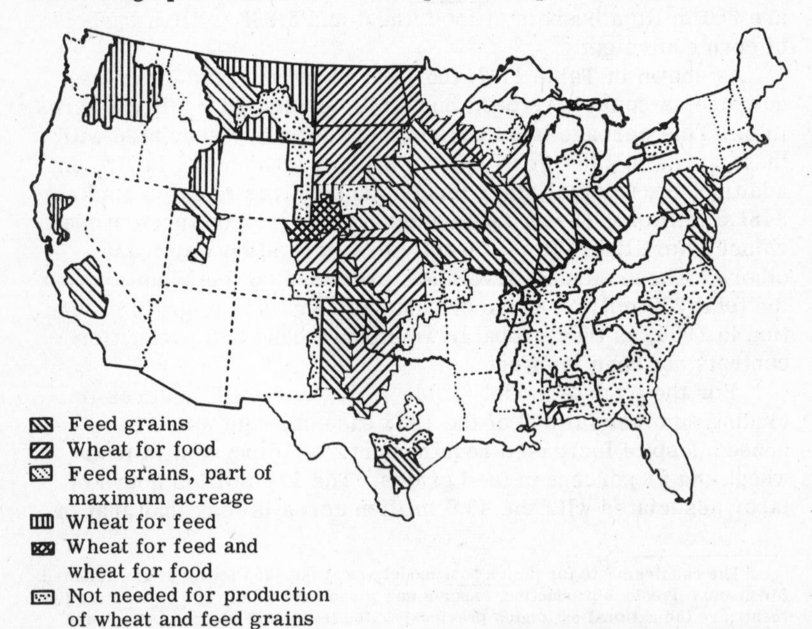

Fig. 11.7. Programmed production location of wheat and feed grains with production practices, resource use and requirements of 1954.

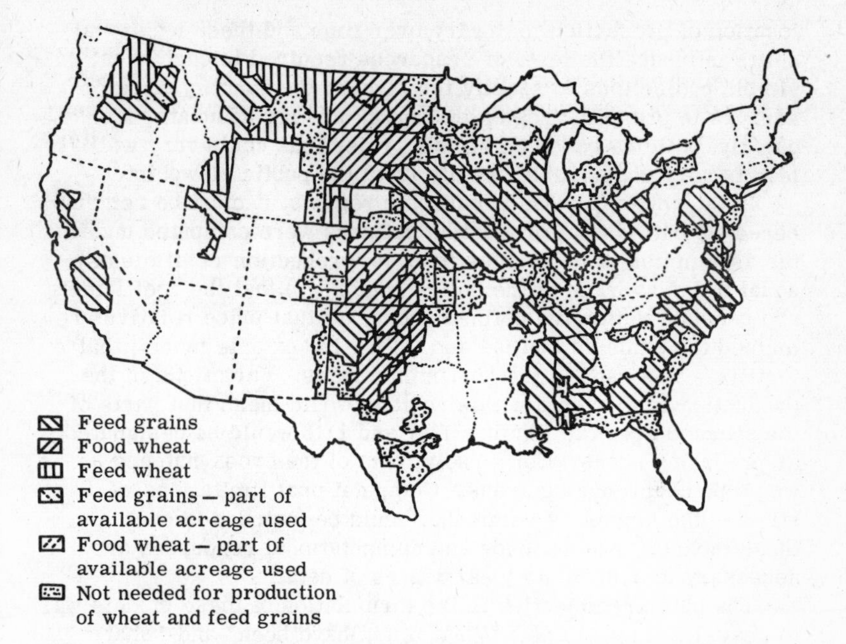

Fig. 11.8. Programmed production location of wheat and feed grains to meet projected requirements of 1985 with optimum fertilizer use and all production mechanized.

production patterns had been consistent with minimum costs by regions in 1954. The stippled areas designate the regions that would not have been needed to produce the specified grain requirements under the assumptions of the model. These regions are in the Southeast, in upper New York, Michigan, northern Wisconsin, eastern Kansas and Oklahoma, western Missouri, southeastern Colorado, eastern New Mexico, south-central Montana, eastern Wyoming and a few other scattered areas.

The regional-production pattern resulting from the *ex ante* model as shown in Figure 11.8, differs from that of the *ex post* model in these respects. Production would be shifted to regions in Virginia, North Carolina, South Carolina, Georgia, Mississippi, Tennessee and Alabama. Producing regions shown in Figure 11.7 but not in Figure 11.8 are in southern Indiana, southern Illinois, central Minnesota, eastern North Dakota, eastern Kansas and southwestern Texas.

These changes in the regional production pattern from the *ex post* to the *ex ante* model bring out this point, which was emphasized previously. Changes in technology can have a significant impact on the location of least-cost production. Because the location of production may vary over time and these locational shifts influence the level of resources required in each area, simple projections to specify the level of the quantity of resources in prospect, region by region, are not adequate. Consequently, policies based on simple projections could very well lead to very undesirable results from the public viewpoint.

In interpreting these results for regions, it must be remembered (1) that spatial production patterns were computed under the assumption of techniques (that is, production coefficients) equal to the average of the entire region, (2) that the coefficients are constant within the defined areas, (3) that price relatives remained the same as in 1954 and (4) for the ex ante model, that fertilizer was used at the "optimum" rates. Variations in the production coefficients within regions would mean that parts of the stippled areas in Figures 11.7 and 11.8 would be designated as producing areas. Conversely, part of the cross-hatched areas would be nonproducing areas. Computational limitations restricted the amount of detail that could be included in each of these models. Ample funds and computational resources are necessary to achieve an ideal degree of detail.

The primary objective in the formulation of these models was to answer the questions: "What might have been" and "what could be" the production pattern of a balanced grain industry, given the adjustment to least-cost areas?

CONCLUDING REMARKS

We have presented estimates of potential excess acreages in wheat and feed grains based on (1) national aggregates and (2) "restricted" regional comparative advantage. The latter is normative in nature but does illustrate the fundamental thesis of this chapter: Surplus estimates based on national aggregates (1) do not provide realistic estimates of surplus resources in agriculture and (2) do not aid in identifying, understanding and solving regional problems resulting from excess production.

We believe we have presented some evidence that shows that the surplus grain problem is not a spectre that will surely fade away if we sit back and wait for consumption to overtake production.

The results presented here are not meant as predictions, even in the loose sense of the term. The significant analysis limitations mentioned should not be overlooked. As was emphasized at the beginning, the specification of surplus resources in agriculture at present or in the future is fraught with difficulties and pitfalls. But analysis is needed and the results presented seem to us to be a step in the right direction.

Chapter 12

J. CARROLL BOTTUM
Purdue University

Land Retirement As a Solution of Supply-Demand Imbalance

FROM THE FOUNDING of this nation until the early part of the twentieth century, the land policy of the United States was in essence one of getting the potential farm land of this country into the hands of individuals and getting it developed. Since 1920, the land area in farms has not changed substantially, and such change as has occurred in harvested crops has been downward.

Even so, aggregate farm supplies since 1920 have tended to press upon prices with the exception of the periods dominated by war and postwar demands. We have been, and are now, in a period where the central land problem has changed from one of obtaining expansion and development to one of getting the potential farm land into its proper use from the standpoint of the nation's requirements.

Near the close of World War I, a significant event within United States agriculture occurred. The rate of gain in agricultural output per farm worker began to exceed the rate of gain in population and the domestic demand for food. For the first time, this made possible an absolute decline in the number of farm workers.

This high rate of gain in output per worker laid the basis for the decline both in the number of farm workers and in the number of farms. This ratio is largely responsible for the human resource adjustment and the size of farm adjustment problems which we face in agriculture in 1960.

During the 1950's a second significant event occurred: Crop yields in the nation began to increase at a more rapid rate than the rate of increase in population and demand for food. In the 1950's crop yields increased one-third while domestic demand for food increased one-fifth.

It just doesn't take as many acres to feed and clothe our larger population in 1960 as it did in 1950. This makes possible an absolute decline in the number of cultivated crops in the United States.

Even if one allows for rather wide changes in the average price of land and in product prices, the optimum combination of resources with present levels of technology does not require as many acres under cultivation as we have today to meet the nation's food and fiber needs adequately.

We have and are adding capital inputs, such as chemicals, machinery and technical know-how at such a rapid rate that supplies are growing faster than the demand for agricultural products.

This has occurred, not only because of new technology, but also because of changed price relationships for capital inputs, which makes it more profitable to substitute them for land. The cost of fertilizer, which is priced only slightly higher now than in the 1920's, is a good example of this.

Therefore, we now have, in addition to an excess supply of human resources, a second resource, an excess supply of cultivated land.

The enlargement of farms does not materially change this resource combination with respect to land. It may raise the average income of farm operators, because it will tend to raise the income of those individuals who do enlarge their units, but it does not correct the imbalance of agriculture.

In fact, the enlargement of farms probably increases total output, because the small unit is more often incorporated into a better managed unit, and the production per acre is raised rather than lowered.

If we continue to have a progressive agriculture, and if we do not discover additional market outlets other than those now in prospect, the retirement of cultivated land becomes an economic consequence of progress in agriculture. The political phase of the problem is not whether we retire land, but rather what land is to be retired and under what circumstances.

Under our present socio-economic system and our emphasis on progress, it is further assumed that we will not limit the non-land inputs.

If we should follow any one of the six most proposed approaches for adjusting agricultural production, or any combination of these approaches, they all would retire land. These proposed six approaches are:

1. Free prices.
2. Mandatory quotas on all products.
3. Mandatory land retirement.
4. The purchase of land.
5. Grass and livestock or crop easement programs.
6. Retirement of land under rental arrangements.

The type and location of the land retired from crop production would vary under each of the approaches. It might or might not be used for other purposes such as grass, trees and recreation.

MAGNITUDE OF THE ADJUSTMENT

An analysis of our recent production and demand situation would indicate our agricultural plant is geared to produce from 4 to 8 percent more farm products than the market will take at socially acceptable prices, as indicated by Congress on numerous occasions.

The accumulation of commodities in storage for the six-year period from 1953-59 amounted to approximately 2 1/2 percent of total annual production.

The adjustment needed above 2 1/2 percent to bring supplies into reasonable balance depends upon the exact assumptions made relative to foreign needs and the level of prices assumed possible and socially acceptable. However, most assumptions and analyses would place the total adjustment needed between the 4 and 8 percent level.

The United States has a total land area of approximately 1,904 million acres. Of this, about 450 million acres are in plowland. Approximately 965 million acres are in permanent hay and pasture. The remaining acreage is in nonpasture forests, waste and nonagricultural lands.

If an agricultural adjustment of the 4 to 8 percent level is achieved, it would require a shift of from 40 to 80 million acres of land out of cultivation. The exact amount would depend upon the type of program used to bring about the shift as well as the type of land shifted. Thus, a 60 million acre figure might be used to indicate the magnitude of the land adjustment problem.

If this shift occurred as a result of low farm prices or a negotiable marketing quota program, the figure might be nearer the 40 million acre level. If it occurred from a program which was directed towards shifting whole farms in the marginal areas or a fraction of every farm out of production, it might require nearer the 80 million acre level.

Our studies indicate that if a program were directed at the farm in the marginal areas or towards a percentage of each farm, about 1 percent adjustment in output might result from each 2 percent shift in land out of cultivation at the 60 million acre level. Very little reduction occurs where small amounts of land are shifted out. However, as acreage increases, the reduction of output becomes greater in proportion to the land taken out.

POSSIBLE APPROACHES

Under any land retirement program, certain limitations on bringing new cropland into production might be desirable. Likewise, practical programs for expanding markets, both at home and abroad, would be consistent with a land retirement program.

Programs designed directly for retirement of land may take varying approaches, such as mandatory controls, land buying, grass and livestock or crop easement programs or retirement by rental agreement.

Mandatory Controls

If mandatory controls are used, it usually means it is necessary to take a given percentage out of each farm, or at least to make uniform adjustments on farms of a given type. Mandatory control, therefore, cannot take out land in certain areas and still meet the qualifications of treating people equally. Little flexibility is available in the program from one area to another.

Land Buying

A land buying program may take out various types of land in certain areas and would allow much more flexibility in the program. However, such an approach requires many immediate social adjustments and does not appear as an acceptable approach, if conducted on a scale to meet the magnitude of the current land adjustment problem.

Grass and Livestock or Crop Easement Programs

Under a grass and livestock program, certain inducements might be given to farmers for shifting their soil depleting crops into grass, which they would use in their livestock program. Under a crop easement program, the government might purchase from landowners the right to grow soil depleting crops in certain areas. The producers could continue to use the land for all other purposes.

Such programs would require approximately a 50 percent greater shift in harvested crop acres than where the land was not used for grass. These types of programs would increase roughage-consuming livestock at the expense of grain-consuming livestock, but it would reduce the over-all production of calories for food.

Retirement by Rental Agreements

Under this approach, a land retirement program could take any one of the three following approaches:

1. It could be used to shift a uniform percentage of plowland on each farm. Under this plan, in most instances, the least productive land on each farm would be retired.

2. Funds could be allotted to each state, to be distributed on a whole or partial farm basis, in the same proportion as the agricultural production of each state is to the total production of the United States. The program could be used to move lower to average grades of plowland out of cultivation in each state.

3. A program could be developed to retire from production the lowest to average grades of land, wherever they are in the United States, on a whole or partial farm basis.

A program also could be developed to take out only the higher producing land. However, such an approach would not bring about the most desirable long-time shifts and seems less likely to be used.

Thus the question, under the rental arrangement, becomes one of whether we retire the less productive plowland on each farm, the lower grades in each state, or the lower grades in the nation as a whole, or some combination of the three.

The implications of these different approaches are self-evident, in most cases. A program which only retires a percentage of each farm would be more costly than a program which retires whole units. A farmer who puts part of his farm in retirement cannot reduce his expenses as much per acre as the farmer who puts his entire farm in the program.

On a partial farm basis, a farm operator must spread his labor, machinery and other costs over fewer acres. In most cases, by putting a small portion of his farm in reserve, he reduces only his cash costs for seed, fertilizer and other capital inputs. These costs which he can reduce in the corn and wheat areas are equal to about 25 percent of his total costs. In the cotton and tobacco areas, they may equal 40 to 50 percent of his costs. Once such a program is discontinued, the land would likely go back into production. While this approach does not solve the fundamental land adjustment problem, it does have political advantages since it tends to distribute funds to many farmers and results in minimum social and economic adjustment.

If whole farms are retired, either on a state or national basis, the costs of such a program are less. From the standpoint of the greatest long-run efficiency and from the dollar and cents standpoint, the retirement of whole farms in the marginal farming areas is the most efficient for the nation and in line with what might happen with competitive prices.

Such a program, however, would concentrate participation in certain areas. It would create the greatest immediate social and institutional problem, especially where population shifts are involved. It would likewise concentrate the payments in certain areas, which would raise political problems.

Analysis made under IRM Project 1[1] indicates if this approach were used, approximately two-thirds of the adjustment in acreage would occur in the cotton and wheat areas of the country (Table 12.1). However, once institutional adjustments were made, it might be publicly acceptable for the government to purchase the land.

Some individuals argue, with validity, that the criteria for retiring land should not be the degree of marginality of the land for cultivation, but rather that criteria should be based on the least difference between the present use of the land and its next best alternative use, whether it be recreation, trees or grass.

They also argue that in some areas with relatively good quality land its value for recreation purposes might make it the land

Table 12.1. Comparison of Two Methods of Reducing United States Soil Depleting Crop Acreage by 42.5 Million Acres[a]

Area	On marginal land for U.S.		On marginal land in small areas[b]	
	Acres shifted	Percent of payments to area	Acres shifted	Percent of payments to area
I Range	2,300	5	3,400	9
II Wheat	12,300	29	9,900	16
III Dairy	3,300	8	3,600	9
IV Corn	3,300	8	13,200	38
V Tobacco	3,100	7	3,300	8
VI Cotton	17,700	42	7,600	10
VII Fruit and Truck	500	1	1,500	10
Total U.S.	42,500	100	42,500	100

[a] Based on estimated crop costs and returns only, 1955.
[b] Estimate if taken out uniformly in 80 acres, then added together for major areas.

Source: Unpublished data, IRM 1 Research Project, Ind. Agr. Exp. Sta., Lafayette.

[1] IRM Project 881, unpublished data, Ind. Agr. Exp. Sta., Purdue University, Lafayette, Ind.

which would cost the least to shift if the value of its alternative use is considered.

SUMMARY

Technological advances in agriculture have created agricultural surpluses because of the failure of the human and land resources to adjust rapidly enough to offset the supply increasing effect of these advances. The government has spent vast sums for programs to protect farmers' incomes from the effects of these excessive supplies. It appears likely that such programs will be continued. If they are, they should be directed toward the twin goals of not only protecting farm incomes, but also of bringing about land and human resource adjustments which are necessary to bring the size of the agricultural plant into better equilibrium with the agricultural needs of society.

Chapter 13

Land Use Patterns Towards Which Adjustments May Be Directed

R. G. BRESSLER
University of California

THE PRELIMINARY program for the seminar on which this book is based described the scope of this chapter as follows:

An ideal land use pattern will be developed. This includes the location of production patterns for particular crops with indicated productions.

Most of the preceding chapters develop information absolutely basic to mine, while most of those following present the institutional arrangements through which desirable land use adjustments can be accomplished.

Janus was the Roman god who could see in both directions simultaneously. Could I but emulate him, and add to these godlike attributes that of divine insight into the future, I might be reasonably well equipped to tackle the problem of an ideal land use pattern for future agriculture in the United States.

If the preceding chapters had accomplished their assignments perfectly and in great detail, if their results had been available to me before this writing, if I had a large staff of able economists and computers – not to mention a better brain – my contribution might have come reasonably close to the mark. In these unlikely events, my chapter might well have sounded the death knell for the Center for Agricultural and Economic Adjustment, for I should have solved the major problems to which it is dedicated. With this thought in mind, I have been content with a less ambitious objective and with a presentation along broad and general lines which should leave at least a modicum of future work for the Iowa staff.

THE CONCEPTUAL MODEL

While this book focuses on land resources, particularly the agricultural uses of land, it is clear that any serious attempt at solution must involve general equilibrium — interrelations between agricultural and nonagricultural sectors of the economy, between land and other resources and between farm and nonfarm uses of land. We visualize a complex interaction of available resources, technology, alternative uses, consumer demands and preference — all in a spatial context with appropriate interconnections in the form of transfer, processing and marketing costs. The model should be dynamic, of course, to allow for changes in technology and tastes, for interactions between and within major sectors and for all the serial interconnections of these variables.

Despairing of our ability to specify or to manipulate such a complex model, we are forced to rely on a simplified and partial analysis. Attention is directed to adjustments within agriculture. Demand is considered an exogenous variable, in the form of a projected consumption pattern for farm products. Technological change is also taken as exogenous, incorporated in a projected pattern of production functions. The model itself is static and competitive — the latter because we want an "ideal" pattern rather than an estimate of what may occur, and because the competitive norm appears to be as consistent with production efficiency criteria as any we can devise.

My land economics colleagues may visualize this in terms of economic rents for parcels of land, with land and markets interconnected in a multiple von Theunen framework, and with the desirable utilization patterns emerging from supply-demand interactions which in equilibrium assign each parcel to its highest rent-earning use. In the language of the programmers, this is an elaborated transportation model; each parcel of land is characterized by production coefficients and costs for all alternative uses, connected to all possible markets for all alternative products by transfer-processing costs, with a final solution which minimizes costs, maximizes rents, satisfies all consumption requirements, allocates land by product and among markets and determines the structures of product prices and land rents.

That this is oversimplified cannot be denied, but our knowledge is hopelessly inadequate even for this model.[1] Our approach must be in very broad terms, therefore, with only a fraction of the detail suggested above. First, we consider future prospects for the aggregate demand for farm products — primarily domestic but with some allowance for exports — and the composition of this demand by major commodity classifications. We assume that

---

[1] The Egbert-Dumenil models, while limited to food and feed grains, represent a good first step in this direction. See: A. C. Egbert and L. C. Dumenil, "Nature, magnitude and physical areas of potential supply-demand imbalance," Chapter 11, this volume.

desirable future production patterns will be closely correlated with these consumption projections and, by contrast with present production, obtain general indications of desirable changes in aggregate output and in the product mix. When these desirable changes are viewed against the background of geographic production patterns and type-of-farming areas, they suggest the dominant production adjustment problems for the major agricultural regions. This can be modified by a consideration of differential population growth by regions and the probable impact on production patterns for market-oriented commodities. Finally, we add the general effects of some technological advances in production and handling on the location of production. The end product will be a far cry from an ideal land use pattern, but it will exhaust my abilities in that direction.

PROJECTIONS OF CONSUMPTION AND PRODUCTION

Many excellent studies of consumption trends and requirements are available, the details of which I shall not reproduce here (see Chapter 3 by Nathan Koffsky). In general, however, such studies involve the following steps: (1) projections of population growth; (2) projections of income and purchasing power; (3) projections of per capita consumption rates – in total and for commodity classes – based on changes in income and on trends in consumption habits; and (4) from the above, projections of future domestic consumption requirements. To these are added guesses as to possible exports of farm products, usually at levels about equal to those of the mid 1950's.

Projections of the 1975 population for continental United States now range around 220 to 230 million, or more than 35 percent above 1955 levels. Per capita real income is assumed to increase during this period by 40 to 60 percent. With this increase in income and with a continuing shift away from cereals and to livestock products, it appears that the aggregate per capita consumption of farm products might increase by 8 or 9 percent. Thus, domestic consumption of these products might rise by roughly 45 percent. Exports in the mid 1950's amounted to 10 to 12 percent of domestic consumption. If the absolute level of agricultural exports could be maintained, total utilization of farm products in 1975 – at home and abroad – apparently would stand at some 40 percent above the 1955 levels. Requirements by commodities would range from roughly 10 percent increases for wheat, potatoes and beans to 50 percent or more for most of the livestock products, feed grains and fruits and vegetables.

Table 13.1. Output of Major Agricultural Products To Meet Projected 1975 Requirements

Commodity	Actual 1959[a] (1953 = 100)	Projected 1975[b] (1953 = 100)	Projected 1975[c] (1959 = 100)
Livestock and products	112	149	133
Meat animals	112	153	137
Poultry products	124	155	125
Dairy products	105	135	128
Wool	96[d]	124	129[d]
Crops	115	130	113
Feed grains	142	142	100
Food grains	96	86	90
Fruits	109[d]	148	136[d]
Vegetables	102	148	145
Potatoes	110	107	97
Dry beans	96[e]	104	108[e]
Sugar	126	106	84
Fats and oils	154	144	94
Cotton	90	123	137
Tobacco	88	158	180
Total farm output	115	138	120

[a] Based on statistics published by the USDA, especially Agricultural Outlook Charts, 1960, Table 44.
[b] Based on Rex F. Daly, "The long-run demand for farm products," Agr. Econ. Res., Vol. VIII, No. 3, July, 1956, Tables 9 and 10. Projection II data have been increased by 5 percent to allow roughly for 1975 population forecasts of 220 to 230 million rather than 210 million.
[c] Projected 1975 divided by actual 1959.
[d] 1958 data; 1959 estimates not available.
[e] 1957 data; 1959 estimates not available.

Because of agricultural surpluses during the 1950's, production would not need to expand as much as utilization to satisfy 1975 requirements. Rex Daly's classic study, modified for somewhat higher population forecasts, suggests increases in production between 1953 and 1975 of 49 percent in livestock products, 30 percent in crops and 38 percent in total farm output (Table 13.1).[2] But output has already expanded materially; the index of farm output is 15 percent higher for 1959 than for 1953. With allowance for this, the production job facing agriculture in meeting 1975 requirements involves an expansion of only 20 percent over present output, with an increase of 33 percent in livestock products and only 13 percent in crops.

Viewed from the 1953 base, the modified Daly projections indicate needed production expansions of more than 50 percent for

[2] Rex F. Daly, "The long-run demand for farm products," Agr. Econ. Res., Vol. VIII, No. 3, July, 1956, pp. 73-91.

meat animals, poultry products and tobacco. Feed grains, fruits and vegetables and fats and oils requirements were up 40 to 50 percent, dairy products 35 percent, and cotton and wool about 25 percent. The output of potatoes, beans and sugar would increase less than 10 percent, while food grain production should be curtailed by nearly 15 percent. The 1953-59 production changes were amazing, however, for some commodity classes — 54 percent for fats and oils, 42 percent for feed grains, 26 percent for sugar and 24 percent for poultry products. At the other extreme, output of wool, food grains and dry beans each declined 4 percent, while cotton and tobacco production fell 10 and 12 percent respectively. It is significant that the crops with output decreases are primarily those subject to production control and that expansion in such crops as feed grains and oilseeds was encouraged by the restrictions on controlled crops. The increase in sugar crops — primarily sugar beets — involves less-than-quota output by the industry in the mid 1950's, increasing profitability of sugar beets relative to other alternatives, the availability of diverted acreage and, especially since 1956, an increase in the domestic allotment. The combination of these factors increased the proportion of sugar consumption supplied by domestic beet and cane producers from 26 to 32 percent of the total.

From the standpoint of land use, the projected one-third increase of livestock products from 1959 to 1975 is already encompassed in the projection of a 13 percent increase in crop production. Within crops, it appears that present production is already adequate or slightly overadequate for 1975 requirements for feed grains and potatoes. Fats and oils need to be curtailed by 6 percent and food grains by 10 percent. The calculation suggests a restriction of 16 percent for sugar crops, but this does not allow for the recent changes in domestic quotas. With this modification, it would appear that the 1953 to 1975 requirement would be at least 130, so that 1975 would require a further increase of 5 percent as compared with 1959. Moreover, there is some evidence that total per capita use of sugar is holding constant rather than declining; if this is correct, the 1975 projections would be further increased in line with population changes.[3] Major production increases will be needed for fruits and vegetables (36 and 45 percent), for cotton (37 percent) and for tobacco (80 percent).

In the past, I have been known to argue that the future production job confronting United States farms will represent a more

---

[3] Leonidas Polopolus, U.S. Beet Sugar: A Study of Industry Structure and Performance Under Protection and Control (Ph.D. dissertation manuscript, Department of Agricultural Economics, University of California, March, 1960).

substantial effort than the record-breaking performances of the past because of certain nonrepetitive factors.[4] I still believe this to be true, but with actual 1959 levels of crop output only 13 percent below 1975 projections it seems clear that there will be "surplus" land in this immediate future. When allowance is made for the possibility of adding new and improved land equivalent to 5 percent of total cropland, it seems certain that an ideal land use pattern for 1975 would involve the retirement of some marginal lands as well as major shifts among crop uses.

REGIONAL ADJUSTMENTS

We now come to the section where we try to outguess or second-guess the regional experts. Let us start by considering population statistics. Nielson has projected 1975 population for the continental United States at 221 million.[5] His estimates for major census regions are given in Table 13.2. While substantial growth is to be expected in all regions, the rate of change is expected to be lowest in the East South Central (12 percent between

Table 13.2. Population of the United States and Census Regions, Actual 1954 and Projected 1975

Region	Population		Increase
	1954	1975	
	(Thousands)		(Percent)
New England	9,843	12,850	30.6
Middle Atlantic	31,463	40,500	28.7
East North Central	32,529	45,300	39.2
West North Central	14,579	17,300	18.7
South Atlantic	23,035	32,523	41.2
East South Central	11,682	13,100	12.1
West South Central	15,571	20,200	29.7
Mountain	5,762	9,582	66.3
Pacific	16,733	29,439	75.9
Continental United States	161,999[a]	220,794	36.3

[a] Adjusted to include count of children omitted by the census.

Source: Howard C. Nielson, Population Trends in the United States Through 1975 (Menlo Park: Stanford Research Institute, 1955), p. 5. Processed.

[4] R. G. Bressler, Jr., "Farm technology and the race with population," Jour. Farm Econ., Vol. 39, No. 4, Nov., 1957, pp. 849-64.

[5] Howard C. Nielson, Population Trends in the United States Through 1975 (Menlo Park: Stanford Research Institute, 1955), 57p. Processed.

1954 and 1975) and the West North Central regions (19 percent), while it will be highest in the Mountain States (66 percent) and the Pacific States (76 percent). I report — with more horror than pride — that the California projection is 23.6 million.

Population and its geographic distribution are roughly synonymous with the geographic patterns of markets for farm products and so are important factors in the location of farm activities. By far the dominant forces shaping the regional patterns of agriculture, however, have been differences in soils and in climate. I have admired the USDA maps showing major type-of-farming areas for more than a quarter century. Two things have especially impressed me about these maps. First, in more than two decades, there have been only minor changes in the general regional character of American agriculture. Second, the broad type-of-farming areas strongly support the above statement as to the dominant influence of soil and climatic factors. The Cotton Belt lies across the southern tier of states because of climatic conditions — not proximity to market — and it has expanded west into Texas and California because of a combination of climate, soils, irrigation and topography, plus farm size amenable to mechanization. Feed grains and livestock dominate the Corn Belt in large measure because the climate favors corn, and this organization gives way to small grains in the Great Plains because rainfall permits small grain growing where many other crops cannot survive. Similarly, grazing is dominant in the Mountain States and Intermountain States because of a combination of rainfall and topography. Specialty crop areas — potatoes in Maine and Minnesota; fruits and vegetables in Florida, along the Gulf and in California; apples in Washington — find their locations in spite of, rather than because of, the geographic pattern of markets. Perhaps only in the major dairy areas are location principles clearly evident, with fluid milk regions in the Northeast, manufacturing milk in the Lake States, and with smaller fluid milk areas in the vicinity of large cities throughout the country.

Possible implications of the projected trends in population and in United States agricultural production are explored below.

New England

From the standpoint of land use, the dominant agricultural enterprise is milk production for metropolitan markets. Specialty crops such as potatoes, vegetables and tobacco occupy much of the better land. Fruit production is important. Eggs and broilers have become an important component of the agricultural total, but these enterprises have little impact on land use. With an anticipated 31 percent increase in population, major changes in agriculture should be in market-oriented enterprises. Dairying might expand 20 to 25 percent, largely through higher production per cow and imported concentrate feeds. Population growth will provide an increased market for locally produced truck crops in season, but the availability of suitable land limits this possibility. The agricultural margin has been contracting in New England for more than a century, and this will continue. Recreational uses and suburban residential expansion will continue to remove land from commercial agriculture, while the gradual shift of poorer lands from crop-livestock uses to brush and forest uses should continue.

Middle Atlantic States

Population increase of 29 percent means 9 million more persons in this three-state region. As in New England, the land use pattern is dominated by dairying. Fruits are important along the Great Lakes, vegetables for fresh markets and for processing are a major enterprise in southern New Jersey, and there remains a considerable amount of "general" farming in Pennsylvania and upstate New York. In spite of continuing "surplus" milk problems in the New York-New Jersey pool, 1975 should see a substantial increase in fluid milk production in this region. In this connection, it should be emphasized that aggregate projections of increases in dairy production at a rate less than the rate of population growth reflect a further decline in consumption of manufactured products; per capita consumption of fluid milk and cream is expected to increase nearly 10 percent over this period. With increased demands from population growth and from higher per capita consumption, it seems probable that vegetable production for the fresh market will expand, probably at the expense of processing crops.

East North Central

This census region includes segments of three major type-of-farming areas: (1) the eastern part of the Corn Belt, extending from mid Ohio across Indiana and Illinois; (2) the Michigan-Wisconsin-northern Ohio dairy area; and (3) general farming with livestock, dairy and some tobacco in the southern parts of Ohio, Indiana and Illinois. Fruit and truck crops are important along the eastern shore of Lake Michigan and the southern shore of Lake Erie. With the Detroit-Chicago complex of manufacturing industries, total population is expected to increase nearly 40 percent between 1954 and 1975. Because of natural factors, dairy production will continue to be important and should expand, but with a continuing shift from manufacturing to fluid outlets. The Corn Belt section of this region represents an efficient, concentrated agricultural area. With projected increases in requirements for meat animals of 37 percent, there would seem to be little change for this area except in terms of increasing efficiency in livestock feeding. This would also be true of the southern section of the region, with the possibility of some small expansion of tobacco production.

West North Central

This region encompasses the westward extension of the Great Lakes dairy area, the Corn Belt through Iowa and Nebraska, the small grain regions centered on the Dakotas and Kansas, and it extends into the grazing lands of the northern Great Plains. Population is expected to increase by about 3 million, or only 19 percent. As in the case of the East North Central Region, dairy production should continue or even expand, with some shift towards local fluid market outlets. The butter industry, centered especially in Iowa and Minnesota, has already made a substantial adjustment but may well decline further with shifts into other livestock enterprises. The primary adjustment problems, of course, are in the small grain areas. Large wheat surpluses now exist, and present levels of food and feed grain production are either at or above projected 1975 requirements. Ideal adjustments of small grain production would not contract acreages in the Corn Belt or in the eastern sections of the wheat areas but would call for a substantial shift of acreage along the western "frontier" from small grains to permanent grass where low and erratic rainfall results in agriculture that is unstable both physically and economically.

South Atlantic States

The South Atlantic Region extends from Maryland and West Virginia to Florida. Broad agricultural uses range from general farming — livestock, dairy, fruit and truck crops — and tobacco, through the Old Cotton Belt, and into the special fruit and vegetable areas of Florida. Population is expected to increase by 7.5 million by 1975 at a growth rate higher than the national average. With projected United States production requirements showing increases of 45 percent in vegetables and 80 percent in tobacco, it seems clear that the region will have opportunities for expansion along these lines. Citrus acreage should also expand, since consumption requirements are projected at more than 80 percent above 1953 levels. The downward trends in cotton acreage in the face of low-cost competition from Texas and the West should continue. Population growth and a gradual increase in per capita income will put a premium on the expansion of livestock and especially dairy production.

East South Central

The agriculture is dominated by livestock and tobacco in the north and by cotton and peanuts in the south. Projected population growth is the lowest for the entire country — an estimated increase of only 12 percent. Tobacco acreage should increase, although this will mean little more than the enlargement of existing small acreage allotments. There should be some moderate expansion in cotton acreage, especially in western sections.

West South Central

Farming varies from wheat and small grains in the north through cotton in the central sections to range livestock in the southwest. The Gulf Coast area is devoted to rice, sugar cane and truck crops. With population growth of nearly 5 million, there should be some expansion in dairy production. This region also should participate heavily in the 37 percent increase in needed cotton production, with expansion both in delta and highland sections. There is little prospect for economical expansion of rice or sugar cane, but truck-crop acreages should increase. Wheat and small grain acreages should decline, especially in the transition zones with permanent grazing.

Mountain States

From the standpoint of agriculture, this large region is an extensive grazing area with cropland limited to the western fringe of the Great Plains and a sprinkling of irrigated and non-irrigated valleys. Population density is very low, and even with a projected increase of 66 percent, the 1975 population will be less than 10 million. Principal land use adjustments should be an expansion of range livestock and of livestock and dairying on present and potential irrigated land; an increase in acres in cotton, fruits and vegetables and dairying on irrigated land in the southern states; and the conversion of small grain areas to permanent grass east of the Rocky Mountains. With the exception of Idaho and Utah, where surpluses will be available for manufactured products, the dairy industry of the region will be keyed to the fluid milk requirements of its expanding population.[6]

Pacific Coast

This three-state region is characterized by large nonagricultural areas but with intensive agriculture in irrigated and non-irrigated valleys. Land use in Washington and Oregon includes dairying and general farming near the coast, fruits and specialty crops in irrigated valleys and wheat in the Columbia River Basin. In California, cotton in the San Joaquin Valley is the most important field crop in the state; hay and feed grains are important in support of the dairy and livestock industries; and large areas are devoted to the production of fruits, vegetables and nuts. Regional population is expected to increase 75 percent by 1975, with most of this in California. Projected regional production adjustments include expansion of fruits and vegetables in line with national requirements, some increases in livestock and an increase in cotton acreage in California. The dairy industry and related hay-feed crops are expected to increase by 60 percent, largely to satisfy fluid milk needs but with some manufacturing uses in the Columbia Basin in Washington.

SUMMARY AND MODIFICATIONS

To summarize, projections of crop production to meet 1975 requirements call for an expansion of only 13 percent above 1959 levels. Aggregate output per acre of cropland increased very little from 1944 to 1954 but now stands 25 percent above the 1947-49 base. While the recent rapid increases may be abnormal, it

[6]Richard L. Simmons, Optimum Adjustments of the Dairy Industry of the Western Region to Economic Conditions of 1975 (unpublished Ph.D. dissertation, Department of Agricultural Economics, University of California, 1959), 352 pp.

seems clear that yield increases, coupled with potential new and improved crop acreage additions of as much as 5 percent, should provide a land base substantially above 1975 requirements. Projections of the magnitude of this land surplus must be in the nature of "wild guesses," but it is quite possible that the figure would range as high as 30 to 50 million acres.[7] Food and feed grains now occupy some 60 percent of total harvested acres in the United States, and production already equals or exceeds 1975 requirements. It seems evident, therefore, that the major land use adjustment for the immediate future in American agriculture is a substantial reduction in grain acreage, with most of this taking the form of transfers to permanent grasses in the low-rainfall areas.

The Corn Belt is our most productive and concentrated agricultural area, and efficient land adjustments would certainly not call for reductions in this region; this will intensify the adjustments necessary in the grain-range areas of the Great Plains. Population growth in the Northeast and the Lake States stresses the need for increases in the production of fluid milk and fresh fruits and vegetables. The South Atlantic States should see an increase in tobacco acreage to meet rapidly increasing demands, although this may mean little more in the over-all land use pattern than enlargement of the presently very small tobacco allotments. Other adjustments for this region should involve increases in fruits and vegetables and livestock and dairying, with a continuing decline in cotton acreage.

Even with increasing yields, cotton requirements 37 percent above present output will call for acreage expansion, especially in the Delta, Texas and the irrigated areas of California and Arizona. Expanded needs for fruits and vegetables will stimulate these enterprises in the Pacific States, while rapid population growth will encourage expansion in dairy-livestock enterprises and the associated hay and feed crops.

Technological changes can have marked effects on the aggregate situation and on the competitive position of the several regions. Failure of aggregate crop yields to increase significantly above the high levels of 1958-59 would create a cropland shortage rather than a surplus in 1975. Failure of livestock feeding efficiency to continue its relatively rapid increase could have a similar effect. Competitive advantages of states and regions can be

[7]Under varying assumptions, it has been estimated that 1959 wheat and feed grain acreage would exceed 1965 requirements by 15 to 25 million, with 25 million acres in the Conservation Reserve Program. R. P. Christensen, S. E. Johnson and R. V. Baumann, Production Prospects for Wheat, Feed, and Livestock, 1960-65, USDA, ARS 43-115, Dec., 1959.

changed materially and in a relatively short time. The development of a commercial strawberry that was a heavy bearer over a long season gave California advantages both in production and in processing, for example, and resulted in very rapid increases in production. The perfection of plants with similar characteristics adapted to Washington and Michigan, on the other hand, could easily reverse this trend.[8] External forces are also important: The development of nonfarm employment opportunities and a consequent increase in farm wages in the Southeast could significantly alter the competitive position of this area in broiler production.[9] In spite of such possibilities, however, it seems probable that the major picture of regional specialization in agriculture will not change materially between 1960 and 1980.

Adjustments in land use, and especially the removal of large blocks of land from crop production, are most difficult to accomplish. Perhaps for that reason, past agricultural programs have emphasized two approaches: (1) spreading any required acreage reduction over all producing areas in an "equitable" but inefficient manner and (2) avoiding the adjustment problem through attempts to stimulate domestic and foreign consumption. We have already seen that projections of rapid population growth and substantial increases in per capita income do not mean substantial increases in needed crop production. Prospects for expanding commercial exports of farm products are not bright. At the 1958 conference of the Iowa Center for Agricultural Adjustment, Cochrane pinned his hope for important increases in the demand for farm products on the use of agricultural surpluses in a long-term program to finance economic development in the impoverished areas of the world.[10] I quite agree that such a program would have many virtues and also that it could eliminate the bothersome problem of shrinking our agricultural productive plant. I leave to the following chapters, however, the task of devising programs and institutions to cope with either the land adjustment problem or the use of farm commodities as an effective instrument in international diplomacy.[11]

---

[8]Carleton C. Dennis, Interregional Competition in the Frozen Strawberry Industry (unpublished Ph.D. dissertation, Department of Agricultural Economics, University of California, 1959), 236 pp.

[9]William R. Henry, "Broiler Production Regions of the Future," Jour. Farm Econ., Vol. 39, No. 5, Dec., 1957, pp. 1188-98.

[10]Willard W. Cochrane, "Demand expansion – opportunities and limitations," in Problems and Policies of American Agriculture, Iowa State University Press, Ames, 1959), pp. 272-91.

[11]While the Seminar was in session, the U.S. Government announced the signing of an agreement with India calling for the shipment of some 600 million bushels of wheat during a four-year period, for development purposes. At average yields, this is equivalent to roughly 10 million acres of wheat land.

While the projections presented in this volume strongly support the idea that there will be substantial surpluses of farm lands and of agricultural productive capacity during the 1960's and 1970's, it should be emphasized that these are not forecasts of the probable future. The truth is that we know little about the future, and that the 1975-80 situation may differ substantially from the "medium" projections; this is true for population, for general economic growth, for trends in per capita consumption, for yields per acre and for general agricultural productivity. If we should have more rapid than projected growth in population and in per capita demand, coupled with less rapid growth in agricultural productivity, current surpluses would disappear in the near future. Under such conditions, the land use solution for an essentially temporary problem might well resemble past and present programs. If population and demand lag while productivity increases rapidly, on the other hand, then agricultural surpluses will be long term and this will call for major adjustments at the intensive and the extensive margins of agriculture. Confronted with such uncertainty, wise planning for the future calls for flexible programs that can be adjusted readily to meet changing and developing needs.

Chapter 14

R. BURNELL HELD
Resources for the Future
Washington, D.C.

Can Other Use Be Made of Agriculture's Excess Acres?

A SERIOUS IMBALANCE exists between the agricultural sector of the American economy and the rest of the economy, an imbalance that scarcely needs documentation, although this can be done quite vividly with some quick comparisons of changes that took place during the 1950's. Price movements give us this opportunity. The index of wholesale prices of industrial goods rose during the period and was 27 percent higher in 1959 than in 1949. On the other hand, the price index for farm commodities, even with the operation of the highly condemned price-support program, was 4 percent lower at the close of the period than it had been at the beginning.[1]

The factors which supported demand in agriculture's domestic market from 1949 through 1958 were not depressed. Per capita disposable personal income, in constant dollars, rose 18 percent; the population of the United States increased by nearly 25 million persons, or 17 percent. Agricultural output kept pace with these changes, increasing 17 percent during the same period. Domestic consumption of agricultural products, however, rose by only 12 percent, and exports followed an erratic pattern but accounted on an average for less than 8 percent of the total utilization during the period.[2]

OVER-COMMITMENT OF RESOURCES

The consensus of economists is that there is an over-commitment of resources in agriculture, primarily land and labor, but neither of these showed any permanent increase from 1920 to 1960. The increase in farm output during the 1950's has

[1] Economic Indicators. Prepared for the Joint Economic Committee of the U.S. Congress by the Council of Economic Advisors. April, 1960. Washington, D. C.

[2] Measuring the Supply and Utilization of Farm Commodities. Agriculture Handbook, No. 91. USDA. Supplements for 1956 and 1958, Tables 1b and 28.

come about with no appreciable change in the combined value of production inputs measured in constant dollars. The number of man-hours used for farm work actually dropped 31 percent during the period and cropland planted was reduced 35 million acres, or nearly 10 percent. Increased use of other production items offset almost completely these declines.[3] And yet, another 30 to 50 million acres of cropland, depending upon its quality, could be withdrawn from cultivation now without seriously impinging upon current levels and patterns of consumption.[4]

We are not confronted with a temporary phenomenon either. Although land is, and will continue to be, an extremely important input in agricultural production, its relative contribution to farm output is smaller in 1960 than it was even in 1950, and this is part of a trend which can be expected to continue into the future. The opportunities for such things as fertilizers, supplemental irrigation, improved crop varieties, insecticides, herbicides and chemical growth regulators and greater managerial skills to substitute for land are increasing, particularly as they are used in combination rather than singly. These new inputs in effect replace land, but a comparable quantity of land is not withdrawn from production. True, some land is idled. Some is taken for highways, reservoirs, urban expansion and other uses as such needs arise, but the bulk of the land remains in production. Only through the operation of the Soil Bank program have significant acreages been removed from agricultural production.

It is often difficult to shift land from crop production to other uses. First, although it would be advantageous to agriculture as a whole if production were curtailed, the competitive structure of agriculture prevents an individual farmer from making such a move, for he will lose rather than benefit from it. Further, the continuing changes in technology just mentioned have made it both possible and necessary for many farm operators to increase, rather than reduce, the scale of their operations. Additional land often enables them to make more economical use of the relatively expensive new equipment in which they must invest and to utilize more fully their labor and their management skills. While many farms contain some cropland of low quality which logically should be retired in favor of higher quality land, it is either difficult, or not worth the trouble, to separate this from the other land, and perhaps just as difficult to find additional land of higher quality elsewhere to replace it. Furthermore, although cropping such

---

[3]Agricultural Outlook Charts '60. USDA, and Crop Production, 1959 Annual Summary. USDA, p. 45.

[4]Alvin C. Egbert, Programming Regional Adjustments in Resource Use for Grain Production. Unpublished doctoral dissertation, Iowa State University, Ames, 1958.

land may yield only enough income to cover the cost of planting and harvesting the crop, and the farm operator would be just as well off to let it remain idle, he may not appreciate what the cost and return situation really is on that land.

If a tract of marginal cropland is of sufficient size, it may have some potential in grazing, timber production or recreational use. This assumes of course that either the present owner or someone else has the desire and the resources to so develop it. Isolated small tracts are a problem, however. Imagine, for a moment, what might be accomplished were it possible to consolidate them and make them accessible. But land cannot move to take advantage of an unsatisfied demand for land elsewhere. The would-be user must be able to get to the land instead and, thus, location and access become strategic factors. Land which enjoys such an advantage with respect to the user's requirements enjoys an advantage that cannot easily be offset by the superiority of other attributes of land more distantly located, or by the willingness of that landowner to accept a small price or rental for the use of the land than that which must be paid to the owner of the other land.

FLAWS IN THE LAND MARKET

The failure of more land to move out of agricultural uses may also be a reflection of certain weaknesses in the land market. Is the land market less rational than the markets for other resources, or is it simply that we sometimes fail to appreciate influences at work other than those with which economists are commonly concerned? Land may continue in agricultural use, even when returns to it in this use are lower than the returns from other uses because of psychological, social, political and other institutional influences. For example, farm land is as much a consumption good as a production good in some areas. Production for the market may well be of minor importance compared with the other satisfactions the farm produces for its operator. In some communities, farm ownership in and of itself is a prestige symbol. In other communities, the life and identity of a religious sect, the Mennonites for instance, are closely tied to the agricultural society it has established. Agricultural communities with birth rates higher than those necessary to provide the necessary replacement of farm operators and where emigration is hindered for some reason may cause farm rents or land prices to be bid to levels out of line with rents or prices for land of comparable quality and situation elsewhere.

The land market is definitely imperfect in a number of respects. Other factor markets are not perfect either, but are probably relatively more perfect. The land resource is in the first place absolutely immobile, while other factors are at the most only relatively immobile. Immobility immediately puts a premium upon the location of the resource over and above other characteristics or qualities of the resource. Transactions are relatively infrequent, and a series of transactions may involve situations differing so much from each other as to give only a very inexact picture of what the market would be for land of a particular quality and a particular location. Information on prices may be guarded and communication between potential buyers and sellers poor. A significant imbalance in the number of potential buyers and sellers is not uncommon.

This is not meant to be a complete inventory of the factors which prevent the use of assumptions approximating a market under perfect competition when examining the allocation of land for agricultural purposes. The influence of such factors is suggested by the anomaly of a continuing upward trend in the index of farm real estate values when over a 10 year period the trend of income of farm operators per farm has been down.[5]

If the land market were more rational, would this help to ease land out of farming? Would the alternative opportunities for the land surplus to crop production become evident if an effort were made to remove the market imperfections or adopt measures to offset them? Such efforts would undoubtedly bring about some shifts of land from agricultural use to more intensive uses as well as other uses more extensive in their use of land. But how much greater would the shift of farm land into urban related uses be today, given a more responsive land market? How much greater would the shift be to grass and timber?

SHIFTS TO MORE INTENSIVE USES

Since users of land for urban-related purposes are able, for the most part, to bid well above the level than can anyone who wants the land for agricultural purposes, and since the power of eminent domain is also available for the use of governmental units for the purchase of highway rights-of-way, reservoir sites and the like, it would seem unlikely that the present trends in land acquisition for such purposes would be greatly changed.

[5]Agricultural Statistics, 1958. USDA. Table 615, p. 431, and The Farm Income Situation, USDA, Feb., 1960. Table 10, p. 33.

There likely would be a much greater change in the shift of cropland into grass and into timber. Considered in terms of the quantities of land that might be absorbed by such uses, the potential in the relatively extensive uses is much greater than in that of the more intensive uses.

Although there is a more liberal use of land for urban purposes of various sorts when the price of land is low, if the demand function for land were determined for a large urban area and contrasted with that of a smaller urban area, it is quite possible that the demand for land in terms of the price of the unimproved land itself would prove to be much more inelastic for the larger urban area than for the smaller urban area. The larger the area, the more important the location becomes, and for a business enterprise of any size, increments of space beyond an optimum level may actually have a negative value.

CHANGING URBAN PATTERNS

The automobile is now changing the pattern of urban development. It has enabled suburban development to take place at a greater distance from the business centers of the central city. It has also made suburban shopping centers attractive to the suburban customer who must drive instead of walk or use public transportation to a shopping area and who wishes to avoid the congestion and parking problems of the older established downtown area. The new suburban shopping areas probably make a much more lavish use of space per dollar of sales than the downtown business districts, but no matter how inexpensive additional land might be, there is an advantage in limiting the surface area of the development to keep the shops closer together for the shopper on foot and as close as possible to the car parked in the surrounding 5,000 car parking area.

Even the suburban householder, desirous of a spacious lot for his house, does not want so much land that he would have to either hire a staff of gardeners to keep it up or run a flock of sheep on it. And, of course, there are city dwellers who gladly forego the pleasures of occupying surface space and piloting a power lawnmower over it every week when the grass is growing rapidly and prefer to occupy the air space above the surface by living in an apartment house.

The rate at which land is moving into nonagricultural uses is difficult to determine but it is sometimes estimated to be of the order of $1\frac{1}{2}$ to 2 million acres a year. Accepting the highest figure for the moment, assuming no change over time in this rate of transfer and that 25 percent of this land would be cropland, these uses would exhaust 35 million acres of surplus cropland in 70 years. Of course, the rate may increase. The need for cropland may also increase. Furthermore, it is important that one know more precisely the productive capabilities of the cropland that will be taken. Land relatively unproductive in agricultural uses must possess qualities which make it productive for other uses and must be strategically situated or it will be passed over in favor of productive farm land.

THE IMMEDIATE SITUATION

The probable impact of the events of the quarter century from 1960-85 upon agricultural production with particular reference to the use made of agricultural land is an important area of study, but the more immediate concern of farmers is the present, or at most, the next five years. It is little consolation to a farmer today to be told that perhaps, and only perhaps, the competition for land for other uses will have absorbed a sufficient quantity of land now in agricultural production which, together with an increased demand for agricultural commodities themselves, will have restored equilibrium to the agricultural economy by 1985. If there was not the human element to consider in this matter, perhaps we could be satisfied to wait out the 25 year period. But even then, this kind of thinking completely ignores the dynamics on the supply side. The increases in the productivity per acre which agronomists, agricultural engineers and other workers from the biological and physical sciences have told us are within the realm of physical achievement and which have been considered to be economically feasible, offset, in some degree, the expansion of the demand side of the market.

If the chances of "growing out" of this problem in the next twenty-five years are slight, then there is even more reason for turning attention first to the immediate situation. If it can be done, the goal of diverting land to uses in which its contribution to the sum of social satisfactions is increased is a highly desirable objective, not just for 1985, but for today. Is there any possibility of accomplishing that sort of reallocation of land to different uses?

IDENTIFYING MARGINAL PRODUCTION AREAS

Before alternative uses for cropland are considered, we must have some idea of what land is marginal in crop production. A pioneering attempt to identify this land has been made by Alvin C. Egbert and Earl O. Heady.[6] Even with the reservations which they make for their study, this work gives us the best point of departure now available. The study presents a picture of only the feed grain and wheat situation, but these are the crops that are now the major problems. We have no indication of the chain reactions that would be set off if some of the land diverted from wheat and feed grains went into the production of other crops and helped to create surpluses there. Additional information is necessary concerning the alternative opportunities in the production of other crops in such regions.

Elsewhere in this volume, Egbert presents two models of the regional distribution of grain production based on that study and related work. One model represents the farming techniques of 1954, and this will be considered first. The second model represents conditions anticipated by 1985 and allows for changes in costs, yields, etc.[7]

What regions would go out of grain production if total production were limited to normal requirements? Model 1954 calls for the reduction of nearly 29 million acres of land in grain production.[8] Of this, about 11 percent of the acreage would come out of the Great Plains. The regions which are predominant in spring wheat and the winter wheat production would not be touched except for the fringes. Small areas in southeast Wyoming, southeast Colorado and the southern high plains of New Mexico would also be surplus. The other cropland to be withdrawn exists as scattered tracts, or islands, in the short-grass range country. The immediate alternative for this cropland seems to be grazing or the production of hay.

GRAZING

In his study, "The Economics of Seeding Wheatland to Grass in Eastern Colorado,"[9] Harry Sitler found that at prices of $1.70 a bushel and 1954 costs, wheat which in that region averaged 8 bushels or less per seeded acre was of doubtful profitability but that yields had to drop to 5 or 6 bushels before grazing the land

[6] Earl O. Heady and Alvin C. Egbert. "Programming regional adjustments in grain production to eliminate surpluses." Jour. Farm Econ., Nov., 1959, pp. 718-33.

[7] Alvin C. Egbert and Lloyd D. Dumenil. "Identification of nature, magnitude and physical areas of potential supply and demand imbalance," Chapter 11.

[8] Heady and Egbert, op. cit., p. 727.

[9] ARS 43-64, Agricultural Research Service, USDA, 1958.

with yearling steers would be a more attractive alternative than wheat production. His investigation indicated that while there would be problems, they need not be insurmountable if the operator took advantage of the assistance, both technical and financial, offered by existing programs of the U.S. Department of Agriculture. The only exception to this might be the cost of providing stock water.

Cropland withdrawn from production in the Edwards plateau and Rio Grande plains of Texas, and from the cross timbers region of Oklahoma would undoubtedly be shifted into grazing with little difficulty. However, as portions of areas such as the black prairies, the coastal and alluvial plains of Texas, come up for consideration, other alternatives are called for, but what will they be? The same question arises as the fringe areas of the Corn Belt are dealt with. A livestock grazing enterprise is beyond consideration unless such already exists, or, unless a consolidation of operating units is accomplished sufficient to permit organizing an enterprise of sufficient scale to be economically rewarding. Land prices would have to work down in order for this to be accomplished.

Seeking a solution to the problem of excess cropland through its diversion to grassland, particularly as we consider the alternatives available in the Southeast where 48 percent of the unneeded grain acreage is located, is not without further problems. Granted that demand is relatively more elastic for livestock products than it is for grain, none of us is blind to the fact that the price elasticity of demand for livestock products is less than unity. A solution for the problem of one region merely transfers the problem, changed in form, to another region. What would the impact of a large expansion of the range livestock industry in the Southeast be on the West? (And what would happen if the public domain land now used for grazing were to be withdrawn from use?) But perhaps more to the point is the question of what would happen should the farming techniques in the Southeast improve sufficiently to retain a portion of the area in grain production. This is exactly the situation that the model for 1985 presents.

TIMBER PRODUCTION

Timber production can be an attractive alternative on the coastal plains of the Southeast. Southern pine is capable of rapid growth. Under good management a well-stocked stand might be expected to produce an annual increase in volume which, with stumpage valued at $30 a thousand board feet, would be worth over $13 an acre and would net nearly $12.[10] (Returns of equal value or more might well be obtained from grain production if a comparable level of managerial skill were applied.) The period of waiting until the first returns can be obtained from a tract that has been shifted from cropland to timber production decreases the attractiveness of this alternative. In addition, it will not provide an outlet for marketing the labor resources of the operator once it goes out of grain production. But both objections assume that the land will remain in small ownership units, which need not be the case.

Saw timber and pulpwood production probably offer the most attractive long-term alternative for much of the Coastal Plain area. Nearly 80 percent of the lower Coastal Plain area is producing pine trees, and land suitable for timber production is still being sought out. But the quantity of excess land in these regions is much more than just the land not needed for grain. It includes cropland that is in excess for that needed for cotton production, too.

And now, one might ask, what of land for urban uses, recreation, transportation, reservoirs and the like? As noted earlier, with even 2 million acres of land going into such uses each year, there is no prospect of solving the immediate problem of surplus crop acres in agriculture in this way. Certainly this is not the way to remove the land which is least suited to agriculture. The land which will be taken for these uses will be that which best serves their requirements and may very well be some of the best agricultural land. Except for recreation, a land use nearly as extensive as agriculture, there is little immediate prospect of expanding this rate of use significantly in terms of the problem we now face.

OUTDOOR RECREATION

Let us consider the general field of outdoor recreation. Now, rather than look to the areas which are surplus to crop production, we must look to the areas which are the most desirable in terms of what they can provide in the way of recreational services. The land areas which best fill this need may not be cropland at all, at least, not the most productive or intensively used cropland. This, of course, comes as no surprise to anyone

[10] Resources for the Future, Inc. "Forest credit in the United States." Washington, D. C., 1958. Table 2, p. 11.

familiar with agriculture. The attributes of the landscape which give a tract of land value for the purposes of recreation are probably inversely correlated with crop yields. For recreational use, the more rugged the terrain, the more interesting it usually is and the greater challenge it is to hikers and climbers. A relatively level area may be more desirable than rougher land for certain types of camp sites and picnic areas, but an open field does not have the additional qualities usually required — shaded areas or bodies of water. A golf course may easily come out of land formerly in crops, but to best serve the purpose the course will be laid out, wherever possible, on undulating rather than level terrain.

Hunting and fishing may or may not take cropland out of production. Lake fishing may require the acquisition by governments of ready access to the lake and boat launching sites. Stream fishing will call more and more for the acquisition of smaller streams and some adjoining land if the state conservation agencies responsible for stocking trout streams are to provide and maintain minimum habitat conditions and if fishermen are to have access to the streams. Relatively little cropland need be taken for these purposes.

Hunting is a somewhat different matter. Land and water areas are required for the use of waterfowl, for nesting, refuge areas during migration and for wintering grounds. Over 8 million acres of land are now used for these purposes — most of it in state or federal ownership. At least 4 to $4\frac{1}{2}$ million acres of wet lands are the minimum of additional land that must be obtained in the near future according to John T. Farley, director of the Fish and Wildlife Service.[11] Without them, a ceiling on duck numbers is likely to be reached soon, if it is not already at hand. The acquisition of land for this purpose is necessary to replace wet lands which, in private ownership, have often been drained for agricultural purposes.

Where would this acreage come from? Undoubtedly a good part would come from the upper Middle West. It would come out of cropland, but cropland that is not necessarily marginal in grain production but is taken out of production. The production that is lost there would be supplied by the production in marginal areas, although the substitution would not necessarily be a one-for-one exchange of acres.

The special requirements for waterfowl have been met in the past in multiple-use arrangements on reservoir areas in

[11] Annual Report of the Secretary of the Interior, 1956. U.S. Government Printing Office, Washington, D. C., p. 283.

connection with irrigation and flood control activities. This kind of arrangement can be expected to be made in the future but is not likely to provide the entire amount of land desired. It should also be noted that while the propagation of waterfowl is given primary attention on the lands obtained for that purpose, recreation facilities are also a secondary possibility.

WILL HUNTERS PAY?

The production of other types of game has usually been possible without the acquisition of particular special-use tracts of land. Up to a point, a population of wildlife species is usually welcome or at least tolerated on farms by farm operators. Wildlife, game in particular, is sometimes referred to as a crop itself, but it is a crop from which the farmer generally derives no gain, and probably experiences a loss after the population of animals reaches a certain level and begins to compete in a serious way with crop production in one way or another. This competition sometimes is not recognized by those who wish to see the wildlife population increased. If there is a desire to increase the yield of such game above present levels, as evidenced by a willingness of hunters to pay the price to make this possible, one might seriously consider the probability of a transfer of some land from commercial agricultural use to the production of game. This is not an immediate possibility, but it is conceivable that the time might come when hunting on private land would be considered less a right that should be available at no cost to the hunter, and more a privilege that he must pay for even though the game which he hunts would still be regarded as public property. Several methods of handling this might be arranged. In some states, public hunting grounds are being purchased. Private clubs which either own the land directly or acquire hunting privileges for their members on private land also exist.

A third arrangement has also been tried wherein the farms within a contiguous area agreed to accept hunters who had paid a special fee which permitted them to hunt on any farm land of the cooperating farm operators. Institutional devices such as these are required if there is to be any shift of land resources from agricultural production to the production of increased quantities of wildlife.

Hunting and fishing are important aspects of the outdoor recreation picture, but only a part of it; they are closer competitors for agricultural land than are most other recreational uses, but they are usually compatible with agricultural use.

ACQUIRING LAND FOR PUBLIC USE

The demand for the services of land in recreational uses does not always find expression in the market as effective demand, for the simple reason that the type of service -- facilities for hiking, camping, canoeing, picnicking, etc., as well as those providing satisfaction to a yearning for a place of solitude in an awe-inspiring natural setting, is something that the average American expects to obtain at no direct or out-of-pocket cost. With large holdings of public lands it is possible for far-sighted individuals to press for the preservation of the great spots of unique character in this country, and thus a good part of the National Park System was obtained, and the National Forests as well, without cost, in the sense that the land was already in public ownership. The only acquisition cost was the opportunity cost which, although increasing, is still low. State and municipal parks, forests and related tracts have often been acquired as gifts from public-spirited citizens, as have some of the National Parks, or from the Federal Government. Others have been purchased with funds in part from the Federal Government or were improved by labor furnished by the CCC enrollees in the 1930's. Other tracts were acquired through the reversion of tax-delinquent lands. Outright purchase of Central Park in New York City was made in 1856 while it was still merely hilly countryside north of the city. If Central Park did not exist today, could New York City afford to dedicate an equally large tract within its boundaries for park purposes now? Is Central Park worth its opportunity cost to the city today?

These are not just academic questions. They are the kinds of questions municipalities, states and even the Federal Government must now consider. How much can governments afford to pay for land for recreation purposes? How can this be determined as long as park services are socially provided, but where there is no ready measure of the value the citizen-consumer of these services derives from them and what he is willing to pay for them? The public may be inarticulate in these matters now, but public officials charged with providing park services cannot afford to wait for an answer. It is not just a matter of rising land prices; it is also a matter of obtaining the necessary land while it is still available.

There is some evidence of a growing awareness of this problem. Not only is there an increasing concern that more open land be provided in the newly developing areas and that more natural areas be preserved to absorb the increase in population, but also that open areas be created in the heart of our cities, a goal largely impossible except where costly urban redevelopment or renewal projects are under way. Attempts to control or direct development on the fringes of suburban areas to preserve open space have been made in some areas through minimum lot-size zoning ordinances, in some instances through the public purchase of land development easements and in some instances by rationing the issuance of building permits.

Measures of this type also might be used to advantage in enabling municipalities to obtain park and recreation areas (by holding it out of other use until their budgets permit its purchase). Some of the land might be acquired through the use of options. But in many instances, the only way to acquire the land will be through immediate purchase.

If present recreational facilities are inadequate and additional land is required, much of it could, or should, be acquired now. New York State is attempting to launch a particularly ambitious land acquisition program. This is highly significant, for although no other state can match it in absolute population, New York, even on a per capita basis, is exceeded only by Maine in providing non-federal public land for recreation purposes. Yet, 96 percent of the state's vast holding of 2.6 million acres is concentrated in three huge units. This makes its land less useful, in some respects, than it would be if the land was spread about the state in a number of smaller parks. The largest, the Adirondack Forest Preserve, is larger than any of the National Parks except Yellowstone. Because this situation does not satisfy the requirements of the state, additional recreation areas are to be acquired.

What would be the impact on cropland if other states were similarly to increase their programs of land acquisition? To the extent that the land came out of cropland, it would have little direct impact on the areas that have been designated surplus. But to the extent that an acre of cropland is removed in Iowa, Illinois or Ohio, an acre displaced from production elsewhere would return to production, or perhaps more than one acre, for although "A rose is a rose is a rose," an acre is not an acre is not an acre. There are quality differences to be taken into account in these geographical shifts in production. Shifts from the humid areas into the arid, non-irrigated areas will bring more land back into production, but hardly enough to make any dent on the surplus problem. The best immediate solution appears to be the Conservation Reserve of the Soil Bank program which to date has withdrawn nearly 28.5 million acres from production.[12]

But after the Soil Bank what? Recreation may require the

[12] USDA. News Release 1056-60, April 13, 1960.

largest absolute quantity of land. If an expanded effort to acquire land for recreation were pursued, it might take a minimum of 35 million additional acres of land by 1985. The requirements of other nonagricultural uses, excluding forestry, might take another 30 million acres. This is an imposing statistic — 65 million acres of land, which we know cannot come out of thin air. The important thing to know, however, is the location of this land and its present use.

A large part of the increase in land for recreation purposes would probably come from forested areas. The U.S. Forest Service sees the possibility that some 10 to 15 million acres of National Forest may be transferred to such use.[13] Not all of this would come from commercial stands of timber, however. To the extent that it would take commercial timber, its loss might be partially offset through more intensive management and use of present forest areas. Other suitable but unplanted, or understocked, sites could be developed. Some of these may now be cropland. But activities of this sort must get underway now if the timber is to be available when it is needed.

Hugh Johnson and Hugh Wooten have estimated that at most, 25 percent of the expansion of urban, transportation, parks, wildlife refuges, reservoirs, national defense areas, etc., comes from former cropland.[14] And some of this will probably have been idle cropland prior to the change in use.

Thus, if a figure of 65 million acres is an acceptable one, it should be reduced to 16 or 17 million acres to indicate the probable loss of cropland. Even if the additional land required for uses outside of agriculture by 1985 were as high as 100 million acres, this would mean a loss of perhaps only 25 million acres of cropland.

Thinking in terms of the impact of these changes in agriculture, it is important that we attempt to locate them as well as we can. Will the growth areas coincide with the areas of present surplus land? In some areas, yes. The Southeast is one example. The upper Atlantic seaboard is not. Lower Michigan is. California is not. Yet, while these areas may not all coincide with the surplus regions, if they remove cropland from production, this indirectly brings land previously in surplus back into production. The same reasoning holds when the 2 or 3 million acres of land are removed for transportation purposes and land is taken for other purposes.

---

[13] Richard E. McArdle, Address before the American Paper and Pulp Association, Feb. 25, 1960.

[14] "Extent and significance of non-agricultural uses of rural land and water," Jour. Farm Econ., Dec., 1958, pp. 1315-26.

Taking a look at what might be considered surplus cropland by 1985, using Egbert's model in which we must assume that the land now available for crops is still available, we note that much of the land in the Southeast, withdrawn from production under today's circumstances, would be producing grain in 1985 while sections of the Dakotas, Minnesota, Wisconsin, Illinois, Indiana and Missouri would be left out.

Again, we have the benefit of a starting point. This picture would be greatly modified, however, by other changes which could not be taken into consideration in the model. The land required for nonagricultural uses may have absorbed 16 million acres or more of this cropland by then. Probable differences in the productivity of the land withdrawn from crop production for other uses and the land replacing it would be likely to call into production a greater number of acres than those removed, but again, this difference would not be sufficient to absorb large surplus which the model indicates would exist by then — 40.5 million acres.

The shift of cropland into forest production is not ruled out. It is perhaps misleading to depend too much upon the 1985 model at this point for information that it was never intended to supply. If the price of forest products rises sufficiently, as it well may do, the grain production called for the Southeast may not come about, while the regions programmed for current production of grain crops, but set aside by 1985, might well be producing farm crops.

Yes, there are alternatives, seldom direct alternatives for the land that is surplus to present agricultural use, but alternatives that hold promise of the production of goods and services of greater social value than unwanted stocks of grain. Further, the most important alternative uses, in terms of the acreage they can absorb, can be reversed if by some chance the requirements for agricultural land should be greater than those now anticipated. But the alternatives may not be sufficiently large to absorb all the land that is surplus, or, the transfers between uses may be too slow in coming about. A real question ahead seems to be one of whether we will have the institutional machinery available to assist in making the required shifts in land use and capable of overcoming the innumerable obstacles that are bound to arise.

Chapter 15

JOHN A. SCHNITTKER
Kansas State University

Appraisal of Programs and Impacts on Land Use Adjustments

COST-BENEFIT ANALYSIS in land and water development in the U.S. is a wonderland which uninitiated but cautious economists view from a distance. It is applicable not only to land development but also to price supports and land retirement under public auspices. The public is vaguely aware that additional crops produced with reclamation water are counted among the benefits of resource development projects and that the costs of the contemporary price support program are results of excessive crop output. To cap the contradiction, crops not produced are the primary benefits from the Soil Bank. These programs operate side by side in most regions of the U.S.

The public has selected or at least acquiesced in our farm price goals or price-support levels. In doing so, it has committed itself under present open-ended price-support programs to indefinite investments in farm commodities. Unless price goals are revised downward sharply or unless price goals are to be achieved mainly by marketing limitations in the 1960's, the public's investment in farm commodities seems sure to rise each year. Even with farm price supports as much as one-third below 1959-60, U.S. farmers in 1965 would produce and market far more than could be consumed at those prices. When we are faced with such production prospects, nearly every addition to land area in cultivation must be counted a contradiction. Unless new land is uniquely suited to the production of some scarce product, it must add to public expenditures either in acquiring stocks for storage or in buying out the production rights in land so further acquisition and storage may be avoided.

The world, however, is full of contradictions which are not *ipso facto* intolerable. If we are to make good use of the limited time we can spare to purge ourselves of economic paradoxes, we must deal with those which are most pressing.

LAND DEVELOPMENT

We have many public programs which increase farm land area or affect land use. Reclamation is one of the most visible and, to many, the most virtuous. New irrigation projects are modern frontiersmanship. Like cowboys and covered wagons, they hold a special place in the public mind. It would not be easy to convince many of us that the lush fields often seen in the colored pages of the farm magazines are producing large public liabilities.

How much have reclamation projects added to farm land and production? And under what circumstances was the land developed? In 1957, 6.6 million acres, 2 percent of all cropland harvested, were watered from reclamation facilities. Only one-sixth of this was added since 1950 – the modern surplus era. Reclamation land produced $928 million in crops in 1957 – 5 percent of the value of all crops, and the following percentages of certain crops:

Corn	.6 percent	Dry beans	27.6 percent	Tomatoes	10.6 percent
Wheat	2.2 percent	Sugar beets	40.6 percent	Apples	8.1 percent
Barley	7.9 percent	Carrots	23.2 percent	Peaches	7.9 percent
Upland cotton	7.4 percent	Lettuce	20.9 percent	Grapes	26.2 percent

Many of these are produced almost exclusively under irrigation. Further, some are crops whose demand expands as incomes rise. Under private auspices or public, it will be desirable to add to lands capable of producing fruits and vegetables.

The Bureau of Reclamation is rather self-conscious about its role in adding to crop surpluses, and has constructed a defense. Not all the dried beans, wheat, corn and cotton produced on reclamation land adds to surpluses, according to the defenders. Instead, it is argued that if 10 percent of all wheat (for example) is surplus, the same share of reclamation-produced wheat should be called surplus.

At first glance, it seems curious that reclamation officials should be concerned about their contribution to farm surpluses. After all, we were very fortunate to have 5 million extra acres and nearly $1 billion in extra crop production from 1940 to 1952. Reclamation can rightly claim great contributions in the past, and at a small cost. The entire program since 1903 has cost only $4 billion in public funds. We have spent as much in buying, storing and disposing of farm surpluses in a single year. The largest annual expenditure – $300 million in 1950 – would not even store present wheat stocks for a year. History may thoroughly vindicate past reclamation projects.

The future may be another story. Sympathy for the family farms which could prosper in now-arid valleys should not obscure the fact that much, perhaps most, of the reclamation projects of the 1960's and 1970's are self-contradictory. For the primary and ultimate purpose of reclamation is irrigation; from a national and a public standpoint, there are few activities with a lower priority for the 1960's than the expansion of crop acreage or encouragement of irrigation.

It ought to be possible to determine which irrigation projects proposed by regional groups or public agencies will produce crops with genuine consumer value (benefits), and which will produce chiefly cotton, grains and dry beans (costs) in the 1960's. It is clearly possible to place the Malthusian argument "out of bounds" to reclamation enthusiasts if economists and public officials will speak up forcefully.

Projects will not stand or fall, however, chiefly on "solid" economic grounds, but will probably continue on the basis of regional power structures and romance. What then, can be done to put them into a defensible national perspective?

Local and personal financial interests in the reclamation program often are made to appear subordinate to the national interest. Congressional hearings bulge with efforts to remove the onus of special pleading from the reclamation program. It is claimed that (1) reclamation pays its own way, (2) that a food shortage is imminent and (3) that the West was robbed of its resources in the past and reclamation projects are a partial restitution. The first item appeals to non-West members of Congress to support reclamation projects as self-liquidating federal investments that place no financial burden on their constituents. The second appeals to the national interest in an adequate food supply. The third lays a foundation for equitable treatment of the West.

There is a serious question about the validity of these arguments, but they are likely to continue to attract Congressional support for a substantial reclamation program. Proposals for reorientation of the reclamation program need to take into account, therefore, not only the real economic interests of the West and the U.S. which will provide the prime mover for a genuine development program for the West, but also the institutionalized rationalizations (not too strong a phrase) which help to broaden reclamation's political support and to divert attention from potential unfavorable economic effects.

Aside from whether or not the Federal Government should continue to make large or small developmental expenditures in the West, the need to minimize the contribution of any program to the agricultural surplus problem appears evident. Three lines of strategy might be followed to this end.

The simplest approach would not challenge the basic philosophy of the reclamation program. We would slow the rate of development of new irrigated land on projects already authorized, and select new projects with only moderate effects on farm production, particularly of those staples seriously in surplus.

A second line of strategy would be to recommend new projects selected to place primary emphasis on electric power and water for non-irrigation purposes. This would be a substantial break with historic "reclamation," in which power and non-irrigation water were by-products. But it would not be a sharp break with the total program for western development.

A third approach would begin to build the foundation for a broader action which might eventually replace the reclamation program as the major public investment effort in the West. This would provide legislative basis for a broad regional development program for the West in which reclamation projects would be appropriately timed among other resource development projects. The West is not interested in reclamation projects *per se*, but rather in federal investment to promote economic development. If public funds and enthusiasm were available to develop the resources of the West on a broad front, the pressure for the restricted and somewhat backward type of resource development represented by land reclamation would be reduced. Enough other benefits would accrue so that supposed irrigation benefits need not be counted in order to get an appropriate benefit-cost ratio. Perhaps the present political support for reclamation could be diverted to support for a broader program of resource development.

Price Supports

The role of price supports in land use changes has often been exaggerated, in my opinion. Neither the planting of 15 to 20 million acres of new lands to wheat in the semi-arid plains between 1940 and 1952 nor failure to return those lands to grass since 1952 can be laid mainly to the price supports.

The chronology of higher price support levels for wheat in the 1940's follows that of expansion of new lands — a damaging coincidence. Often overlooked is the fact that the mid to late 1940's were years of exceptionally good weather, that wheat prices were often well above supports and that the discovery and adoption of new cultivation technology was at its peak.

Seldom from 1943 to 1953 were wheat prices raised by the price-support program. The guarantee of 90 percent of parity prices even after war demands were met helped to reduce uncertainty and was thus expansionary. But in retrospect, the practical alternatives to 90 percent of parity were support prices only modestly lower and scarcely less expansionary, as the 1950's have shown.

The argument that price-support levels prevented widespread retirement of such land to less intensive uses since 1953 is scarcely less transparent. First, the level of price support proposed by the critics of the price-support levels we have had, were only slightly lower. If we had gone to wheat price supports at 60 or 70 percent of parity in 1954 (no one seriously proposed this), I doubt that land abandonment or reseeding to grass would have moved noticeably faster than it has. The difficulties of returning semi-arid land to grass are such that only extreme measures will bring it about. Sustained low grain prices would make land retirement less costly and given rental rates more attractive. But taken alone, low wheat prices are more likely to result in capital losses and land abandonment than in a return to grass.

Clearly, the acreage allotment programs associated with price supports have influenced the use made of land, but not the aggregate amount of farm land in use. Acreage controls have been a system of passing the buck, improving one commodity situation at the expense of another.

Soil Management

There are two other public programs with important land development implications — the Soil Conservation Service (SCS) program and the Agricultural Conservation Program Service (ACPS). Public expenditures in the two are $250 million and $80 million per year, respectively. Both programs are justified partly from a genuine conservation standpoint, but are equally dependent on rationalizations of soil and water conservation. Drainage, irrigation, tillage and other pseudo-conservation practices make up a large part of each program.[1] Since ACPS and SCS practices merge with other farming operations, the addition to farm output is incalculable. SCS considers one-third of all farm land as adequately treated (from a conservation standpoint);[2]

[1] Earl O. Heady, "Redirecting conservation programs," National Farm Institute, Des Moines, Iowa, 1960.

[2] Hearings, House of Representatives, subcommittee on appropriations for the Department of Agriculture, 86th Cong., 1st Sess., p. 568.

one-third of all farm land is involved in ACPS practices.[3] The annual contribution to total output of these two programs after nearly 25 years is probably far greater than the 5 percent of annual farm output contributed by the reclamation program, which operates on only 2 percent of all cropland area.

Research and Education

Research and extension are the public programs with the greatest effect on land use adjustments. Properly oriented toward more efficient farm production and more intensive land use during most of their history, they have surely been more influential in determining land use than all the other public programs combined. Crops with drouth tolerance, systems of cultivations which substitute for precipitation, fertilizers which substitute for precipitation, fertilizers which substitute for rotations and high-yielding strains which offset price declines are at the very core of intensive land use. These practices and discoveries are being applied not only on selected acreages, but to some extent on most of the land in the U.S.

To decrease intensity of land use while new discoveries for intensification are available is not an easy task. To do it concurrent with a system of open-ended price supports which encourage intensification on limited land areas (cotton, wheat, rice and tobacco) is virtually hopeless.

LAND RETIREMENT

There has seldom been any doubt that we have had our hearts behind resource development, nor any indication that we had our hearts in land retirement or in production control. The moral neutrality which attaches to idle plant capacity, and in some quarters even to idle workers, has not yet become attached to farm resources. As a public, we are still stirred by speakers who implore us to plant and produce more — not less. And a cloud follows those who argue the contrary.

It will take time to forget the acreage reserve, which gave land retirement a bad name. And it would take ingenuity to devise an expanded land retirement program which achieved the production adjustment it pays for. But these obstacles can be overcome if we can decide whether or not we are serious about it.

---

[3] Ibid., p. 663.

The purpose of land retirement is to implement a price policy. Unknown but discoverable acreages of U.S. cropland idled under appropriate rules would result in selected long-run price levels for crops and livestock without chronic surplus production. The farm price level is terribly important to farm people and to the public. There is much disagreement among farm groups on the desirable level for farm prices for the 1960's. But there is virtually unanimous consent to the idea that farm prices, in the absence of price-raising devices, will be chronically low in the 1960's even in a prosperous general economy. All major farm groups reject this prospect and are searching for means to avoid it. Despite continuing free market incantation, the question of government intervention in the farm economy of the 1960's has thus been answered affirmatively by everyone who counts. Two related questions – the specific price level to be sought and the means by which to seek it – remain undecided.

It is almost axiomatic that if we decide as a public policy to reduce farm resource use, we should not simultaneously choose other public policy goals which are obstructive. Sharply higher prices for farm crops would make public land rental more costly, and would make substitution of other inputs for land on remaining farms or part-farms more attractive. If land retirement for compensation is to be a major tool of farm policy, it can best be used first to end excess output at prices near present levels, not far above. Otherwise, the public will pay three times – in higher food prices, in higher compensation required to attract land to be idled and in a greater acreage required to achieve a given price goal.

Clearly, land retirement even under present law is superior to indiscriminate stock accumulation from the viewpoint of public cost. Claims made by Soil Bank administrators are probably optimistic. Yet the value of major crops not produced in 1959 and 1960 because of the Soil Bank surely exceeded the $375 million cost appreciably in 1959.

Given farm price goals, the choice between adding about $1 billion in farm commodities to stocks each year as at present, or spending $1 billion on land retirement, ought to be resolved in favor of the latter. But that would not solve the "choice of farm program" problem, for there remains the choice between land retirement and direct marketing controls, alternatives not mutually exclusive.

Political reality and history are on the side of a pluralistic approach to marketing restrictions. Democratic government, for better or worse, is often crisis government. Commodity crises do not arise simultaneously; we cannot, therefore, expect to adopt a 10 or 20 commodity marketing quota in a short time. We must start from where we are and improve upon our past mistakes.

The first farm policy crisis of the 1960's is in wheat and feed grains, with wheat the most visible. The wheat allotment program since 1954 has added 5 to 15 million tons to the feed grain supply each year since 1954. If the land taken out of wheat since 1954 had been retired permanently for a lump sum or multi-year payment, feed grain stocks in 1960 might be near normal and livestock prices since 1954 would not have been seriously affected.

Wheat marketings will be reduced further in the 1960's, to the detriment of the feed-livestock economy if the released acreage is permitted to produce any other product for use. This would hasten the day when direct marketing controls on livestock would be demanded in the interest of price maintenance. In my opinion, there is much to be lost in comprehensive direct controls, while the price gains might be achieved partly through indirect programs not yet tried. Selective land retirement coupled with selective marketing quotas on crops is one such indirect approach to reduced marketings, and should be tried first.

SUMMARY

Land development is a modest effort in the U.S. While contradictory, it is in many ways unassailable. Yet we are not absolved from pointing out its contradictions.

Effective land retirement, like effective production and marketing controls, has not yet been tried. Obituaries for both are premature. I believe they will not only survive the failures of the 1950's, but can be joined in a lasting marriage of convenience in the early 1960's. Properly supervised, they should get along well, for they have the same ends. Like succeeding generations, they will be modest improvements on the past, not permanent solutions for the future.

Chapter 16

PHILIP M. RAUP
ELMER LEARN
University of Minnesota

Effects of Alternative Programs of Supply Control Upon Land Withdrawal[1]

WE USE THE TERM supply control to refer to purposive action designed to restrict the quantities of agricultural products coming to the market. The restrictions involved are measured by the adjustment needed to relate supply to demand, commodity by commodity, at prices judged to be "fair" to producers and consumers. Alternative program proposals to achieve the required adjustment are many and varied. In general, they involve either a system of marketing quotas established on saleable agricultural commodities or a system of input restrictions aimed at control of production.

To date, most of the attempts at supply control have been of the input restriction type where the input directly involved has been land. This is true of the acreage allotment programs and of the more recent Soil Bank legislation. No serious consideration has been given to production control through restrictions on other classes of inputs, with the possible exception of labor. Some sporadic discussion has taken place regarding a tax on mineral fertilizers. There have also been suggestions for restrictions on agricultural credit, and some recent pronouncements have called for a reduction of inputs devoted to research in agricultural technologies.

Because of land's crucial importance as a production input, it is evident that any form of supply control program will have widespread land use significance. A thorough discussion of land withdrawal and land use implications inherent in alternative supply control programs, however, would require far more time than is available. Furthermore, other chapters have touched on land use problems associated with earlier agricultural programs — which, as we have indicated, were primarily of the land restriction type.

[1] In developing the argument presented in this chapter the authors have benefited from discussions with Walter W. Wilcox and from the comments of Lyle Schertz to an earlier draft.

Therefore, we concentrate our attention in this chapter on land use and land withdrawal questions surrounding the market quota type of supply control program. We will discuss these programs in terms of their probable effect on the extent and intensity of land use adjustments. In so doing, we will attempt to appraise the appropriateness of these adjustments from the standpoints of landowners and users, the community and the economy. The discussion of land use implications requires that we not consider the adjustment of agricultural supply to demand in isolation from other goals of society. Our evaluation, therefore, must include discussion of a wide range of problems associated with land use and land withdrawal. Included are land needs for urban expansion, for recreational purposes, tenure relationships and tax structures.

We will not concern ourselves with the problem of goal setting — i.e., what level of control is required. Neither will we attempt to justify the need for supply control. We begin with the assumption that supply control is to be considered seriously as a potential solution to the agricultural adjustment problem. The question of the land withdrawal implications of alternative programs is, therefore, a legitimate topic for discussion.

Relatively little research has been completed regarding the detailed operation of a widespread supply control program utilizing marketing quotas. Our remarks are thus liberally sprinkled with questions, hypotheses and highly tentative conclusions.

Although the term supply control is conceived and discussed as a global concept, it is emphasized at the outset that controls upon marketings must of necessity apply directly to specific commodities or products. The degree of limitation on marketings will be different for different products, and the continental expanse of American agriculture will guarantee that the impact of marketing restrictions will vary geographically. We can identify in this regard three classes of products in terms of the dominant forces influencing the decision concerning the location of their production:

1. Products whose zone of production is sharply delimited by climate and soil considerations. Tree and bush crops and forest products are prominent examples.

2. Products for which perishability, storage, transport or institutional considerations dominate the decision of where to produce. Fluid milk is the outstanding example of this class.

3. Products whose zones of production are dependent upon factor and product price relationships, with a wide range of choice available to the producer faced with the question: What to produce? The conventional hog-corn-soybean-beef feeding types of

farming of the Middle West provide the dominant examples in this group.

The mechanics of supply control and consequent land use adjustments are less difficult for groups 1 and 2 above. The area of critical difficulty for any supply control program involves products falling under type 3 above, for which the land user enjoys a wide range of substitution possibilities. The success or failure of supply control programs depends on the effectiveness with which the supply of this class of products can be controlled.

The market quota type of programs to which we have reference would involve the national imposition of marketing quotas implemented through certificates to be presented when any agricultural food product was offered to the market. It is beyond the scope of this paper to present in detail the mechanics through which a program of this kind would be administered.[2] The principal variations, however, center around the nature of the marketing certificate and the freedom with which it can be transferred.

In most proposals, initial allocation of the certificates would be based on some historical record of past marketings, specific to a land area and to an individual. Under one version, the certificates could be made to "run with the land," and in this form they would differ only in detail from past programs of the "acreage" or "planting" quota type.

The certificates could also be made to "run with the person" in that they would expire at his death, or would revert to some national administrative agency after a specified period of nonuse or following a decision of the certificate holder to quit farming, for whatever reason. Alternatively, the certificate could be made an unrestricted personal right, independent of the land, and freely negotiable by the original holder. It is this third alternative that has been most prominently considered in recent proposals for this type of supply control effort.[3]

Let us consider the probable effects upon land use and withdrawal of a system of supply control based on negotiable marketing certificates that do not run with the land. What would be some of the probable consequences of this type of control?

---

[2] See W. W. Cochrane, Farm Prices, Myth and Reality, University of Minnesota Press, 1958, and W. W. Cochrane, "Some further reflections on supply control," Jour. Farm Econ., Nov., 1959.

[3] The feature of free negotiability has particular appeal to economists because of the implications it carries concerning resource mobility within agriculture. Because transfer of certificates is effected through a market system, this form of control also implies greater freedom of individual decision making than would be true of many other supply control mechanics.

It is instructive to begin with an examination of the nature of the right created by the establishment of a negotiable marketing certificate. In the past our concept of ownership rights in land has included the right to dispose freely of the products of the land. It has been an integral part of the core of the "bundle of rights" concept of land ownership, ranking with the right to exclude others and the right of unrestricted use as one of the crucial rights involved in the ownership complex. Where this right of disposition over the product is detached from the bundle and made separately saleable, a fundamental change has been introduced into our conception of land ownership. A right that has in the past been associated with real property has now been defined as a personal property right. Where this change is accomplished it will precipitate fundamental alterations in the structure of legal rights and privileges traditionally associated with land ownership. We have, of course, tested the power of the government to separate these rights in past market quota legislation. Such a separation of rights, in fact, is imposed on producers of wheat and sugar beets currently. We have not had experience, however, with the problems that are likely to arise where this separation of rights to market the product of agricultural land is extended to all or most of agricultural production or where these rights are made separately saleable.

One of the most important problems associated with this change will arise at the outset. Unless the marketing certificates are distributed in some reasonable relation to present structures of land values, they are certain to run afoul of the fifth and fourteenth amendments to the United States Constitution. If, through an exercise of the police power or otherwise, a general limitation is placed on the marketing rights of all landowners, it seems probable that this could be accomplished without incurring any obligation to compensate the owners although their property would have been depreciated in value by this act. If the imposition of the marketing certificate system has a differential impact on landowners, with little relation to the productivity value of their land in its current use, it is virtually certain that this would be adjudged a taking of property rights for which compensation would have to be paid.

These considerations suggest strongly that any imposition of marketing quotas would, of necessity, be based initially on some historic record of acreage of land held or used, or quantity of product marketed. In short, to avoid the problem of confiscation of property rights without just compensation, the initial distribution of marketing rights probably would have to bear some reasonable relation to the present distribution of land ownership rights.

Assuming then that marketing quotas are imposed at the outset in ratio to current patterns of land use and production, what consequences flow from the negotiable nature of the certificates? It would be possible, for example, for an individual to conclude that the effort and uncertainty in continuing to produce his customary crops were sufficiently great to justify his sale of the marketing right to a producer more favorably situated. Two types of circumstances, in particular, might lead to this conclusion. On the one hand, production areas subject to high natural risk have tended in the past to generate a structure of land values based on earnings whose long-term average levels fail to reflect the extreme cyclical fluctuations to which they are subject.

Where the high yields of a few "boom" years must compensate for a possible succession of poor years, it would be necessary for the producer to carry over his excess output from good years for which his marketing certificates would be inadequate. This would involve storage costs, or the emergency purchase of marketing certificates at premium prices. In either case he would suffer a marketing disadvantage. All other things being equal, the producer of the same commodity in areas less subject to climatic risk would have lower costs and fewer occasions to make emergency purchases of marketing certificates in order to dispose of his bumper crops. It seems reasonable to conclude that we might witness the migration of marketing certificates, and production, from areas with histories of extreme year-to-year fluctuation to areas with more stable annual output histories.

The differential availability of alternative nonfarm employment might be another factor affecting the decisions of producers to sell their marketing rights. In spite of generally increased farm earnings under a successful program, some producers' incomes will continue to be unsatisfactory judged in terms of nonfarm alternatives. The difference is likely to be thrown into sharp relief as a result of the relative certainty with which future farm earnings can be assessed under the program. Moreover, the cost of increasing labor income through the purchase of additional marketing certificates would be clear-cut. An additional incentive will be the income that can be earned without sale of the homestead and accompanying farm land through sale of the marketing certificates. It seems probable that in this situation agricultural producers in favorable labor market areas might well conclude that a sale of their marketing certificates and a transfer of occupations is in order.

This reasoning suggests that the strategically placed bidder for marketing rights might be the producer who is located in an area of relatively low climatic risk, but relatively distant from alternative job opportunities. In time, marketing rights might well tend to migrate from the most extensive and most intensive present margins of land use to some middle ground, i.e. from the relatively arid production regions and from the urban fringes.

There are other considerations that might lead to a migration of production away from both the present intensive and extensive margins of land use. The separation of the right to market the products of land from other aspects of land ownership rights would have a differential impact on land values, depending on the extent to which demand elements in the land market reflect considerations other than those based upon the net earnings of the land in agricultural use. In general terms, these demand elements fall into two groups:

1. Demand forces internal to the farm firm but not based upon the capitalized net earnings of the specific tract of land in question.
2. Demand elements that are external to the farm firm and that reflect estimates of present or future land values in uses other than agricultural.

Within the farm firm there are in general two different types of demand elements at work in the land market in addition to the productivity inherent in a specific tract of land. On the one hand is the "internal economies of scale" element, reflecting the fact that some farm units are too small for the effective utilization of modern agricultural technology, or are too small for existing stocks of equipment or skills of management. Where this condition prevails, the price of an additional tract of land sufficient to raise the farm to some threshold level of economic size will be bid out of proportion to the price that would be justified for that particular tract by a capitalization of its specific net earnings. Since the existing farm organization of the potential buyer is out of balance, the advantages resulting from bringing it into balance can be bid into the price of the additional tract of land.

In areas where an internal economies-of-scale problem exists, current levels of farm land values reflect a substantial element of value that is rooted in this tendency to capitalize all of the advantages of achieving an efficient organizational unit into the price that will be offered for the additional land needed. This has been a powerful demand element in the farm land market from 1945 to 1960.

A second demand element that is internal to the farm firm but only weakly related to productivity value arises from cultural patterns or individual preferences that place a high value on a rural-farm way of life. Farm families may choose to remain in farming in spite of unfavorable returns to family labor when measured against opportunity wage rates available in alternative employment. To the extent that this occurs, we can expect to find this voluntary freezing of labor mobility reflected in land values. The land values will be higher than those justified by capitalized net earnings attributed to land when farm labor is valued at opportunity-cost wage rates.

The demand elements for farm land that are external to the farm firm are widely varied. They include the demand for farm land for residential sites for families whose primary source of income is outside of agriculture. Some of these are urban families who have "moved to the country"; others are farm families who have shifted to nonfarm employment but have retained ownership of farm lands. In either case the earning capacity of nonfarm jobs is available to be drawn upon in paying for the purchase of farm land.

Where this occurs, the effect is to "export" a demand for urban housing into the rural countryside, and to convert it into a demand for farm land. This demand element is strongly present in areas surrounding the larger urban centers, and extending out for distances of 30 to 50 miles. The effect is to build into farm land values in these areas a demand element that is unrelated to the productivity of the land in agricultural uses.

In addition to this diffused pattern of nonfarm demand for rural residential sites, there is a variety of more specific urban demand elements for farm land. These include the use of rural land for airport locations, highway improvement and expansion, water supply protection areas, public parks and recreational areas and private golf courses, hunt clubs and the like. While none of these demand elements, by itself, will influence farm land values in any substantial area, their cumulative effect is substantial.

In summary, the urban explosion triggered by the automobile and good roads has led to a sharp increase in the element of nonagricultural productivity value currently reflected in market prices for agricultural lands in the vicinity of urban centers.

We have identified above a variety of demand elements for farm land that are unrelated or only weakly related to the productivity of the land in agricultural use. Where this nonproductivity component in the present structure of farm land values is large, the introduction of a system of mandatory but negotiable marketing certificates to control supplies will have results that may seem surprising on first inspection. Where farms are uneconomically small and there is a consequent strong demand for land for farm expansion purposes, there will be a tendency for this "expansion demand" to shift to the demand for marketing rights, with a probable sharp reduction in the premium that will be freely paid for additional acres alone. Where there have been substantial economies of scale to be achieved through farm expansion, and where this has led to higher priced farm land, it would seem reasonable to expect a rather sharp deflationary influence to be exerted upon land values by a system of negotiable marketing certificates. Where individual farmers had, in effect, paid a premium for their additional land, they now would find themselves more or less compelled to repeat the error and pay a premium for additional marketing certificates to enable them to retain their marginal grip on the threshold of efficient size. They can be expected to be strong bidders in the market for negotiable marketing rights.

Where nonfarm demand elements have resulted in a high price for farm land in terms of its productivity value, it seems probable that this element in the land market will not be greatly affected by the introduction of marketing certificates. The supply price for land in these areas may, however, be somewhat lower because of the additional income that can be obtained by the original owner through sale of his certificates. In any case, it is unlikely that buyers of land for residential or other "urban" uses will be an important influence in the market for marketing certificates except in an indirect manner.

For types of production that lend themselves to geographic concentration, of which chicken broiler and turkey producers are good examples, there may well be both production and nonproduction-oriented reasons why the purchase of marketing rights would be profitable. In this situation the premium for the marketing right would arise from low-cost production advantages and from structural advantages in marketing growing out of large-scale operations. Advantages achieved by vertical integrators, for example, may be even greater under a market quota program.

These considerations suggest that the same broad reasons that have led farm people to pay premiums for farm land for agricultural uses will also tend to lead them to pay premiums for marketing certificates. The nonfarm element of demand for farm land is not likely to be greatly influenced by the imposition of a quota system. If this reasoning is correct, it suggests that there may be two principal groups of strong bidders for these marketing rights:

1. Individuals whose personal value system includes a high premium on a rural way of life.
2. Individuals whose current size of farm operating unit is at

or below the threshold of economic scale under present technological conditions.[4]

If these are the individuals who can be expected to be on the buying side of marketing right markets, who can be expected to be on the selling side? It seems reasonable to suppose that the landowners whose farms are already adequately large, who are situated in areas relatively remote from urban land market influences and who are well within the low weather-risk area of humid agriculture will find themselves under little pressure to enter the market for marketing certificates as premium bidders except possibly in the first year or two that the program is in operation.

In short, the type of firm that might not feel any compulsion or visualize any reward from the premium purchase of marketing certificates may tend to be the larger family-sized farm in predominately agricultural districts remote from urban centers. Although they might not enter actively into the market as buyers of marketing certificates, it also seems probable that they would not enter actively as sellers. As a class of farms, they might well play a passive role.

Where then would the sellers of marketing rights be found? We have already indicated one source of these rights for sale: Producers in areas of high climatic risk whose average yearly marketings reflect an arithmetic fiction compounded from extremes of boom and bust years.

Another class of sellers of marketing rights could well be composed of individuals from a wide variety of farming areas whose decision to sell is prompted not by the size or organization of their production enterprises but by their stage in the family life cycle. With an active market for separately saleable marketing certificates at hand, it seems probable that many elderly farm couples might decide to sell their marketing rights while retaining ownership of the land. This could become an acceptable substitute to an increasingly difficult alternative of farm operation at reduced scale under conditions of advancing age. It might well lead to earlier retirement "on the farm." The fact that land ownership remains in the hands of the farm couple would enhance this prospect. It would be reasonable for the elderly parents to conclude that as long as they held title to the land, they still held the door open for some member of the family to decide that he wished to farm, with the price of entry

[4] Included in this group will be those individuals whose scale of operation is reduced below tolerable levels by the imposition of the program. This latter group will probably decline in importance after the first few years of operation of the program.

represented by the purchase price of the needed marketing rights. In the meantime, the elderly couple would have the proceeds of the marketing rights as a form of retirement annuity.

If this trend should develop, it would represent a partial disposal of the assets of the prospective estate of the farm owner. He would in effect reduce the inheritance expectations of his heirs. He could do this without sacrificing any of the family motives built into the desire to "keep the farm in the family." To the extent that these motives played a prominent role in the value patterns of family members, the reduction in the size of their prospective inheritance would be regarded as tolerable when measured against the alternative possibility that the farm might have to be sold to provide retirement income for the elderly parents. When the alternatives are total sale of the farm land and marketing rights, or sale of marketing rights only, it might well be that parents and heirs alike would conclude that sale of the marketing rights was the less undesirable alternative.

Based on this reasoning, it is suggested that one possible source of supply of marketing rights would be provided by elderly farm couples who now feel compelled to continue farm operation well beyond the years at which they might otherwise choose to retire.

Another source of supply of purchasable marketing rights might be provided by landowners whose motivation for ownership is strongly influenced by a desire for an anti-inflation hedge. Landowners who are not dependent upon land income for their principal source of support might nevertheless desire to hold land minus marketing rights as a form of insurance against war or economic disaster. It would be reasonably predictable that in time of war or economic collapse a system of transferable marketing rights would be drastically altered or would break down. Should a crisis in international relations develop overnight, a rapid change in the issuances of marketing certificates could be predicted. Some landholders might well reason that they could afford to continue the ownership of land without appurtenant marketing rights as a form of disaster insurance. Should disaster occur, they would have every reason from past history to believe that the marketing quota system would be quickly abandoned in favor of a total drive for "all out" production. The strictly inflation-hedge landowner might thus develop as a relatively ready source of saleable market certificates. Because of the opportunity cost of holding highly productive land out of use, it is likely that most of the land held for these purposes would be marginal in terms of agricultural use.

Much of the ultimate success of a supply control system

based on separately saleable marketing certificates will depend on the tax treatment accorded the certificates. They represent a form of wealth ultimately based on real property. Under present law they would unquestionably be included in the personal property tax base. The fact that they are saleable separately from the land will increase the possibility of tax evasion, complicate the task of assessing this form of personal property and give rise to some difficult problems of periodic re-evaluation. In addition, in any areas where a substantial volume of marketing rights had been sold off of the land, the local units of government would find themselves called upon to provide local public service out of all proportion to the remaining local property tax base.

The twin pressures of need for replacement revenue and need for new devices of appraising this unfamiliar form of "property" might well bring about a thoroughgoing change in the rural use of the property tax.

In speculating on the possible directions that this property tax change might take, it is necessary to ask: What will be the nature of the markets in which these separately saleable marketing certificates are exchanged? On the one hand, the sale of these marketing rights could take a form comparable to a central commodity exchange in which some right, roughly similar to a warehouse receipt, was being exchanged.

Alternatively, the markets in which these certificates were exchanged could be more nearly akin to the traditional land market, rooted in the county register of deeds office, in which titles to real property and any incumbrances against it are registered. In view of the property tax crisis that would be occasioned by any substantial sale of marketing rights separate from land, it seems probable that the markets in which these will be transferred will include a transaction recording device that will be more nearly comparable with the register of deeds office than with a commodity exchange.

It is possible, for example, that some separate register of titles to marketing rights could be established, parallel to conventional registers of titles to land, in which all parties interested in a particular marketing right could be shown. Registered in this fashion, the marketing right would be available as a base for personal property taxation, and the disruption that this method of supply control would cause in the traditional sources of local public finance would be reduced.

It is also possible that a property tax treatment for the marketing certificates would be difficult, if not impossible, for local units of government to exercise because of the difficult problem of assessment and levy. As a consequence, one possible alternative might be the imposition of a turnover tax on the marketing certificate whenever products were sold, the tax to be levied against the seller. The proceeds of this tax could be aggregated at regional or state levels and distributed to local units of government in accordance with some standard of need, in much the same fashion that centrally collected sales or income taxes are now distributed.

One point seems clear: Any turnover tax levied against the marketing certificates would need to be uniform among states. If it were not, the flexibility in the location of production introduced by the device of the separately saleable marketing certificate could be seriously impaired.

If we shift our view from that of the community in need of revenue to that of the seller of a marketing right faced with a potential property tax bill, still another dominant consideration comes in sight. Some immediate reduction in property tax burdens would be mandatory whenever there was a sale of marketing rights independent of the land. Unless the landowner could reckon with a sharply reduced fixed charge for carrying his land minus marketing rights, he would have a greatly reduced incentive to dispose of these rights separately.

In agricultural areas close to urban centers it is conceivable that the remaining value of the land after the marketing rights had been separately sold may be almost as high as was the level of value when marketing rights were included. At the opposite extreme, on the extensive margin of arable farming, it is also conceivable that the separate sale of the marketing rights may virtually extinguish any value in the land. Only where recreational uses, forestry or mineral production were realistic alternatives, would the land have any productivity value minus the rights to market its agricultural products. At both the intensive and extensive margins of use, it is thus probable that a method of determining the remaining value of the land that depended upon subtraction of the capital value of the marketing right from the current market price of land would yield intolerable results. For land uses in areas feeling the full force of urban expansion or recreational uses, this method would result in remainder values that were unrealistically low. At the extensive margin in farm-forest or semi-arid regions the resulting residual value would almost certainly be too high, reflecting the fact that land value levels in these areas are currently unrealistically high in relation to prospective earnings at the new and reduced levels of permitted output.

It seems reasonable to conclude that the introduction of this form of supply control program would force a radical alteration in conventional methods of assessing property taxes. Without this radical revision the potential effectiveness of this type of control program would be seriously jeopardized.

A parallel readjustment in conventional forms of land-based credit would also be required. With marketing rights separately saleable, prospective creditors would need the security of a mortgage against the land plus some form of chattel mortgage or assignment to cover the marketing right. With this dual form of security in hand, it seems probable that institutional lenders would consider loans against the land plus marketing rights for a sum that would total a larger percentage of the consolidated value than is presently considered safe in conventional mortgage credit circles. Since the marketing right would be immediately saleable, in a much larger potential market than is normally available for the sale of farm land, the security represented by the two elements of value combined would be upgraded. In effect, the size of the market in which the security could be converted into cash would have been increased.

The extension of this line of reasoning to cover the probable effects upon the land market opens the door to an intriguing possibility. Since the marketing rights are divisible, in terms of commodity units, they would offer a prospect for the serial purchase of one of the assets needed in getting established in farming. The inconvenience, cost and confusion that would be involved in buying a farm one acre at a time would not necessarily extend to the practice of buying the "marketing right" a few bushels or a few head of livestock at a time. The divisible nature of the intangible rights represented by the marketing certificates would also lend themselves to piecemeal transfer between father and son. In this sense, the individual units of the marketing right would be akin to shares of stock in a corporation. One unintended by-product of this method of supply control might thus be the creation of a realistic method whereby farm families could take advantage of present income tax regulations permitting repeated gifts *inter vivos*, in limited amounts and in successive years, free of gift or inheritance taxation.

The credit uses to which the marketing certificates would be put, coupled with the prospective use of these certificates in the piecemeal purchase or transfer of the farm, reinforce the probability that the market mechanism in which these certificates are traded would be similar to the present land market. Title could be based on some form of local registry of marketing rights comparable in form to present systems whereby mineral lease rights are recorded and traded.[5]

There remains one prominent area in which the effects of this form of supply control are difficult to predict. This concerns the lease and rental market for farm land. If marketing rights are separated from the land, it seems probable that the contribution of these rights, in a tenant-landlord relationship, would tend to gravitate into the hands of the tenants. Equipped with the livestock, machinery and working capital that are the conventional contributions of tenants, it would now become necessary to procure suitable land and the necessary marketing rights. The door would be open for a dual form of rental market to emerge: One market for land and another rental market for marketing rights.

If he held marketing rights, acquired through lease or purchase, the tenant would have a direct incentive to apply his equipment and marketing rights to land that would offer the maximum yields for a given unit of effort and capital. We can anticipate that fertile and strategically situated land would command a premium rent, in this circumstance, even if it were devoid of its marketing rights. Since the marketing rights would presumably exchange at a "national" market price, adjusted for differences in cost of transport, it seems reasonable to anticipate the emergence of differential rents for land without marketing rights that would approximate present differentials in land values. To push this line of thought one step farther, it also seems probable that the differential levels of rental values for land without marketing rights would be more sharply graduated than are present land value structures. With price uncertainty reduced, attention would shift to production efficiency and to the differential fertility levels of alternative tracts of land. Our reasoning on this point suggests that the introduction of this type of supply control program would enhance the desirability of the "good" lands.

However this may be, one point seems certain: This method of supply control would result in a substantially more complex tax, credit and tenure structure than has been customary in American agriculture. New institutions would be needed, coupled with radical changes in existing ones. To select one prominent example, radical changes could be expected in the conventional crop-share leasing arrangement now dominant in many agricultural regions of the United States.

---

[5]Some of the possible lines of development are suggested in L. A. Parcher, "Some factors influencing mineral rights separation in land sales," Okla. Agr. Exp. Sta. Bul. B-431, July, 1954, and in "Mineral rights management by private landowners," Great Plains Agricultural Council Publication No. 13, Okla. Agr. Exp. Sta., Stillwater (no date).

Let us summarize briefly. The land withdrawal pattern that we envision in earlier pages does not differ greatly in form from the trends in land use that we have witnessed from 1945 to 1960. We do anticipate that the rates of withdrawal and shifts in use would be accelerated, and that the differential levels of land rent would be more sharply graduated than is now the case. It also seems probable that land remaining in production will continue to be consolidated into larger-sized units, and at an accelerated rate.

A system of supply control with negotiable marketing quotas will occasion major institutional changes, both in the form of a new market for the marketing certificates and in the form of radical changes in present land tenure institutions. We would expect the land-based tax structure in rural areas to undergo drastic revision. In addition, rural credit institutions, farm transfer and inheritance practices and established forms of landlord-tenant arrangements will require an extended period of adjustment to the forces put in motion by creation of saleable marketing rights.

Chapter 17

WALTER E. CHRYST
Agricultural Research Service, USDA

JOHN F. TIMMONS
Iowa State University

The Economic Role of Land Resource Institutions in Agricultural Adjustment[1]

THIS STUBBORN PERSISTENCE of agriculture's problems after nearly four decades of public adjustment programs, from 1920 to 1960, suggests that public efforts have not as yet come fully to grips with agriculture's fundamental difficulties.[2] The purpose of this chapter is to direct attention to certain overlooked or unattended aspects of the agricultural problem complex.

THE PROBLEM

The thesis explored in this chapter holds that land resource institutions influencing resource allocation and income distribution within agriculture, between agriculture and other industries and between time periods provide some of the basic causes of agriculture's difficulties and present serious obstacles to remedial action.

More specifically, the institution of property in land with all of its attending implications induces the capitalization of many kinds of benefits into land values. Included are benefits from farm income-increasing programs, land development programs and production control programs, as well as benefits from cost-reducing technology and a host of other minor measures such as

[1]The authors are grateful to Mark M. Regan, ARS, USDA, for some of the suggestions contained in this chapter, and to Professor W. L. Gibson, Jr., Virginia Polytechnic Institute, and Professor Wilfred Pine, Kansas State University, for permission to use data not previously published. The authors' views expressed in this paper do not necessarily represent the views of the United States Department of Agriculture.

[2]The literature on agriculture's income and production problems contains abundant evidence of the persistence of agriculture's difficulties. During the 1950's the gross national product increased 60 percent, yet income to farm people declined. On a per capita basis, farm people realized less than one-half the increase in income that nonfarm people received. In addition, about $11 billion worth of farm products are in public storage and 25 million acres of cropland are withheld from production.

homestead tax exemptions. Once the benefits become capitalized into land values, the higher values are reflected in amortization, interest and tax commitments. These commitments constitute fixed costs to the farmers and may in turn (1) magnify uncertainties of economic and natural origins and (2) necessitate increased production to meet these fixed commitments in periods of falling prices. At this point, acreage control and price support programs further enter the picture to relieve resulting surpluses of products and declining farm income. However, since the programs themselves are usually tied to land, program benefits are in turn capitalized into land values, which may lead to a circle of more program benefits, higher land values and an increasing need for further layers of program benefits.

This situation places agricultural programs in the position of supporting a system of land values which the programs helped create. As a result, the system builds up an artificial surplus of land estimated between 45 and 75 million crop acres which would not exist if land could move freely to other uses and substitute more freely for capital in all uses. In addition, the claim of the land factor brings lower net income to farmers and higher costs of farm products to consumers both through higher taxes to support farm programs and through higher costs of certain products resulting from withholding land from production. As a further consequence, excesses of products may be produced by farmers in an attempt to meet their fixed commitments as a necessary requisite for maintaining an equity in land and a position in agriculture.

This thesis does not imply that land resource institutions alone are responsible for agriculture's difficulties. These difficulties are complex and many faceted. However, the thesis does suggest that institutions have been instrumental in fostering misallocations of resources (1) between agricultural and nonagricultural uses, (2) within agriculture and (3) between time periods.

This thesis is further explained and developed in subsequent sections. Inadequate empirical evidence requires that the development of the thesis be largely conceptual, using such scattered data as are currently available in an illustrative manner. From this exposition, however, may come certain reorientation of research and thought essential to an improved understanding and amelioration of agriculture's difficulties.

CONCEPTS AND ASSUMPTIONS

Prior to exploring this thesis further, certain underlying concepts and assumptions should be stated. The term "land resource institutions" means the entire body of rights and responsibilities created by society regulating the use and control of land resources.[3] These institutions specify how rights in land are owned and transferred, who receives the value of land, how income is shared in the use process and the range of uses to which land may be put.

The term "land resources" means all attributes of a particular tract of land including (1) natural attributes, i.e., soil and climate; (2) socially created attributes, i.e., location and publicly supplied improvements such as highways, drainage and flood control; and (3) capital investments in land which become fixtures, i.e., terraces and fertility. Labor and capital are used to exploit the opportunities created by land resources. In most agricultural activities, land resources may serve as substitutes, within some range, for labor and capital.

A basic assumption of the subsequent analysis is that a particular gross national product is preferable from a public viewpoint to any smaller national product, given the amount of labor and capital used in productive processes. This assumption embraces the application of the familiar principles of maximization and equi-marginality, and applies to the use of resources within agriculture and resources that can be transferred between agriculture and other employments. These principles provide the criteria for appraising land resource institutions in terms of effects upon achieving or obstructing efficient use of resources.

HOW LAND RESOURCE INSTITUTIONS AFFECT RESOURCE USE AND THE DISTRIBUTION OF INCOME

Land resource institutions determine land use and income distribution as a consequence of three conditions.

1. A right to use some land is indispensable to the productive process in agriculture.[4] Labor and capital usually may be

[3] For further discussion of land institutions, see John F. Timmons, "Land institutions impeding and facilitating agricultural adjustment," Chapter 10 in Problems and Policies of American Agriculture, Iowa State University Press, Ames, 1959.

[4] As stated by Marshall, "The use of a certain area of the earth's surface is a primary condition of anything that man can do; it gives him room for his own actions, with the enjoyment of the heat and the light, the air and the rain which nature assigns to that area; and it determines his distance from, and in a great measure his relations to, other things and other persons. We shall find that it is this property of 'land' which, though as yet insufficient prominence has been given to it, is the ultimate cause of the distinction which all writers on economics are compelled to make between land and other things. It is the foundation of much that is most interesting and most difficult in economic science." Alfred Marshall, Principles of Economics. 8th ed., p. 145.

substituted for some land, either in a firm or in an economy, but some land must be used, just as some labor and capital must be used.

2. Land, being immovable and serving as a spatial basis with its resources for productive activities, can and does reflect future income claims in terms of present values. Earlier in man's history, productivity of labor was capitalized into laborers through the institution of slavery. With the abolition of involuntary servitude, labor receives a periodic wage or other return tending to reflect current value productivity. Likewise, capital, unless and until it becomes real property (in which instance it becomes a resource of land), receives periodic returns which tend to reflect current value productivity. Unlike land, however, the value of a capital item is limited by its cost of reproduction.

3. The property institution in land requires that payment for the use of land for satisfying direct or derived demands must be committed ex ante, even though value productivity of land may be realized periodically over time in conjunction with the use of capital and labor. Once commitments are contracted on present values of rights in land, the institution of property enforces economic claims to and from land in the form of taxes, mortgage payments, payments on low equity nonmortgage contracts (i.e., land installment contracts) and rents. In addition, land rents and land prices (committed without debt claims) reflecting partial and lump-sum payments for the services of land in the production process are notoriously inflexible and lag behind changes in the value productivity of the factor.

Results of these three restraints surrounding the use, control, and valuation of land yield a current value of all farm land (with its resources) equivalent to about eight times the total current net income to agriculture.

Let us proceed by searching further into the implications of these restraints.

Through the capitalization process the burden of variability of output is shifted, in large measure, from land to labor and capital. The numerous examples of farm families reducing their levels of living and neglecting the maintenance and replacement of capital items to pay land costs are familiar. Familiar also is the memory of the thousands who failed and started over again as tenants with depleted resources or who sought public relief. One out of every four farms in Iowa, for example, was foreclosed or transferred under duress of debts and taxes between World Wars I and II.

Two other effects of land resource institutions stemming from the introduction of fixed land costs into the farm financial structure are (1) market instability and (2) inefficiency of resource use.

With respect to market stability, it may be argued that high fixed commitments for land for any large proportion of farms producing a specific commodity can, after an initial decline in the price of the commodity, generate subsequent declines with the consequence that supply becomes inversely correlated with demand and a generally unstable situation is created. Let us anticipate the behavior of a farmer with heavy mortgage and tax commitments when the price of his products declines. As a competitive producer with no influence upon price, he can meet his obligation only by increasing output, by throwing into the current struggle for economic survival resources – for example, machine maintenance, breeding stock, and soil productivity – reserved for future production periods. Since his fellow producers are in similar straits and the expanded output is offered on an inelastic market for farm products, the prices of products again fall and new sacrifices are required. Thus, under some circumstances land institutions may create a supply of commodities that is an inverse function of their price, which generates general instability in the market.[5] Further, there may be an intertemporal transfer of returns from the future to the present, i.e., some premium from the future is attached to present prices in order that the farm firm may exist in the future. Thus, resources are transferred from future to present uses, with the consequence that excessive production in the current period has the additional cost of more expensive production later.

In addition to the intertemporal aspects of resource use, there is reason to believe that some entrepreneurs adjust to economic hazards by restricting the ratio of liabilities to assets. The proper ratio depends, of course, upon the individual's taste for risk, but in general, the lower the ratio the greater the economic shock that one can successfully withstand. Usually, no other single farm investment is as large as the investment in land, and there is an abundance of empirical evidence to suggest that the hazard is met by restricting farm size, with the consequent restriction upon debt and financial vulnerability. Other data suggest that owner operators tend to substitute capital for land, and labor for capital.[6] To the extent that these substitutions

[5] The application of the Hicks type analysis to this phenomenon would yield an upward-sloping excess demand curve. Hicks demonstrates that a downward-sloping excess demand curve is an essential condition for a self-correcting market, i.e., market stability. J. R. Hicks. Value and Capital. Oxford University Press, N. Y., 1946, 2nd ed., p. 63 ff.

[6] See Miller, Chryst and Ottoson, Relative Efficiencies of Farm Tenure Classes in Intrafirm Resource Allocation. Iowa Agr. Exp. Sta. Res. Bul. 461, 1958.

are required by the methods of holding and transferring land without additional resources or output being created thereby, it is difficult to see how the public interest is being served.

In summary, land institutions tend to imbed the prosperity of the past into the costs of the present. The mood of the buyers and sellers of land may be a major factor affecting the welfare of farm people; when they are pessimistic, cautious and uncertain, and when land values do not respond to an increase in commodity prices, those who work in agriculture will benefit. But when those who deal in land are optimistic and sure, a Procrustean bed may be made for agriculture that will require painful adjustments when prices decline.

NATURE OF PUBLIC INTERVENTIONS AND THEIR CONSEQUENCES – IN RETROSPECT

The plight of agriculture viewed through income and production consequences has induced the public to intervene in an attempt to remedy agricultural problems. Through the years, these interventions have been substantial in cost and varied in approach. At this point, it would be well to review some of these recent attempts to bring about agricultural adjustments and to ascertain, at least conceptually, the results of these attempts.

In the main, the resources directed toward the improvement of the situation in agriculture have been used in three ways: (1) direct intervention in production and in the market to increase the price of farm products above the levels that would otherwise prevail, (2) the development of resources through irrigation and drainage or the protection of existing resources through such measures as flood control and soil conservation and (3) the development of techniques, through research and education, of obtaining a given output at less cost.[7]

These public activities are justified on the basis that a contribution is made to national welfare in general and to the welfare of farm people in particular. No doubt there exists the inherent belief, reasonably founded at first glance, that if prices are relatively high and stable, new lands are being developed and cheaper ways are being found to grow crops and produce livestock, the agricultural sector will be well off. This apparently is not the situation.

---

[7] This is not, of course, an exhaustive enumeration. Other items which quickly come to mind are farm credit, rural electrification, market news services, crop insurance, production credit, drouth relief, disaster loans and homestead tax exemption.

Publicly sponsored research and education in the agricultural sciences dates back to the Morrill Land-Grant College Act of 1862, reclamation has been a permanent feature of our national government since 1902, and direct intervention in the prices of agricultural commodities has been with us since the Agricultural Marketing Act of 1929. All of these activities have been greatly accelerated from 1930-60.

Questions may be appropriately raised about the effectiveness of these measures in alleviating the economic distress of farm people. If there is current concern about agricultural income after a sustained achievement of favorable prices, notable successes in agricultural research and education, the completion of large projects in reclamation and two decades which have seen the agricultural income divided among fewer and fewer people each successive year, perhaps it is time to see if there is something in the environment that prevents the methods from operating as expected.

The incidence of benefits and costs of these public programs has never been investigated on other than a nominal scale. Despite the many years of operation of these programs, there is practically no knowledge about who has been helped and by how much or who has lost and by how much. In attempting to assess the welfare implications of these public interventions in agriculture, there is recognition that many economists have avoided distributive problems on the basis that "interpersonal comparisons of utility" are difficult, if not impossible, to make. Despite this trammeling factor, however, it would at least be of interest to speculate upon who gets the benefits and how land resource institutions help pick the beneficiaries.

Price Support — Acreage Allotment Measures

The consequences of a program which restricts the quantity of land that can be used in agriculture and which guarantees a per unit product price greater than that which would otherwise prevail appear to be as follows:

1. Marginal physical productivity of land increases and marginal physical productivity of labor and capital decreases.
2. Marginal value productivity of land increases, and marginal value productivity of labor and capital may increase or decrease, depending on whether or not gain in price offsets the reduction in marginal physical productivity of the two factors.
3. If the marginal value productivities of all factors are increased, it would seem reasonable to expect labor and capital

to flow into agriculture (or more realistically, the rate of outflow to be reduced) until these factors would earn only slightly more at the margin than before the program was put into effect. At the new equilibrium, since all labor and capital in the economy are somewhat less productive physically as a consequence of fewer natural resources being employed in conjunction with them, these factors can be expected to earn somewhat less in real terms than was earned in the original situation.

4. As the marginal value productivity of land increases regardless of the change in the marginal productivity of labor and capital, which can earn little more than was earned before the initiation of the program, most of the benefits of the program must accrue to land.

5. If the program has positive benefits, these benefits will be primarily reflected in land values and rents with little or none of the benefits accruing to labor or capital.

Evidence commensurate with this conclusion has been found in a study of tobacco acreage allotments in Virginia for the period 1954-57. A regression analysis of 213 farm sales in Pittsylvania County indicated that an acre of tobacco allotment accounted for $962 of the selling price of a farm in 1954 and $1,673 of the selling price in 1957.[8] The value of an acre of cropland without the allotment was $22.70.[9] Similar evidence has been found in Greene, Wilson, and Pitt counties of North Carolina, where the regression estimates yielded $2,327** in 1954 and $4,036** in 1957.[10]

The impact of this capitalization of tobacco allotments upon farm purchases may be seen by referring to Figure 17.1. The chart represents data derived from the regression estimates for Pittsylvania County. The average sale price of the 213 farms was $10,243, and an estimated $5,650 was paid for the right to grow tobacco on a specified number of the purchased acres. For the $5,650, the purchaser received a franchise to grow tobacco — nothing physical. A subsample of the transactions indicated that the buyers borrowed an average $3,677 per farm — an amount roughly equal to two-thirds of the value of the allotments. If the

[8] Standard error: $143 in 1954, $208 in 1957. R = .88**. (Double asterisk: significant at 1 percent probability level.) From Maier, Hedrick and Gibson. "The sale value of flu-cured tobacco allotments," Va. Agr. Exp. Sta. Tech. Bul. No. 148. Apr., 1960, p. 27.

[9] Estimate on pooled data for four years. Standard error, $12. Intercorrelation of cropland with tobacco allotment may have biased noncropland estimate downward.

[10] Strong intercorrelation of the acreage allotment with cropland and noncropland suggests that this estimate is biased high. Use of "informed man on the street" estimates of the value of cropland and noncropland reduced the acreage allotment estimates to $1,290 and $2,500, respectively, for 1954 and 1957.

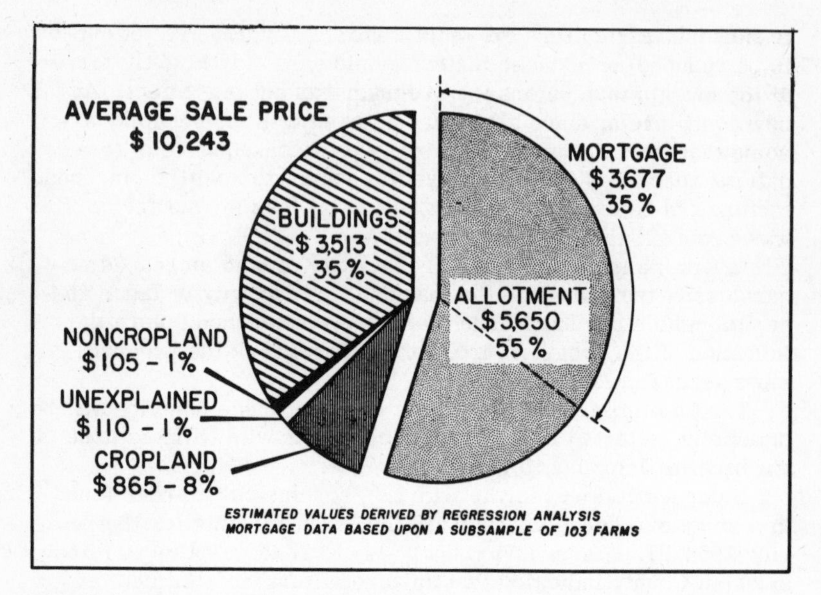

Fig. 17.1. Value of components of sale prices of 213 farms transferred in Pittsylvania County, Virginia: 1953-57.

program benefits were capitalized on the basis of the mortgage rate of interest, it would appear that two-thirds of the benefits are going to lenders on the land.

A regression study of land values in Kansas has yielded similar information on the value of wheat allotments. According to the study, the right to grow wheat added $53 to the value of an acre of wheat land in the Anderson area and $58 in the Logan-Wichita area in 1956.[11]

The data support the hypothesis by showing that benefits accrue to land but the data do not give the full picture. We do not know, for example, the total amount of the benefits of the tobacco program and how these are divided between land and labor. We do know, however, that there is a flow of labor from the tobacco areas to the mills, and can conclude that the program apparently has not succeeded in raising the labor return of farm operators above the wages of a millworker. Perhaps, in the long run, it is the alternative employment in the mills that sets the reward of agricultural labor in the section.

With respect to the allocation of resources in agriculture, it

[11] R^2 = .88 and .98, respectively. The study was sponsored by ARS, USDA, and the Kans. Agr. Exp. Sta.

is reasonable to expect the usual consequence that follows the limitation on the quantity of a factor. As the available supply of the factor is reduced, it becomes more expensive; the new minimum cost situation includes less of the restricted factors and more of its substitutes. When the restricted factor is land, there is a social cost attached to this process in terms of the potential earnings of the substituted factors in other employments. While the earnings of the mobile factors may be no greater than their alternative opportunity, it may be reasonably anticipated that more of these factors will be employed than the minimum cost situation with full use of the land would require. This substitution has as its consequence concealed underemployment and higher cost food than is otherwise obtainable.

The land withdrawal programs may be expected to have similar effects in terms of land values. If some land is withdrawn and labor and capital applications are adjusted to their new earning opportunities, either through the retention in agriculture of supplies that would have moved or by the movement into agriculture from the outside, it cannot be anticipated that the return to labor and capital would be greatly enhanced. The marginal physical productivity of land was increased, however, and if we assume some positive effect on price, we must assume that marginal value productivity of land will be increased and the principal effect will be upon the return to land.

Resource Development Programs

Many resource development programs can be expected to yield effects similar to those previously outlined for the acreage allotment programs. Consider a program that involves the application of public capital in an area to increase yields over time (irrigation, drainage, or clearing) or in specific years (flood control). If the program is successful, the economic productivity of land, labor and capital in the project area will be increased. If labor and capital flow into the developed area to the point that their marginal earnings are again equivalent to their opportunities outside of the project, and if these opportunities are influenced in only a minor way, if at all, by the project, nearly all of the increased return can be expected to go to the land involved, some control of which is necessary for labor and capital to earn a greater reward. This effect has, of course, been long recognized by legislators, and some publicly sponsored development projects have had features to discourage land speculation.

Agricultural Research and Education

Gains in technology can usually be expected to reduce rent and land values. Technology, in general, results in a lowering of the cost schedules; price finds its way down to the minimum average total unit cost of the marginal firm; rents to all firms are reduced and, according to capitalization theory, land values should follow accordingly.

Let us suppose, however, that for institutional reasons the price is maintained in some fixed relationship to some price that may have existed before, say, from 1910-14. Let us say that, as a result of innovations, the cost structure drops vertically, i.e., any given quantity can be produced with fewer or less expensive labor and capital resources than before. The difference between price and the average cost of production (AUC) is increased rather than diminished, and in the absence of marketing quotas, rents (and land values) may be expected to increase with little or no effect upon the return to the other factors.

We may assume another, but a more realistic situation. As a result of gains in the technical processes of production, the cost curves move downward and to the right, i.e., the minimum average cost of production is not only less than it was before but occurs at an output greater than most firms are producing. The marginal cost schedule likewise shifts to the right for all levels of output. We assume again that labor and capital are not perfect substitutes for land at the new optimum level of production. All firms operating with a plant too small to take advantage of the gains in technique have an incentive to add land. If a number of firms existed which had greater capacity than that which was economically feasible, land offerings would possibly equate with the new demand and no change in land price would result. The distribution of holdings, however, is badly skewed toward the small operator, each of whom now has an incentive to hold more land and can pay up to the difference between the new average unit cost and the commodity price for the land necessary for the expansion.

This argument can, of course, be reversed. If, in a competitive market, the farmer must exchange all of his anticipated gain for the land necessary for expansion, i.e., if he is left no better off after the expansion than before, he has no incentive to adopt the techniques. Perhaps the interaction between the land transfer process and the price support program as an obstacle to technological progress is an appropriate subject for research.

TRENDS IN FACTOR REWARDS IN AGRICULTURE

It is not our intention to say that the public programs have not provided any benefits for the agricultural population. We would suspect, however, that the benefits of these programs have had their greatest impact in improving agricultural welfare in those periods in which the uncertainty existing about their continuity was sufficient to preclude them from being capitalized into land values. The doubling of net farm income during the period 1933 to 1941 (and this increase must be attributed in part to the operation of the various public programs) was accompanied by an increase in land values of only slightly more than 10 percent (Figure 17.2). Again, during the period 1941-45, the wartime prosperity in agriculture was considered a temporary phenomenon, various educational measures were employed to refresh farmer memories of the 1920-21 experience and the increase in land values was considerably less than the increase in net income. Following 1946, however, confidence in agriculture prosperity apparently was placed on a firmer basis, and we have seen land values more than double (from $61 billion in 1946 to $125

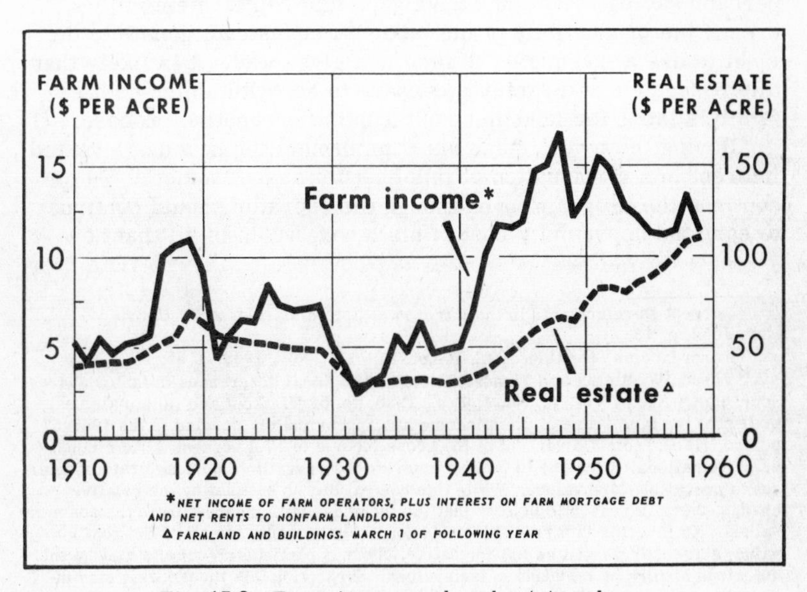

Fig. 17.2. Farm income and real estate values.

billion in 1959)[12] while farm net income has slightly declined ($17 billion to $16 billion from 1946-58).[13]

This has also been a period of rising interest rates, and the hypothesis that land is now claiming well over twice the agricultural income it claimed in 1946 would seem to be at least worthy of consideration. In this connection, it is of interest to note that the Ruttan-Stout estimates of labor's share of the gross farm income has declined from 51 percent in 1946 to about 24 percent in 1957.[14]

To suggest, at this point, that this capitalization is immaterial because farmers own their farms is to miss the real point. The farmer in Pittsylvania County, Virginia, who must spend $5,650 for the right to produce tobacco and who must borrow $3,700 of this amount, probably is not comforted by the fact that he may be buying these rights from another farmer. Due to the price stabilization features of the program, his expectations of variability in prices are no doubt less but will he not have to pay, through land, for this gain also? As he now owes interest and amortization, vulnerability to crop failure and risk to his personal health appear to have been increased. We must assume, since he borrowed, that he does not have unlimited resources; perhaps savings that could have gone into capital items to increase the productivity of his labor have, instead, gone into the right to use a given tract of land in a given way. It is likely that this purchaser will find it necessary to substitute his and his family's labor for land and capital in the productive process.

Having, however, made his commitment, he now has a vested interest in a continuation of this economic environment. To discontinue the program, even though the operator should continue to earn the opportunity cost of his labor, which is all that he

[12] Current Developments in the Farm Real Estate Market, ARS, USDA, 43-101, May, 1959, p. 13.

[13] Farm Income Situation, AMS, USDA, FIS-174, July, 1959, p. 35.

[14] Vernon W. Ruttan and Thomas T. Stout, "Regional differences in factor shares," Jour. Farm Econ., Vol. 42, No. 1, Feb., 1960, pp. 52 ff. Stout and Ruttan also estimate that the land share of farm income has approximately doubled in the 1946-57 period, rising from 7.5 percent of the gross income to 12.4 percent. The method employed allocated income to land by applying the prevailing mortgage rate of interest to prevailing land values. While this has validity in estimating the relative change, there is reason to believe that the technique will underestimate the absolute values. An investor in a rented farm is not likely to capitalize all of the rent into value; some margin will be left for safety. This is particularly true in view of the notorious history of variation in land values. Supporting this thought that land income is not capitalized like government bonds are the numerous production function studies which indicate that farmers have seldom carried their investment in land to the point where the marginal productivity of a dollar is less than 10 cents. Handling land and capital items by using protected earning rates and treating labor as a residual may seriously overestimate the return to labor.

could expect in the first place, would work an appreciable hardship upon the individual. He can only recover his investment through a continuation of the existing situation. It is also likely that the lender has a strong interest in the maintenance of the value of the program rights. The value of these rights is also basic to the local government, as most local governmental services, such as schools, secondary roads and police protection, are financed in large part from taxes on the real property.[15]

Looking backward from this point, one may appropriately raise a question about the inflexibilities that land institutions may have introduced into the structure of agriculture. The record value of farm property rests upon a specific pattern of land use and a specific set of commodity prices. Many have invested upon the basis of this pattern of use and set of prices, and they will, quite naturally, resist any adjustment in either prices or use which would result in their inability ultimately to recover their investment. Shifts downward in land use can only be accomplished at the expense of the return to labor and capital; and as the quantity of capital would be adjusted to its new return, the brunt of the decrease in the return to land would have to be borne by agricultural labor.

CONSEQUENCES OF PUBLIC INTERVENTIONS – IN PROSPECT

Inadequate as our understanding of program consequences remains, the future is even more obscure. However, viewed through the ideas presented in this chapter, certain guidelines may help lift the veil of obscurity. If, for example, some assistance is to be rendered through price supports to each generation of farmers who must obtain land, commodity prices must rise more rapdily than benefits can be capitalized into land values. If this is not the situation, benefits from price-supporting activities will accrue to new farmers only as the land market may fail to function, as both reason and history indicate that it will. Such a technique of assistance is not economically feasible in either the short or long run, and certainly might not be politically feasible for any prolonged period of time.

The possibility of the long-run effects of further land withdrawals should be examined closely. No doubt gross agricultural

[15]Beyond the local community, of course, is the storage industry, whose basis stems in part from the inability of the programs to limit output to the amount that consumers will take at the predetermined price.

income could be further increased by such withdrawals or by transfers of some lands to lower uses. Ignoring the effects of this action upon the efficiency of resource use in the national scheme for the time being, such action will not likely be of much benefit to those who must buy or rent farms in the future.

The Virginia-North Carolina tobacco studies have indicated that after adjusting the 1954 and 1957 estimates of the value of an acreage of allotment, the increase in value was in direct proportion to the reduction in the average size of the allotment (Table 17.1). The rapidity with which the acreage cuts were reflected into land values is surprising. Not only will further withdrawals not have a lasting benefit for most of the people in agriculture, but the resulting increased value of the land that can be used will probably introduce further rigidities, increased risk and additional inefficiencies. It is difficult to see how any long-term improvement in the welfare of agriculture can be achieved through any program which requires access to its benefits through rights in land.[16] On the other hand, an adjustment toward a more economic use of the agricultural resources cannot be accomplished

Table 17.1. Estimation of Impact of Reduction in Tobacco Acreage Allotment Upon Value of Allotments

Factor	Counties	
	Pittsylvania, Virginia	Greene, Wilson, Pitt, N. C.
Estimated value of acre of allotment, 1954	$962	$2,327
General rise in land values, 1954-57	1.18	1.16
1954 estimate corrected to 1957 for land value change	$1,135	$2,699
Adjustment for allotment[a] reduction, 1954-57	1.49	1.49
Estimate based on price and acreage changes, 1954-57	$1,691	$4,021
Regression estimate, 1957	1,673	4,036
Difference	$ 18	$ - 15

[a] Acreage allotments were reduced by one-third during the period. The test is for a linear effect upon land values, i.e., a rise of three-halves.

A similar table appears in Maier, Hedrick and Gibson, *op. cit.*, p. 40.

[16]The reasoning leading to this conclusion is equally applicable to any device relying upon a negotiable right, franchise, license or marketing certificate.

without considerable hardship upon those who have invested in the rights to produce.

But the problem of resource adjustment is upon us. As Professor Boulding has pointed out, agriculture tends to be chronically depressed in a progressive society because the immobility of the labor resource prevents adjustment as rapidly as technology would require to maintain a constant income.[17] The distress in agriculture is accentuated by the effect of the retained labor force in depressing the reward of labor and increasing the reward of land.

In the long run, our land transfer processes may leave farm people facing the necessity of making payments on past prosperity from an ever diminishing income. The question now exists as to whether the income position of farm people should be protected by fostering further inefficiency of land use, or whether land income can be used to facilitate a long-run adjustment. Some possibilities of the latter type might be explored.

SOME RESERVATIONS ABOUT THE CONCEPT OF SURPLUS LAND

Few subjects, if any, have engaged more of the attention of those working in agricultural policy than the matter of surplus land. One hears many references to the surplus land that we now have, and a number of estimates have been prepared suggesting that there will be a great deal more surplus land in the future. The concept of surplus land has gained broad, if not almost universal, acceptance, and the central decisions that we are urged to face deal with the mechanics of getting this surplus land out of use: whether it is best to idle some land from each farm or to idle whole farm operations, and which of the available methods (lease, purchase or easement) are most suitable for this operation. There is a ring of urgency in the voices of those calling attention to these problems as they point out that new land substitutes are already en route and the problem of surplus land is already critical.

It would be helpful if the measure that is being employed to determine which quantity of land is usable and which quantity is "surplus" were restated. Once, no doubt, this measure was rather rigorously defined, but an occasional review along with a resurvey of the underlying assumptions would be helpful.

---

[17] Kenneth E. Boulding, Economic Analysis, Harper and Brothers, New York, 1941, pp. 778-79.

Is the measure wholly oriented around the income position of agriculture to exclusion of all other questions of national interest? Do these estimates assume that economic substitution is a one-way street — that capital and the resources which go into the development of technical innovations can be substituted for land, but that land cannot be substituted for these resources? Is the amount of nonsurplus land simply the maximum amount of land that can be used if a predetermined price, production and land value pattern is to be maintained?

If we were to escape the limits of our own economy or our own era; perhaps we could see the economic role of land in a light different from the one that has illuminated the subject from 1930 to 1960. And while we might, for a moment, escape to glimpse the economic problems of another economy or another generation, we are likely to remain prisoners of the thought that any economy has only four items with which to satisfy its wants: human energy, human ingenuity, some tools that have been accumulated at the expense of consumption and some "tools" provided by nature, i.e., the natural environment. Are we not likely to conclude that the fullest possible substitution of the tools provided by nature for the energy and the tools that can only be brought into being through a sacrifice in consumption is a necessary condition for the maximization of the economic welfare of the society? If we were to find two islands alike in every respect — populations, tastes, tools and the state of the arts — and each with a quantity and quality of land such that the cultivation of each acre would yield a product greater than the amount the labor and capital used would bring forth in other use, is it conceivable that one island can raise its per capita consumption above the other by refusing to use all of the land that it has available? Would we conclude, if 25 percent of the land can be offset by additional investments of labor and capital assigned to agriculture and agricultural development, that 25 percent of the land is surplus? If 50 percent can be offset by taking labor and capital from other employments, is 50 percent of the land surplus? Is any land to be considered surplus if its abandonment cannot be offset by the application of more labor and capital? If we look beyond our own shores, we will not find many places where a productive physical environment is considered a national handicap. It is difficult to understand how this phenomenon of natural wealth, responsible as it is for industrial growth of the United States by initially freeing labor from nonagrarian employment and by providing the balance of payments needed to repay European capital investments, has now become a burden.

If economists are motivated toward the maximization of real

income reflecting the preferences of the consuming group, in a world of diminishing returns with a labor supply that cannot exceed a finite number during any one production period, isn't there only one single definition of surplus land that is compatible with this objective? We define as surplus that land which, if used, would not (1) increase output, given the quantity of other factors employed, or (2) substitute for any other factor in maintaining a given level of output. Land of this type is clearly surplus and it also is clearly worthless.

It should be noted that these two conditions reduce to the same thing if there is continuity in the production function. Taking the first condition, if we can increase output by using more land with a specified set of labor and capital inputs, the original output could be achieved through the increased use of land and a reduction in the amount of labor and capital employed. The contribution of land in the productive process is the release of labor and capital to other employments, that is, the substitution of tools provided by nature for the tools and energy provided by man; and the value of land is whatever the tools and energy for which it substitutes would earn other employments.[18]

If this hypothesis is valid — if the value of land rests upon the productivity of those factors that it could replace — a considerable portion of the land now considered surplus would not be surplus under the definition above. The separation of the $129 billion value of farm land into its components of capital considered as real estate, social investments in roads and land and associated production franchises is difficult, but few would argue that the capacity of land to substitute for other factors is not a major element of this value. This value is evidence that "surplus land," as defined in this chapter, does not exist. In the same manner, the payment to farmers for land placed in the various surplus land reserves is evidence that this land is not surplus.

---

[18]Even those who say that "land is capital" and those who say "land is like any other factor of production," may grant some validity to this theory of land valuation. A farmer, balancing his intensive and extensive margins, will not offer for land more than the cost of the labor and capital necessary to achieve the same increase in output on his existing acreage.

This argument has recently been stated very succinctly by Hawtrey:

> "The producer who is calculating how much capital to employ with a given amount of labour and land will see the limit at the point at which the cost-saving efficacy of any additional plant ceases to cover the cost of the plant. That is why the price and the cost-saving efficacy of any factor tend to be equal. But the cost of land is zero, so that the landowner offers land of any cost-saving efficacy, however low, to producers for what it will fetch; only marginal and sub-marginal land are unused and fetch nothing."

Ralph Hawtrey, "Production function and land — a new approach," Econ. Jour., Vol. 70 (227), March, 1960, p. 114 ff.

Two effects of the policy of restricting land use are worthy of note. If a farmer cannot use land, he may use something else. If the nitrogen from the organic matter in soils in the Soil Bank is not available, he may find it profitable to get nitrogen from a sack. There are a number of commercial substitutions available to assist in achieving a certain output if land is not available. To the extent the purchased factors, the "nonfarm inputs," replace land that could be used, the net income of agriculture is correspondingly reduced by their value. Purchased inputs expanded by 40 percent in the 1940-59 period.[19] It is possible that some of these inputs could be offset by the substitution of the already available land, and the net income to agricultural people, as a group, increased thereby.

The second consequence of the restriction upon the use of land pertains to employment. To the extent that the labor is being used, either on the farm or in the manufacture and distribution of the nonfarm inputs, that could be replaced by land not being used, it is difficult to see that this labor is effectively employed. At first glance, at least, it would seem likely that the method of idling usable land would result in concealing the underemployment of the resources that are used to replace it.

SUGGESTED CRITERIA FOR REORIENTING RESEARCH AND INTERVENTIONS

Significant and rapid shifts in land use within agriculture and between agricultural and other uses are necessitated by (1) the relative price elasticities of demand for farm and nonfarm products and services and (2) the application of product-increasing technology to a unit of land in agriculture. Current farm programs tend to prevent these shifts directly by freezing certain uses in land through the capitalization of benefits into land values and through routing program benefits through land. Let us observe more closely the economic reasons for adjustment as a basis for appraising land resource institutions, including programs involving the land factor.

With an increase in gross national product and income to consumers, consumer outlays for products possessing income elasticities greater than 1.0 will enjoy an increasing absolute and relative share of the consumers' outlays. Since the income elasticity of demand for food products provided by farmers is estimated to be less than .25, food-producing farmers cannot expect

[19] USDA. ARS-AMS, Agricultural Outlook Charts, 1960, p. 58.

to share in increases in national income. Furthermore, for certain food products, i.e., potatoes and cereals, possessing negative demand elasticities, actual decreases in demand per capita for the physical products may be expected despite increases in national and per capita income. Land resource institutions which restrict the intra-agricultural shifts in land use seriously interfere with providing consumers with the products they seek as identified by relative demand elasticities. As a result, agriculture and the nation experience misallocations of resources, with attending consequences on costs, prices and production.

From the supply side, the development of new techniques and expanded use of capital has resulted in fewer acres being used to produce given quantities of many commodities. For example, corn yields for the nation have increased fairly steadily from 28 bushels per acre in 1940 to 46 bushels per acre in 1959. Major technological factors accounting for this increase are hybrid corn and fertilizer.[20] But the acreage shift away from corn has not been sufficient to offset the productivity per acre flowing from fertilizer and hybrid corn. As a result, public granaries and Soil Banks are being overflowed with corn and acres. This is even more true with wheat. And other major crops are in a similar situation.

There remain other uses of land where the income elasticities of demand are much higher than for food. Recreation, timber and grazing are notable examples of uses, with high capacities to absorb land but obtaining relatively low returns. Other uses, with more limited capacities to absorb land, but with high returns, are industrial, residential, highways and airports.

Thus, supply and demand conditions flowing from production technology and demand elasticities are continually changing and charting a course for needed changes in land use both within agriculture and between agriculture and other uses. However, land resource institutions, including the property-capitalization complex and farm programs, obstruct these shifts. Although labor and capital might be expected to be relatively mobile and move about in search of higher returns, land being immobile physically, and pressed into economic immobility by its institutions, is particularly stubborn in shifting to uses demanded by society.

Underpinning the suggested criteria for reorienting research and public interventions in agriculture are two basic assumptions stated earlier in this chapter. First, the maximum gross national product is desired from a particular level of resources

[20] L. N. Thompson, Iver Johnson, John Pesek, and R. W. Shaw, CAA Report No. 24. Iowa Agr. and Home Econ. Exp. Sta., 1959, p. 24.

devoted to production. Second, factors within agriculture and between agriculture and other industries should shift freely between uses on the basis of their relative economic rewards, i.e., rewards to factors in agriculture should approximate similar resources from various uses within agriculture and outside agriculture.

From ideas presented in this chapter we may generalize certain criteria for guiding future efforts to remedy the nation's agricultural problems. These criteria are as follows:

1. Land must be freely substitutable for labor and capital wherever such a substitution is economically feasible.

2. Productivity of past uses of land should not be a determinant of current and prospective uses.

3. Methods of guiding land use should not create franchises of value but, instead, should contribute to the improvement of the welfare of the agricultural population and to the public welfare to the measure that this welfare is concerned with the efficiency of resource use.

Application of these criteria and the reasoning leading to their development have been attempted in the program proposal presented in the next section. As developed here, the proposal is concerned with the creation of an institution to address the basic problem of income equality of labor in agriculture with labor outside of agriculture, subject to the condition that agriculture render its maximum economic service in the long run. The relationship of this institution to other institutions, such as law and the political process, is not explored. The relation of the proposed program to certain other historically held goals, such as the family farm, conservation, reduction of tenancy, and so on, is not treated. The first impression is that the proposal, or its variants, would contribute to the attainment of some of these goals while others, such as conservation, would have to be dealt with in separate approaches. For these and kindred reasons, the proposal in its present form is not being advocated by the authors, but it is hoped that consideration of its methods will help clarify the role of land and land institutions in agricultural adjustments.

A SUGGESTED APPROACH TO THE ACHIEVEMENT OF BETTER RESOURCE USE IN AGRICULTURE

The objectives sought by this approach are: (1) adjustment of the supplies of agricultural products, (2) development of incentives for a more efficient use of agricultural resources and

(3) the creation of a mechanism to facilitate the voluntary redistribution of the labor force in the national economy. This suggestion looks forward, optimistically perhaps, to the day when earnings of agricultural labor are commensurate with the earnings of comparable urban labor, with public intervention in agriculture at a minimum level. Basically, the approach seeks to divert the program-created income stream now flowing through land titles toward a long-run adjustment in the earning opportunities of farm people.

Observations and reasoning presented earlier in this chapter support the belief that no program can diffuse its benefits widely throughout the population if the instrument of control is of a permanent or semi-permanent nature and negotiable in the market. If such a diffusion is desirable, then control programs cannot rest upon acreage allotments, franchises, licenses or marketing certificates, or any other device of a transferable and permanent nature.

Therefore, it is proposed that production rights be made temporary for the production period and attach to the individual rather than to the land.

Further, it is proposed that the administrative agency determine each year the amount of each commodity that can be reasonably absorbed in domestic consumption and foreign trade. The price corresponding to this amount would be announced.

The agency would then let certificates, valid only for the forthcoming production period on the basis of competitive bid, the amount being paid for the certificates being deposited with the agency.

The purchaser of a certificate would be free to employ any combination of land, labor and capital he chooses in producing the amount of the commodity for which he holds certificates of entitlement. It would, of course, be to his advantage to use the least-cost combination, fully utilizing land as a substitute for labor and capital in order to make his production as efficient as possible.

The proceeds from the sale of the certificates would approximately equal the amount now being paid annually, through amortized land purchase and rentals, to obtain these production rights. It is proposed that these funds be used to facilitate an adjustment in the earning opportunities of farm people by (1) grants and loans to cover moving expenses of farm people to nonfarm employment; (2) unemployment compensation, as needed, for those who move for the first two years or so after leaving farming; (3) development of an extensive system of vocational training in rural high schools to prepare youth for nonagricultural occupations; (4) establishing a program of college scholarships for the more talented young people; and (5) where economically feasible, assisting in the establishment of industries and other nonfarm businesses in rural areas.

The use of the funds for this purpose would continue until the number of people who had transferred was sufficient to make the earnings of farm people comparable to those of their urban counterparts. At this point the program would be abandoned.

There appear to be several advantages to an approach of this type. First, the full use of land in the production of food and fiber at minimum cost is encouraged. Second, the average and marginal productivity of labor in agriculture would be increased. Third, the uncertainty and economic vulnerability facing farmers would be reduced, as the production permit cost would be on a year-to-year basis.[21] Fourth, the approach would contribute to a greater total national product by assisting underemployed people now in agriculture to transfer to more remunerative employment and by developing technical skills in farm youth that might not otherwise be developed.

There are, of course, difficulties as well as advantages with this program. Once initiated, this program should not be more difficult to administer than most of the current or proposed programs. The principal difficulty appears to involve the initiation of the program and its effect upon land values. This program, like most proposed modifications of the income-supporting programs in agriculture, would tend to reduce land values through increasing the supply of land available for use and reducing the amount of labor applied. And while these changes can be expected to have beneficial effects in the national interest, at least to the extent that the national interest is served or disserved by changes in the national product, the question will invariably be raised concerning the interests of those who have invested in farm land with the expectations that the present price and production situation would continue to prevail.

Consideration of the basis of the public obligation to maintain a static situation to prevent disappointment of the land buyers, or to compensate them for any change that might be made, is beyond

[21]Objection to this point has been raised. It has been suggested that the year-to-year letting of permits will not provide the certainty of expectations necessary to carry on agricultural operations. In response, it may be pointed out that buying a temporary certificate is not greatly different than renting a farm in order to produce, and that in 1950, the latest year for which production-by-tenure data are available, 54.5 percent of the farm products sold came from farms that were rented wholly or in part. Numerous studies have indicated that the one-year lease is the modal type. The uncertainty facing these producers under the temporary certificate program would not be greater than the uncertainty they face in the farm rental market.

the subject of this chapter. If, however, it is deemed desirable to minimize these disappointments in the course of the initiation of this proposal, this could be accomplished by easing into the program gradually. For example, the first issue of certificates could be made to farmers on the basis of their historical production and would be valid as long as they were being used by the individual. These certificates could not be transferred to any other individual or transmitted through inheritance. Upon the death or retirement of the farmer or a prolonged failure to use the certificate, the production rights involved would revert to the issuing agency. Present farmers would thus receive a return on their labor and capital plus the program benefits now being assigned to land. Owner operators would receive approximately the same amount that they could have expected to receive in their lifetime.

As farmers retire or take up other occupations, the administrative agency could let the reverted certificates, withholding such parts of them as necessary to maintain the desired commodity supply situation, on a bid basis. This issue would be temporary and nontransferable to prevent capitalization. The purchasers could be expected to pay whatever they are now paying for production rights by acquiring these rights through the purchase or renting of land, and they should be left no worse off than they would be through the continuation of the existing situation. In time, of course, all certificates would revert, leaving the agency with the control and the funds needed to effect a long-term adjustment. This is, admittedly, a leisurely approach to the solution, and several alternatives are available to hasten the process. For example, the lifetime certificates could be issued for 75 percent of the production and the balance let upon a bid basis in order to have funds to start the adjustment immediately.

This suggestion is obviously incomplete in many ways and is not offered as a solution to all of the problems confronting agriculture. It is believed, however, that such a program overcomes two deficiencies evident in current programs and in recent proposals: (1) the dissipation of the benefits through capitalization into the instrument of control and (2) the inefficient substitution of human energy and saving for land. Further, the possibility exists that ultimately the approach could lead to at least a temporary solution of the farm problem. On the basis of this hope, however faint it may be, the suggestion is offered to the profession for consideration and discussion.

FUNDAMENTAL RESEARCH NEEDED TO GUIDE LAND USE AND INSTITUTIONS

Information required to facilitate adjustments in land use and land institutions has not been developed as needed in recent years. In order that this deficiency may be overcome so that land can play its maximum economic role, a threefold approach is suggested.

First, research needs to be expanded and reoriented where necessary, to provide data on relative value product returns to factors in the various agricultural and nonagricultural uses. This analysis should be closely related to consumer wants and preferences as indicated by the price elasticities of various products. Basic to this research is the provision of physical and technological coefficients under existing practices and under new practices evolved and evolving from physical research. This involves a comprehensive productivity inventory of soil resources related to possible uses to which particular soils may be put under various levels of technology. Extensions of the envisioned research include development of institutions which will achieve the above criteria within the range of physical possibilities. Further studies are needed on the performance of current farm programs in terms of the initial and ultimate incidences of benefits and costs. Studies reported on tobacco allotments should be extended to other major crops under control. These studies should reveal the land uses in major physical areas (soils areas) created or maintained by public measures in comparison with optimal land uses for providing consumers with the products wanted at lowest average unit costs.

The planning and execution of this research demands the full cooperation of research in numerous disciplines. Economics, soils, engineering and law are heavily involved in satisfying these demands. Isolated results of this type of interdisciplinary research are already in evidence. However, the full realization of possibilities of interdisciplinary studies remains in the future.

Second, results of research in relation to principles underlying studies and interpretations thereof must be made more understandable and more readily available to the general public, legislators and administrators of agricultural programs. Possibly the research man's responsibility does not end with the completion of a technical bulletin or formal article which oftentimes represents little more than communication among researchers. In cooperation with extension workers, researchers might further the objective of understanding research results through special seminars with legislators, administrators of farm programs and farm leaders both inside and outside farm organizations. These special educational measures should be supplemented with extensive educational programs for farm and nonfarm groups alike. Nonfarm people, in particular, should be provided with an improved understanding of agricultural problems and possible solutions. This suggestion becomes increasingly important as the proportion of nonfarm to farm people increases throughout the nation.

Third, based upon research and a wider understanding and appreciation of results of research, institutions (modified to become politically acceptable, which is ultimately necessary in our society) may be forged which will meet the criteria presented earlier. However, political acceptability may likewise become modified through an improved public understanding of economic consequences of various alternative courses of action.

Throughout this discussion, land institutions are considered as means for achieving people's objectives. The objectives in this chapter have been limited to economic objectives. To the extent economic objectives are appropriate, these objectives provide criteria for testing and developing institutions for bringing about agricultural change. These institutions were made by man and may be altered by man to serve his objectives more adequately. Some of the inadequacies of current land institutions have been indicated and possible reorientations have been suggested. These indications and reorientations are offered for further consideration in research, educational and action programs concerned with improving the nation's agriculture in the national interest.

Chapter 18

DONALD E. BOLES
ROSS B. TALBOT
Iowa State University

Governmental Framework for Achieving National Land Use Adjustments

AS A TRUE CONSTITUTIONAL system, the United States operates within the framework of a limited government. Thus, there are restrictions of a higher law placed on the policies and laws that emanate from the lawmakers and policy formulators at any given moment.

CONSTITUTIONAL AND LEGAL CONSIDERATIONS

The Supreme Court is, of course, the final arbiter of whether a policy decision is authorized by the United States Constitution. From a realistic standpoint, therefore, Congress must always evaluate whether a given legislative measure, such as national programs of cropland withdrawal, will withstand the test of Supreme Court scrutiny.

A second major factor to be considered in this connection is the federal system established by the Constitution in which there exists a national government and a series of state governments which both receive their power from the Constitution. Under our system the national government exercises delegated powers and implied powers, while the states retain the reserved powers — those not placed in the hands of the national government or specifically denied to the states.

Despite this seemingly formal and clear division of authority, no federal system is precise or tidy. There inevitably exists a host of areas in the penumbra or peripheral zone where there is no clear-cut rule to determine beforehand whether the states or the national government are legally competent to function. As a result, almost all of the major constitutional debates in American political history have revolved around the nature of our federal system. Constitutional issues arising from the nature of the American system of federalism have played a significant role as a stumbling block to national agricultural programs in the past as in United States v. Butler.[1] This was especially true during the early days of the New Deal when the Supreme Court indulged in the constitutional heresy of dual federalism which rejected many programs of cooperation between the federal government and the states.

The Supreme Court adopted a more tolerant view toward broad national agricultural programs with the change in viewpoint of Justice Roberts in 1937, often called the "switch in time that saved nine" referring to Franklin Roosevelt's court-packing plan. The case of Wickard v. Filburn reveals the willingness of the Court to accept an extension of the commerce clause of the Constitution as a peg on which to hang one type of agricultural program.[2]

If Congress should decide to adopt a national program of large-scale cropland withdrawal, it is clear that the commerce clause is one constitutional provision under which it has proceeded and may continue to proceed.[3] There are, of course, a number of other constitutional principles that may be utilized with, at least, the degree of effectiveness of the commerce clause.

One is the national power of eminent domain. Since this is an incident of sovereignty, the right of eminent domain requires no constitutional recognition.[4] Moreover, the Court has made it clear that the requirement of just compensation in the exercise of the right of eminent domain is merely a limitation upon the preexisting power[5] to which all private property is subject.[6] This national power can neither be enlarged nor diminished by a state.[7] No legal barrier to the national power of eminent domain exists even though state-owned lands taken through proper procedures impair the tax revenue of the state, or interfere with the states' own projects of water development and conservation.[8]

---

[1] 297 U.S. 1 (1936).

[2] 317 U.S. 111 (1942).

[3] Examples of congressional enactments concerned with cropland withdrawal tied to the commerce clause are the Soil Conservation and Domestic Allotment Act, 49 Stat. 1148 (1936) and the Agriculture Act of 1956 (Soil Bank Act) 70 Stat. 188.

[4] For examples of recent articles discussing various facets of eminent domain in relationship to agricultural programs see: P. G. Kauper, "Basic principles of eminent domain," 35 Mich. S. Bar J. 10 (Oct., 1956); "Limitations of the Federal Government to acquire land within a state," 9 S. Car. L. Q. 474; F. Fishman, "Some status factors affecting the availability of public lands for general locations," 34 Dicta 243; J. D. McGowen, "Development of political institutions on the public domain," 11 Wyo. L. Rev. 1 (1956); "What constitutes a public use," 23 Albany L. Rev. 386 (1959).

[5] U.S. v. Jones, 109 U.S. 513 (1883); U.S. v. Cormack, 329 U.S. 230 (1946).

[6] U.S. v. Lynah, 188 U.S. 445 (1903).

[7] Kohl v. U. S., 91 U.S. 367 (1876).

[8] Oklahoma v. Atkinson Co., 313 U.S. 508 (1941).

Still another series of powers at the disposal of the national government for use in developing broad and systematic programs of withdrawing agricultural croplands from production are the taxing and spending powers. A variety of Supreme Court decisions in other areas suggest that a prohibitive tax placed on types of marginal and submarginal lands that national policy sought to take out of production, or which the federal government sought to obtain, would probably receive the Supreme Court's approval. The Court has typically refused to look beyond the face of tax statutes and inquire into the motives of the lawmakers despite such a law's prohibitive proportions.[9] In a recent decision the Court explained:

It is beyond serious question that a tax does not cease to be valid merely because it regulates, discourages or even definitely deters the activities taxed.... The principle applies even though the revenue obtained is obviously negligible...or the revenue purpose of the tax may be secondary.... Nor does a tax statute necessarily fall because it touches on activities which Congress might not otherwise regulate.[10]

Historically, there had been sharp differences of opinion between those who subscribed to Thomas Jefferson's restricted notion of the spending power[11] and the broader and more literal approach favored by Alexander Hamilton.[12]

The Supreme Court was slow to formally accept either of the two competing doctrines, although in 1896 it invoked, "the great power of taxation to be exercised for the common defense and the general welfare" to sustain the right of the federal government to acquire land within a state for use as a national park.[13] In U. S. v. Butler, the Court gave its unqualified support to the Hamiltonian doctrine which maintained that the spending clause conferred a power separate and distinct from any of the enumerated legislative powers and that Congress had the substantive power to tax and to appropriate limited only to the stipulation that its exercise should provide for the general welfare.[14]

In the Butler case, however, the Court, while granting a wide sweep to the spending power, found that this power was limited by

---

[9] McCray v. U.S., 195 U.S. 27 (1941).

[10] U.S. v. Sanchez, 340 U.S. 42 (1950). See also: Megnano Co. v. Hamilton, 229 U.S. 40 (1934) and Sonzinsky v. U.S. 300 U.S. 506 (1937).

[11] For a detailed exposition of Jefferson's views on the subject see: III Writings of Thomas Jefferson, pp. 147-49 (Library Edition, 1904). Jefferson explained his point of view in the following fashion: "They (Congress) are not to lay taxes ad libitum for any purpose they please; but only to pay the debts or provide for the welfare of the Union. In like manner, they are not to do anything they please to provide for the general welfare, but only lay taxes for that purpose."

[12] Hamilton's views may be found in The Federalist, No's. 30 and 34.

[13] See: U.S. v. Gettysburg Electric Railroad Co., 160 U.S. 668 (1896).

[14] 297 U.S. 1 (1936).

the tenth amendment and on that ground the Court ruled that Congress could not use moneys raised by taxation to "purchase compliance" with regulations "of matters of State concern with respect to which Congress has no authority to interfere." Shortly over a year later this decision was reduced to narrow proportions when the Court sustained a tax imposed on employers to provide employment benefits, and the credit allowed for similar taxes paid to a state. The Court held flatly that the relief of unemployment was a legitimate object of federal expenditure under the "general welfare clause."[15] It seems clear that this concept of cooperative federalism would be controlling in any national programs of large scale cropland withdrawal.

The taxing and general welfare clauses have an additional advantage to recommend themselves as a constitutional peg on which to hang federal land withdrawal programs, whether they involve outright purchase of the land by the federal government or programs of indirect regulation and control. The Court has made it clear that neither a state nor an individual is entitled to remedy in court against a questionable or even unconstitutional appropriation of national funds.[16] Some might argue, therefore, that if these clauses of the Constitution are used as a basis, any land-use law passed by Congress would be beyond challenge so long as it fulfilled due process requirements and assured the equal protection of the laws to persons affected.

Another technique which might be used as a method by the national government or even the states in cropland withdrawal programs is the use of zoning regulations. The legal theory behind zoning is that states through the exercise of their police powers may declare that in certain cases and localities specific businesses which are not nuisances per se are deemed nuisances in fact and in law.[17] The Supreme Court has ruled that before a use-zoning ordinance can be held unconstitutional, it must be shown to be clearly unreasonable, arbitrary and to have no substantial relation to the public health, safety or general welfare.[18] While the Supreme Court for years had refused to accept zoning for aesthetic reasons only, this view was completely altered in Berman v. Parker (1954) when Justice Douglas for a unanimous

---

[15]Steward Machine Co. v. Davis, 301 U.S. 548 (1947).

[16]See: Massachusetts v. Mellon and Frothingham v. Mellon 262 U.S. 447 (1923); and Alabama Power Co. v. Ickes, 302 U.S. 464 (1938). A more recent case which suggests an implied obligation of the U.S. Supreme Court to review the validity of taxpayers' suits brought in state courts where a federal question is involved is contained in Doremus v. Board of Education, 5 N. J. 435, 75 A. 2d 880, 342 U.S. 429 (1952).

[17]Reinman v. Little Rock, 237 U.S. 171 (1915).

[18]For example, see: Euclid v. Ambler Realty Co., 272 U.S. 365 (1926); Zahn v. Board of Public Works, 274 U.S. 325 (1927); Cusack Co. v. Chicago, 242 U.S. 526 (1917).

court accepted aesthetics as a proper public purpose in its own right.[19]

Recent programs of rural zoning have also met the test of constitutionality and appear to be functioning successfully in states such as Wisconsin.[20] It would seem that the broad-scale planning concepts implicit in the zoning concept might also be utilized on a national scale concerning agricultural croplands with additional advantages not necessarily to be found in the use of the constitutional techniques discussed earlier.[21] For example, the Soil Bank program might be regarded as one form of zoning.

From the foregoing it should be clear that no major legal or constitutional obstacles at present exist to prevent programs aimed at removing excess agricultural cropland from production. The major impediments are, of course, political and socio-economic in origin. At this point it is necessary to try to identify and analyze some of the major administrative and financial problems for purposes of arriving at a feasible and realistically functional program.

Financial and Administrative Considerations

It is patently obvious that any governmental program that contemplates the withdrawal of between 45 to 80 million acres of surplus croplands will be financially costly. This will be true whether a plan for outright purchase of the lands is adopted or if financial aids are offered to the private owners to continue ownership of the land but keep it out of food crop production. While such programs conceivably could be sponsored by either the local, state or national governments, the enormity of the financial outlays involved is such that only the national government seems equipped to undertake the major burden of responsibility. This is not to suggest that states cannot develop complementary programs of this type on a smaller scale. Approaches such as Wisconsin's Forest-Crop Act, which exempts from state property taxed lands placed in extensive and controlled reforestation programs with the state and the private owner sharing the profits from the ultimate sale of marketable timber, can do much to

[19] 348 U.S. 26 (1954).

[20] See for example: G. G. Waite, "Land use controls and recreation in northern Wisconsin," 42 Marq. L. Rev. 271 (1959).

[21] For an excellent discussion of the legal and practical advantages and problems involved in the use of zoning regulations as planning aids see: "Planning in a democracy," A Symposium, 20 Law and Contemporary Problems 197 (Spring, 1955).

reduce the number of acres devoted to food crop production. Moreover, state rural zoning laws might be directed toward preventing additional croplands from being activated.

Two practical factors militate against any plans to use local governments, such as the county, as the chief sponsoring agencies of broad and systematic programs of land use control. First is the fact that population is diminishing noticeably in most of the strictly rural counties, with the result that the general tax base becomes sharply limited. Second is the fact that there is at least the normal increase of interest in these areas in seeing governmental services expanded in fields such as health, welfare, relief and highways. As a result, in those counties where there is the greatest justification for surplus cropland withdrawal the local governments already have reached the breaking point insofar as their financial abilities are concerned. It is impractical to think, given the present tax arrangement, that they could take on any new programs of the magnitude implied in proposals for cropland withdrawal.

With property taxes the significant burden on rural farm properties, a means of retiring croplands might be suggested by those who are not particularly burdened with humanitarian considerations. This would be to either remove or add no additional tax assistance devices such as agricultural land tax credits. Thus rural land taxes would move inexorably upward to a point where it is conceivable that significant amounts of marginal land might revert to the state because of tax delinquency. Something similar to this occurred in northern Michigan, Wisconsin and Minnesota during the 1930's. In this event the state governments might then adopt a formal policy of refusing to re-sell such lands to private persons or to sell only with the stipulation that these lands could not be used for food-crop production.

Such an approach has two major shortcomings at least. In the first place, it would work a severe hardship upon rural property owners during the transition period when some owners were in the process of being forced off the land. Secondly, it could clearly accelerate the out-migration from rural counties, with the subsequent reduction in tax revenues and diminution of retail and wholesale trade. Thus objections would be forthcoming not only from the farmers but from merchants and private businessmen generally.

From the standpoint of adopting an efficient administration for handling a major program of cropland withdrawal from production, the state and local governments are hardly in a position to take the initiative. In most instances their administrative structure for dealing with strictly local issues is so cumbersome, outdated and consequently ineffectual that it is difficult to perceive how an entirely new program could be handled effectively. On both the state and county levels the absence of executive power, or the sharp limitations placed on the executive, are such that a minimum of centralized direction or responsibility can be shown for programs traditionally falling within the state's jurisdiction. This problem tends to be compounded when new programs are introduced.

Alternative Federal Programs

Thus it would seem that the federal government of necessity must take the lead in developing the administrative structure under which land withdrawal programs must operate. This is not meant to imply that the state and local governments need be ignored. Indeed there may be some merit in decentralizing the day-to-day administration of such programs into the hands of the states or county groups such as agricultural stabilization and conservation committees. The local operation should, however, be confined within boundaries carefully stipulated by the federal government similar to requirements for uniform accounting systems, and definite local agency responsibility in handling the programs such as are prescribed in most grant-in-aid plans at present.

If one accepts the premise that the most effective way to obtain an administratively acceptable and financially feasible plan of large-scale cropland withdrawal is through the actions of the national government, a variety of program actions are possible.[22] A most sweeping proposal would call for outright purchase by the federal government of excess croplands. This land could then be held as part of the public domain with broad scale planning concepts applied whereby it might be utilized as national parks or recreational and conservation districts.

Opposition to such a program would probably come from associations of local governmental officials who would object to the removal of extensive areas from the tax rolls, thus lowering even further the tax base and certainly diminishing drastically the need for local governmental officials — especially if entire counties were acquired by the federal government. Merchants and businessmen of the cities and towns in the region could be counted

---

[22]Several aspects and problems involved are discussed in: "Federal regulation of agriculture: conflict between economic reality and social goals," 5 J. Public Law 248, 1956; D. Gale Johnson, "Government and agriculture: is agriculture a special case," 1 Jour. Law and Econ. 122, 1958.

upon to object to what seems, at first blush, a significant diminution in their sales potential. This objection might be partially answered by likely offsetting increases in trade that might occur from an enlarged tourist or vacationer influx into the area as a result of increased recreational facilities.

It is important in evaluating the advantages of a program of this type to include a host of intangible factors which do not submit to the balance sheet approach intrinsic in the traditional benefit-cost analyses. Although research efforts are being made in this direction, a host of intangible elements defy ready reduction into monetary equivalents. Among factors of this sort are: scenic and recreational values, including the aesthetic asset of additional wildlife; the saving of human life and property through broad planning ventures of flood control; the general strengthening of national security through a better balanced economy, and through greater recreational opportunities for the increasing leisure time of the population. Unfortunately most governmental agencies up to this time have been unwilling to recommend policies or programs based upon such forms of economic evaluation of extra-market values.

There are, of course, a variety of possible cropland withdrawal programs that are less broad in scope or which might operate within the framework of agricultural programs presently in existence. For example, a federal price-income support program including a provision for compulsory land retirement might be one approach. Under such an arrangement land removed from food-crop production could receive support payments based on 100 percent of parity. If this approach was followed, the present administrative hierarchy could be utilized. It would also have the advantage of keeping private lands within the tax-rolls, thus providing the necessary revenues for local and state governmental operation. This plan, however, appears to lack the broad planning potential and workable safeguards that would need to be devised to insure that sufficient land was taken from food-crop production to provide a meaningful solution of the overproduction problem.

Another possible approach would be to adopt a land retirement program based upon a national or regional compulsory conservation farm plan similar to the optional programs provided by the Soil Conservation Service. Within this approach, an index of land classifications could be devised similar to those presently used by the Soil Conservation Service. This index could then serve as a basis for removing specific segments of land on a farm or in a region from production on a compulsory basis with direct or indirect compensation granted for the losses in income suffered from the retiring of such land. Indirect governmental assistance to compensate private owners for the losses suffered in the removal of land could come in the form of tax assistance or tax relief devices from either the national, state or local governments. Because of the difficulty local governments are encountering in obtaining necessary operating revenues, it is unrealistic to assume that they would or could take primary responsibility in initiating such programs. It would be possible, however, for a national program of payments in lieu of taxes to be established to assist the state or local governments in offsetting the loss in tax revenues resulting from this type of land withdrawal program.

THE POLITICS OF NATIONAL LAND USE ADJUSTMENT

It is assumed that a crux of the American farm problem is one of immediate and persistent overproduction of food products, particularly grains. To alleviate this condition we have been examining the possibility that our national policy should be one of increasing the withdrawal of grain-producing farm lands. A decrease in the amount of land under production would, to an undetermined extent, also bring about a reduction in the number of farmers and, perhaps, in capital investment within the farming enterprise.

To bring about a policy of this type, and to view its consummation in political terms, it is necessary to consider the issue of political feasibility within a constitutional-democratic political system.

The issue then becomes: How can the idea of land use adjustment be translated into terms of political reality? What kind of fusions of political ideas, interests and institutions will have to be brought about, within the context of the United States Constitution, if this proposal is to become national legislation? The high costs of existing farm programs, the crucial importance of food costs to the urban consumer and the uses of food and fiber as a tool in American foreign policy have imposed upon the proposal of additional land use adjustment a political dimension which makes it an issue of national and international significance. Consequently, the farm problem needs to be acted on within the general context of national politics and should not be posed and resolved solely by the farmer and the farm organizations operating within the framework of "Committee Government" in Congress.

The federal Constitution was constructed in such a manner

that the centralization of power in political institutions has been extremely difficult to bring about. The diffusion of power has weakened our political parties but has strengthened the growth and power of pressure, or interest, groups in the United States. All democratic nation-states today, apparently, are pluralistic to the extent that many interest groups are prevalent in their political system.[23] There is really no democratic alternative.

Interest groups are to free government as air is to fire, to use James Madison's analogy. Without the one, the other would perish. Nevertheless, this pluralism has meant that policy is made through the interactions of interest groups, public and private. In the case of agriculture, this means the office of president, the farm organizations, certain types of business groups, key committees and individuals in Congress, the United States Departments of Agriculture and Interior and the Farm Credit Administration. What the secretary of agriculture wants in the way of farm policy he will get, assuming that the president will back him with the veto weapon, or, he — the secretary — will at least be able to deny other interest groups the kind of legislation which they desire.

The foregoing outline of the process of policy formation is an oversimplification, but it is useful for the purpose of presenting the Soil Bank Act, more accurately referred to as Title I of the Agricultural Act of 1956.[24] The Democratically-controlled 84th Congress had passed H.R. 12 which, among many other features, provided for 90 percent of parity supports for the basic commodities. On final passage the House voted favorably 237 to 181.[25] The Senate passed the measure without a roll-call vote. However, the House failed to override the presidential veto by even a majority, much less the required two-thirds.[26]

The president — or, more pertinently, the secretary of agriculture — wanted to attack the problem of overproduction and low farm income through the devices of lower support prices and the Soil Bank. The Democratic majorities in Congress were amenable to the Soil Bank provisions (which were a part of H.R. 12) but had included high price support provisions too. This was the primary reason for the veto.

---

[23] H. W. Ehrmann (ed.), Proceedings and Papers, International Polit. Sci. Assoc., Pittsburgh, 1957.

[24] The Soil Conservation and Domestic Allotment Act of 1939 was designed to reduce in quantity the "soil-depleting" crops, but its legislative history will not be developed in this chapter. In actual operation, the ACP program has probably increased production and improved conservation practices at the same time.

[25] For - Dem. 189, Rep. 48; Against - Dem. 35, Rep. 146.

[26] The vote was 202 to 211. (For - Dem. 182, Rep. 20; Against - Dem. 38, Rep. 173.)

The substitute bill[27] then passed both Houses by substantial margins but not without some procrastination. One of the apparent and basic facts about our congressional process is that national elections are always impending. In this instance the legislation was enacted during a presidential election year but late enough so that the economic impact would not be significant until 1957. The political and the economic factors became intertwined — a not unusual situation. Who was to get credit for the Soil Bank payments? Would a "gentle rain of checks" redound to the benefit of the Republicans or the Democrats? Acreage reserve payments were authorized (although never fully appropriated) for up to $750 million a year from 1956 through 1959; in addition, conservation reserve payments up to $450,000,000 a year were authorized, with contracts running from 3 to 15 years.

The prime difficulty with the operation of the Soil Bank program, in terms of congressional politics, is that it has had a low degree of acceptance with those members of Congress who are powerful in the area of farm policy. There has been some support on the Republican side of the House and Senate Agriculture Committees, but even here the backing has been qualified and rather restrained. The Democratic members, particularly those from the South, have been outwardly and aggressively critical. The chairman of the powerful Sub-committee on Agriculture of the House Committee on Appropriations — Jamie Whitten (Dem., Miss.) — has been outspoken in his opposition and criticism. However, his counterpart in the Senate — Richard Russell (Dem., Ga.) — has, on occasion, displayed some agreement with the Soil Bank type of program, even of an extended type.[28]

What has brought about the opposition in Congress? In general, the answer would appear to be that the Soil Bank program has brought in its administrative wake certain social and economic changes which have disturbed the economic and social status quo. These changes, in turn, have forecast some revisions in the political power structure.

Senator Sparkman (Dem., Ala.) stated the anti-Soil Bank case quite pointedly: " . . . the small businesses which have been serving the farmers, namely, the ginners, the fertilizer dealers, the implement dealers, and other small businesses of that kind, have

[27] H.R. 10,875, 84th Cong., 2nd Sess., 1956.

[28] Senator Russell: "I saw the other day where a man introduced a bill to buy $25 billion worth of land. That may be the answer to it [farm problem], something of that kind. Let the Government buy it up and retire it permanently and have some program where they can sell it back to the farmers as the needs of our civilization require additional lands to be opened up." U.S. Congress, Senate, Hearings Before the Subcommittee of the Committee on Appropriations, 85th Cong., 2nd Sess., Washington Government Printing Office, 1959, p. 597.

been severely effected."[29] Congressman Hemphill (Dem., S. Car.) claimed that "our relief rolls are filled with farmers literally put out of business by the Soil Bank. This is particularly true of the colored population of the Southeast who know no other trade."[30]

Senator Milton Young (Rep., N. Dak.) commented: "I would have to vote against additional funds for a program that would take a whole farm out of production" and, further that "both farm organizations in my State [North Dakota Farmers Union and North Dakota Farm Bureau] passed resolutions opposing it [conservation reserve program]."[31] Senator Dworshak (Rep., Idaho) also noted that in his state there was " . . . widespread criticism of the soil bank program."[32]

Assistant Secretary of Agriculture Marvin McLain concurred that "down in the South" the major complaints of the Soil Bank program came from "the cotton ginners, fertilizer sellers and the people that were in the business of handling the commodity."[33]

Whitten remarked that "a fellow from Alabama told me that he put his farm in the soil bank, and put his money in the First National Bank, and he is going down to the fishing bank."[34] In a much more serious vein, USDA testimony made the following calculation: "It is estimated that farm operators [in 1957] will pay out about $360 million less in production expenses, as a direct result of their participation in the acreage reserve program" and that "marketing charges on the quantities of wheat, corn, cotton, rice and tobacco not produced as a result of the acreage reserve program are estimated at about $180.5 million. About $55 million of this amount would have been marketing charges in local markets."[35]

On the administrative side, the Soil Bank program has produced further repercussions. Perhaps members of Congress are, at least on occasion, more eloquent than accurate, but in early 1958 Senator Talmadge (Dem., Ga.) let forth the following denunciation: "Mr. President, what little faith the farmers might have had in the Department of Agriculture has been destroyed by the arrogant deceit and stupid bungling which have marked the signup for participation in the cotton acreage reserve program of the soil bank for 1958."[36]

---

[29] U.S. Congress, Congressional Record, 85th Cong., 2nd Sess., Government Printing Office, Washington, D. C., 1958, p. 3953.

[30] Ibid., p. 7083.

[31] U.S. Senate, Agricultural Appropriations for 1960, pp. 586-87.

[32] Ibid., pp. 588-89.

[33] U.S. House of Rep., Dept. of Agriculture Appropriations For 1959, Part 3, p. 2154.

[34] Ibid., (1958), Part 4, p. 1573.

[35] Ibid., p. 2111.

[36] Congressional Record, 85th Cong., 2nd Sess., 1958, p. 2205.

Congressman Dorn (Dem., S. Car.) was even more derogatory: "Mr. Speaker, ... it is inhumane and unthinkable that elderly people and those afflicted with physical infirmities are required to stand in line all night in the cold and rain to have their applications considered. Mind you, Mr. Speaker, these applications are scheduled in the dead of winter."[37] These statements hardly indicate fulsome praise for the administration of the Soil Bank program, although they do seem to point to a certain hardy steadfastness and desire to participate in it.

More significantly, the acreage reserve program received much unfavorable national publicity because of the amounts of the payments. Senator Williams (Rep., Del.) stated that, in 1957, there were 2,422 individuals who received in excess of $10,000 in payments; that 1,260,000 farmers received almost $614 million (an average of $487 per person) for removing 22 million acres from production.[38] Nationwide publicity was given Senator Proxmire's (Dem., Wis.) charge that three individuals, or corporations, received $322,012, $278,187 and $209,701, respectively, in acreage reserve payments in 1957.[39] Whether this was a wise use of public funds was, of course, widely debated.

Adding to the adverse publicity was Senator Ellender's (Dem., La.) claim, on the Senate floor, that "when the 1956 [corn] crop was gathered, we found ourselves paying almost $180 million, but 220 million more bushels of corn had been produced than in the previous year."[40] These views and figures were, it would seem, widely disseminated; whether or not they were accurate is not the point at issue.[41]

Congressional criticism of the conservation reserve program has been directed largely against taking whole farms out of production. This procedure may reduce production but it also reduces a political commodity — farmers. Congressman Anderson (Rep., Minn.) has been favorably disposed to the Soil Bank program, but even he has expressed his dislike of the "whole farm" approach and wants no more than 50 percent of a farm to be

[37] Ibid., p. 2084.

[38] Ibid., pp. 9273-74.

[39] Ibid., p. 3742. Senator Neuberger (Dem., Ore.) also made a similar criticism — 67 farmers received more than $50,000 each in acreage reserve payments in 1957. 47 of the 67 were from California, Oregon and Texas (Ibid., p. 6781).

[40] Ibid., p. 3743.

[41] The USDA's estimates of the amounts of decreased production brought about by the conservation reserve program are contained in a departmental Press Release, Jan. 29, 1960. Corn production, for example, was some 183 million bushels less in 1959 than it would have been without the conservation reserve, according to USDA calculations.

eligible for the conservation reserve.[42] USDA officials have fought against such restrictions by claiming that, in some instances, the farmer needs " ... to relocate or establish himself in some other more satisfying endeavor," and that a "part farm" approach would bring in the poor land and the farmer would then, in all probability, increase the production on the remainder.[43] These criticisms have, however, pushed the USDA into a compromise situation since under the 1960 conservation reserve program no more than 25 percent of the farm land in a county can be placed in the reserve.

Criticisms of administrative regulations have also occurred in regards to the maximum payment an individual might receive under the conservation reserve program. The early restriction of $3,000 "to any one producer" was interpreted by the secretary of agriculture — upon advice of the department's General Counsel and the General Accounting Office — to mean per farm, not per farmer. Such an interpretation, which ostensibly assisted tenant farmers to receive some of the Soil Bank funds, was widely criticized. The present restriction of $5,000 per farmer for conservation reserve payments has also been attacked because certain ingenious individuals have discovered a few possible loopholes in the law, at least such was indicated by the evidence of the General Accounting Office in 1959.[44]

The ideological issue has also slipped into the debate at this point. Senator Proxmire (Dem., Wis.) remarked: "Since the amount of money available [for soil bank payments] always is limited, the farmer who has a small family-size farm should have the first 'crack' at it."[45]

The national farm organizations — notably, the American Farm Bureau Federation, the National Farmers Union and the National Grange — were not aggressively committed to the Soil Bank approach in its early stages. Their acceptance of the so-called Soil Bank Act in 1956 was probably predicated on about the same reasoning as used by Whitten: " ... it is a relief bill made necessary by the decline in farm income"[46] and that " ... the chief argument I can see for the soil bank idea is that it has become

---

[42] U.S. House of Representatives, Department of Agriculture Appropriations For 1960, pp. 2203-4.

[43] Ibid., pp. 2202 and 2204.

[44] The Comptroller General of the United States, Review of the 1959 Conservation Reserve Program, Commodity Stabilization Service, Dept. of Agriculture, Dec., 1959, pp. 31-40.

[45] Congressional Record, 1958, pp. 3743-44.

[46] Ibid., p. 2751.

absolutely apparent that some form of purchasing power is going to have to be put into the hands of the farmer."[47]

Since the program has been in operation, its acceptance by two of these farm groups has declined. The National Farmers Union is clearly opposed to the "whole farm" provision, according to their publication: Official Program for 1959, and recently James Patton, president of the Farmers Union stated: "As you know, the Soil Bank has not been generally popular in areas where it was used to the greatest extent. We must put the emphasis back on conservation and land use adjustment within the fence lines of operating farms."[48]

The National Grange has not been openly hostile to the program, but their policy position has rather approximated that of the Farmers Union. Any extension of the Soil Bank program should, in their opinion, come about within the framework of some type of a guaranteed price support program, notably of a marketing certificate type.

At the 1959 annual convention of the American Farm Bureau Federation, it appeared that at least some of the Farm Bureau officials were skeptical of the efficacy of the Soil Bank approach, despite the quality and vigor of its espousal by Dr. Carroll Bottum. Nevertheless, in the Farm Bureau's official program, Policies For 1960, an expanded conservation reserve program was advocated. Subsequent public announcements, congressional testimony, and their advocacy of the Hagen-Thomson bills[49] showed that the Farm Bureau favored raising the amount of land in the conservation reserve to 60 million acres within a three-year period. However, it would seem that the Farm Bureau's support for such an expanded acreage is based on congressional acceptance of the Farm Bureau's market price formula for wheat.

The Soil Bank Program — 1960 Version

The acreage reserve program expired at the close of calendar 1959. The conservation reserve program will continue until 1970, assuming that Congress continues to provide the necessary

---

[47] U.S. House of Representatives, Dept. of Agriculture Appropriations For 1957, p. 220.

[48] Statement of James G. Patton on General Farm Income Improvement Legislation before the House Committee on Agriculture, Feb. 29, 1960, p. 3.

[49] H.R. 10,666 - Hagen, Dem., Calif.; and H.R. 10,774 - Thomson, Rep., Wyo.

appropriations for the consummation of existing contracts.[50] However, we are primarily concerned here with the extension of the Soil Bank program, or at least some type of land retirement system. Consequently, is it probable that Congress will act in this session (86th -2nd) to provide for a Soil Bank of some 60-70 million acres? If so, how will this amount of land be retired, and where?

The American political system moves most dynamically when the president provides the principal motivating power. On Feb. 9, 1960, President Eisenhower, in his farm message to Congress, said: "...I urge an orderly expansion of the conservation reserve program up to 60 million acres, with authority granted the secretary of agriculture to direct the major expansion of this program to areas of greatest need."[51] The president's "guidelines" were rather flexible and did not seem to close the door to some type of a production control plan, although Secretary Benson did appear to close it a few days later.[52] However, the president and his secretary of agriculture are committed to a very substantial increase in the conservation reserve program. What kind of a "package deal" they would accept is still not clear.

The background of the congressional scene relative to Soil Bank legislation has already been outlined. Some type of policy action seems to be mandatory, particularly in regard to wheat. In early February, President Eisenhower noted that federal funds tied up in wheat approximate $3\frac{1}{2}$ billion. But what kind of a wheat, or general farm, program? Should we take the "free market" approach of the president-secretary of agriculture and that of the Farm Bureau; or the "production control" route that is advocated by an alliance of congressional Democrats-National Farmers Union — National Association of Wheat Growers — and, somewhat passively, by the National Grange? We need not concern ourselves with the "politics of choice" except to note that either approach calls for a substantial increase in some form of Soil Bank.

The Poage (Dem., Tex.) - McGovern (Dem., S. Dak.) bills[53]

---

[50] Through 1958, the conservation reserve contracts ran approximately as follows:
5 percent - 3 year contracts
60 percent - 5 year contracts
35 percent - 10 year contracts
(U.S. House of Representatives, Department of Agriculture Appropriations For 1960, p. 2212)

[51] U.S. House of Representatives, Message from The President of The United States, Relative to Our Problem in Agriculture As It Relates to Excessive Production of Certain Farm Products, 86th Cong., 2nd Sess., 1960, Document No. 330, p. 2.

[52] Des Moines Register, Feb. 15, 1960.

[53] H.R. 10,355 and 10,563, respectively. These bills represent the legislative efforts of the latter coalition.

would require, if approved by nationwide referendum, that 10 percent of the tillable acres of a farmer must be retired without rental payment, and up to 30 percent of additional tillable acres could be taken out of production with the possibility that payments would be in kind. These bills – sometimes referred to jointly as The Farm Family Income Act of 1960 – include all farm commodities, with the exceptions of tobacco, sugar and wool.

After much deliberation and negotiation, the Farmers Union, Grange and the National Association of Wheat Growers developed a marketing program for wheat which would be acceptable to them, if the Poage-McGovern bill proved to be politically inexpedient. Under the provisions of these bills,[54] wheat growers would have to retire 10 percent of their wheat base each year without rental payment, and, if funds were available, they could put an additional 10 percent of their wheat base in the land retirement program.[55]

The Farm Bureau-sponsored bills have already been outlined: The conservation reserve would be increased to 60 million acres within 3 years, and 17 million of those acres would come from the wheat areas. Senator Hickenlooper (Rep., Iowa) introduced a quite similar measure in early April, 1960.[56]

It may be that no important farm bills will be passed in 1960. At this point the decision seems to be in the hands of a few centers of power in Congress, the national farm groups and the USDA. Of the other public interest groups the Department of Interior might be of some assistance in advancing a Soil Bank program, but that department is caught on the horns of a dilemma: the drive to increase irrigated land in contrast to the need for more conservation for various recreational purposes.

One of the ironies of present-day American politics is the support given the present farm programs by the policymakers in the Department of Interior, notably the Bureau of Reclamation. Program costs, it is argued, are not excessive; population is increasing in a Malthusian fashion; and land is becoming a scarce resource. To some extent these arguments are, perhaps, of a self-enhancing type, but the reader is led to the conclusion that implicit therein is a belief in "The Fifth Plate" (world food shortage) philosophy. The Department of Interior's support of present farm programs, at least as these programs are involved

---

[54] H.R. 11,011 - Breeding, Dem., Kans.; and S.3159 - Carlson, Rep., Kans.

[55] The National Grange, Marketing Program For Wheat, March 7, 1960, 3 pp.

[56] American Farm Bureau Federation, Nation's Agriculture, "New 4 point wheat plan," March, 1960, pp. 12-13, 25; also the AFBF's Official News Letter, March 21, 1960.

The Senate bill was S.3335; co-sponsors were Senators Lausche, Dem., Ohio, and Dirksen, Rep., Ill.

directly in the production of farm products, is clearly more positive and vocal than that of the USDA.[57]

The dilemma arises in the area of purpose and objective. The Fish and Wildlife Service has worked closely with the USDA's Soil Bank Division in instituting fish and wildlife conservation practices. The Service disagrees, however, with the USDA in regard to the latter's wetlands policy:

> ...in that wetlands without a crop history are not considered by the U.S. Department of Agriculture to be eligible lands under the program.... The Soil Bank is a potential opportunity to compensate owners for maintaining wetlands as wetlands; and this, in our [FWS] view, would be in the public interest.[58]

Nevertheless, there has been some coordination and cooperation between the two departments, within the Soil Bank program, in the development of wildlife habitat areas and the construction of dams and ponds.[59]

The National Park Service has been conducting extensive studies of the future demand for nationwide recreational facilities under its Mission 66 program. Although the projected demand for additional areas appears to be quite evident and considerable, the Soil Bank program will be of little value in achieving the goals of the program. The Service does note, in a recent study on the Missouri River Basin, the considerable need for added recreational areas.[60] However, about the only proposal that is at all specific is for "...an example...of the prairie lands which once stretched across the central United States."[61]

The Outdoor Recreation Resources Review Commission has not given any particular consideration as yet to the possible recreational value of land in the conservation reserve, but plans to do so.[62]

The private interest groups that are involved in conservation and recreational activities have given little testimony before congressional committees relative to the land in the conservation

---

[57] For example, the address by William I. Palmer, asst. commissioner, Bureau of Reclamation, before the Sprinkler Irrigation Assoc., March 15, 1960 (Dept. of Interior Information Service Release, March 15, 1960).

[58] Letter, A. V. Tunison, acting director, Bureau of Sport Fisheries and Wildlife, Fish and Wildlife Service, Dept. of Interior, to Ross B. Talbot, March 9, 1960.

[59] U. S. Senate, Agriculture Appropriations for 1959, op. cit., pp. 583-87.

[60] National Park Service, Dept. of Interior, Recreation - Today and Tomorrow in the Missouri River Basin, Washington, Govt. Printing Office, 1959, p. 54 (Map - Plate 9).

[61] Letter, Ben H. Thompson, Chief, Division of Recreation Resource Planning, National Park Service, Dept. of Interior, to Ross B. Talbot, Feb. 11, 1960.

[62] Letter, Norman Wengert, Deputy Director for Studies, Outdoor Recreation Resources Review Commission, to Ross B. Talbot, Feb. 16, 1960.

reserve program. The Wildlife League did testify in behalf of the Soil Bank plan,[63] but the support of these interest groups is not evident in the appropriation hearings.

Assistant Secretary of Agriculture McLain observed that, in his opinion, the consumer has been in support of the program:

> I have talked to many consumer groups and I have talked with many consumers and I have yet to find a consumer who is not in full sympathy, with the approach of this [soil bank] program. He thinks just what I have said: It is wiser to keep our reserve in the ground rather than pile it up here and lose the value of it by storage costs, transportation costs, and so forth.[64]

Perhaps so, but consumer interests in the United States are not recognized as being politically articulate in the halls and committee rooms of Congress.

Thus, the immediate political situation of the Soil Bank program in Congress looks about as follows: (1) the whole area approach is a political impossibility at this time. No interest group, public or private, is sponsoring any such legislation. (2) The whole farm approach might be increased in scope but only, it would appear, if there are some definite restrictions on the number of whole farms that could go into the Soil Bank within a given area, e.g., perhaps not more than 25 percent of the farms per county. (3) The part-farm approach is certainly a political possibility. Just how much land this would put in the Soil Bank would be a hazardous guess: a good deal if the Poage-McGovern bill should pass as is, and not be vetoed; quite a lot less if only a wheat bill goes through Congress and the 1958 Corn Act is left untouched.

SUMMARY

To conclude, the premise has been accepted that an extensive land retirement program would be in the national interest of the United States. It would remove a portion of an important natural resource from food production, and the resource itself could then be used to pursue other national goals, such as soil conservation, recreation and flood control. Nevertheless, there is little, if any, evidence available which leads one to conclude that Congress is proceeding in any other than its traditional piecemeal, interest-oriented fashion. The bald fact seems to be that the primary

---

[63] U.S. House of Appropriations, Dept. of Agriculture Appropriations For 1959, op. cit., p. 2027.

[64] Ibid., 1960, pp. 2213-14.

reason why we have a Soil Bank is because it had political vote-getting possibilities in that the payments would augment the farmer's declining income. If the Soil Bank legislation is extended during this Congress, the principal motive for doing so will probably remain the same.

However, this is not a plea for pessimism or despair. The American political system functions by brief spurts followed by long periods of political sparring. The year 1961 might well be one of genuine accomplishment. There will be a new administration; it will have a program of some considerable magnitude. If Congress is politically amenable, a good deal might be accomplished in the coming session. The ideas, analyses and plans presented in this volume need not fall on plowed soil; rather these efforts may be of some valuable assistance in the fostering of a situation in which large portions of this soil will have a cover crop.

Chapter 19

HOWARD W. OTTOSON[1]
University of Nebraska

Lessening Impacts of Land Withdrawals on Nonfarm Resources and Rural Communities

TOO LITTLE ATTENTION has been given to the adjustments of nonfarm portions of rural communities which have accompanied the continuing shifts of labor resources out of agriculture. This is one reason why the Soil Bank has gone "sour" politically. Thus, it is most appropriate that time and space be devoted to this topic which has been explored only to a limited extent by agricultural economists or others.

In order to set the stage, it is convenient to make some assumptions about the nature of the land withdrawal program about which we are concerned. First, however, it may be helpful to conjecture briefly on the geographical location of the areas which most likely might be affected by land withdrawal programs. There is some evidence on this point. In Figure 19.1 are indicated the areas of soils classified by the Soil Conservation Service as not suitable for cultivation, (land capability classes V, VI, VII and VIII) but which are still in cultivation in the Great Plains.[2] There are nearly 14 million acres of such soils, with the largest areas being found in Kansas, Colorado and Oklahoma, followed by North Dakota, South Dakota, Texas and Nebraska. In addition, some 15 million acres of marginal Class IV land are found in the same states as well as elsewhere in the Plains. It should be noted that the concentration of these areas will not be coincidental with concentration of small towns. Large averages of land of low productivity are sparsely populated. Others are more thickly settled.

Heady and Egbert have used programming techniques to detect farming areas sensitive to production shifts.[3] They delineate

---

[1] I am indebted substantially to the many helpful comments from my colleagues at the University of Nebraska during the preparation of this paper.

[2] A. R. Aandahl, "Location of 'low grade' croplands in the Great Plains States," Proceedings of the 1958 meeting of the Great Plains Agricultural Council, Bozeman, Montana, July, 1958. Mimeo.

[3] Earl O. Heady and Alvin C. Egbert, "Programming regional adjustments in grain production to eliminate surpluses," Jour. Farm Econ., 41:718-33, Nov., 1959.

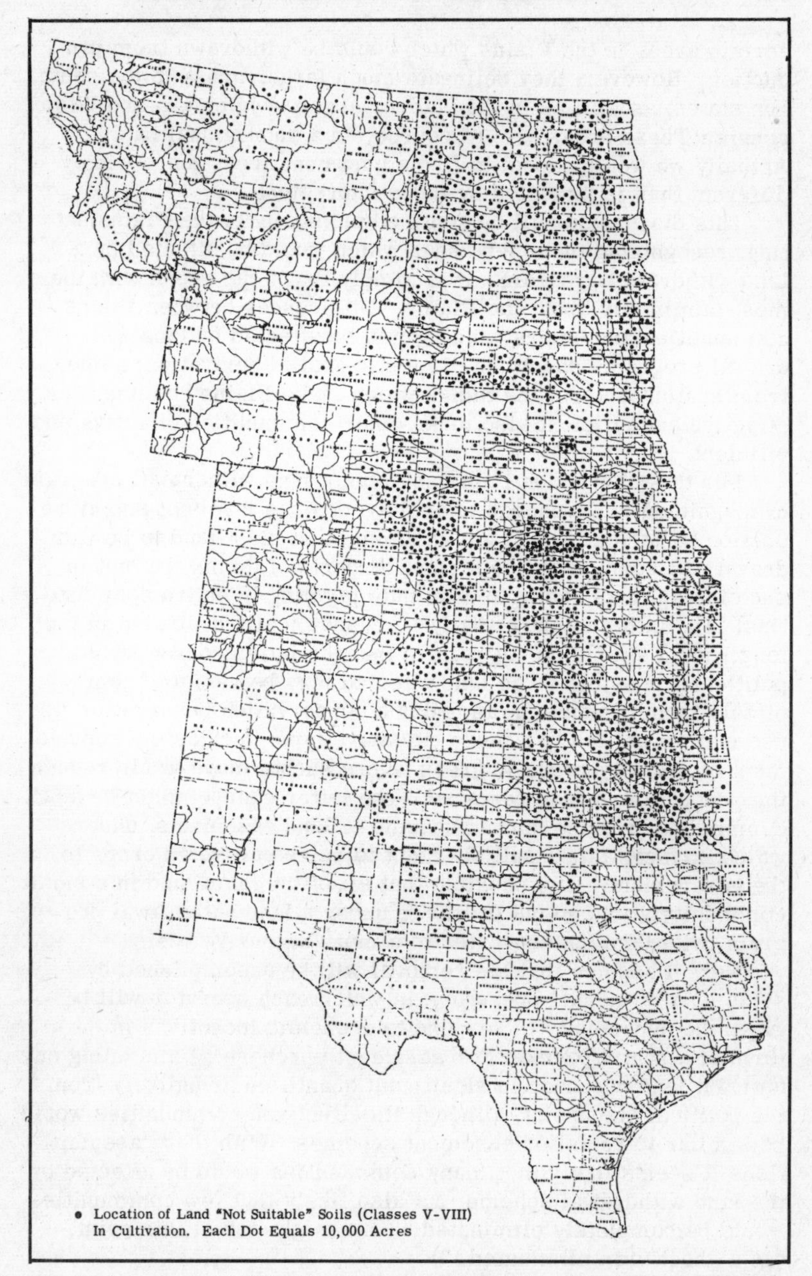

Fig. 19.1. Location of land use classes V, VI, VII and VIII land in the Great Plains. (Source: Aandahl, Andrew R. "Location of 'low grade' croplands in the Great Plains States." Proceedings of the 1958 meeting of the Great Plains Agricultural Council, Bozeman, Montana, July, 1958. Mimeo.)

certain areas in the Plains which could be withdrawn from production. However, they delineate much larger areas in the southern states, as well as in the cutover areas of Michigan and Wisconsin. These areas are, of course, on a subregional basis. Actually we would expect to find adjustment areas more widely different than is indicated by these subregions.

This discussion will be confined primarily to the Plains setting, recognizing the other areas which would be affected by a land withdrawal program. It is simply that I can speak with the most familiarity about the Plains. Differences between Plains communities and others which would be affected by land withdrawal programs should be of mostly spatial derivation; aside from spatial factors, the things which make Plains communities effective and efficient also make other communities effective and efficient.

For this discussion I am assuming a land withdrawal program of magnitude large enough to achieve desired levels of supply reduction in agriculture. I am assuming that most land to be withdrawn will come as whole farms, or parts of farms, but not in such intensity as bodily to eliminate farming in entire communities. The latter might actually be economically desirable in the long run. I simply do not believe that the latter course would be politically possible. The land affected may be removed completely from production, as under a conservation reserve, or its use may be shifted to a more extensive type, such as the replacement of grain by grass in areas where such a move would reduce the production of feed per acre. The latter course might be accomplished by some sort of scheme of land easements, under which farmers might sell the right to raise cultivated crops to the government. It is possible that all of the farm land in a small community would go out of tillage under a land withdrawal program, with farming converted to a more extensive basis.

Next, I assume that the removal will be accomplished by some sort of market operation, in which each operator will be given the opportunity to respond to economic incentives in the form of a rental payment, or easement purchase. I am ruling out outright land purchase in significant quantities as unlikely from the political standpoint, although its effects on communities would be similar to rental or easement schemes. With these assumptions it seems likely that many communities would be affected by the land withdrawal scheme, but also likely that few communities would be completely eliminated. (One might ask at this point, "Is a ghost town eliminated?")

Finally, I assume that the withdrawal program will be set up so as to encourage economically desirable long-run land use adjustments; that it will be efficient in the sense that the cost of withdrawing given units of production, or units of standard resource inputs, will be minimized.

NATURE OF IMPACTS OF LAND WITHDRAWAL ON FARM COMMUNITIES

General Effects

Rural communities in the Plains and elsewhere have been experiencing the results of the outmovement of labor resources and the extensification of farm production since the 1930's; thus the institution of a land withdrawal program would not be qualitatively a new phenomenon. For example, between 1930 and 1950 the farm population of Nebraska declined by 33 percent, while the total population declined by 4 percent. The total population of the state had exceeded the 1930 level only by the year 1956, while during the same period the population of the United States had increased 32 percent. More dramatically, the decline in total population in the six-county Plains-Corn Belt transition area in central Nebraska was 28 percent during the period 1930 to 1950. If we examine these data more closely, we find that the farm population declined by 40 percent during the period, while nonfarm population fell by 4 percent. (The exclusion of the town of Broken Bow, with a 25 percent increase in population, brings the decline in the nonfarm sector to 9 percent.) At the same time the composition of the population shifted from a ratio of 66 percent farm/34 percent nonfarm to 55 percent farm/45 percent nonfarm. The extent of disengagement of farm labor resources from farming already accomplished during this period in areas at the margin between intensive and extensive types of farming is sometimes not fully appreciated.

We must distinguish between small communities and large ones in considering population dynamics. It seems that the larger communities have been getting larger, and the small ones are getting smaller. For example, the relation between the size of towns in 1930 in the six counties in the central Nebraska transition area and the percent of their population changes between that year and 1950 is shown in Figure 19.2. Data from the whole state show the same relation.

The geography of the land class data previously noted when examined along with the geographical distribution of towns in Nebraska emphasizes the implications of land withdrawal to the towns. In Figure 19.3 are shown the towns and villages of

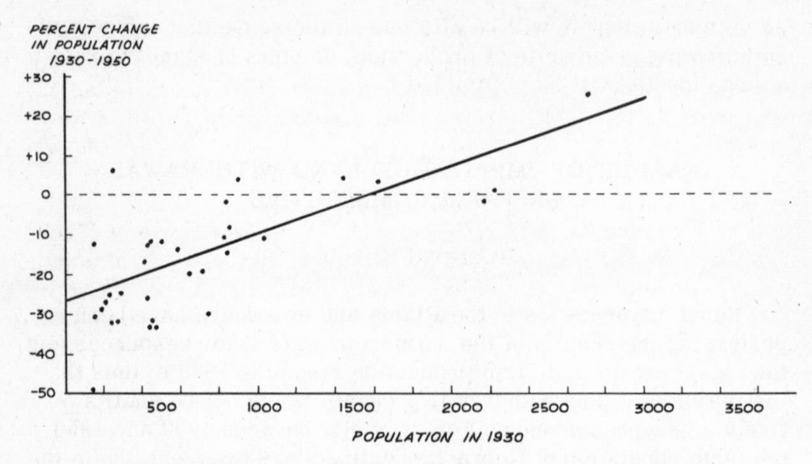

Fig. 19.2. Relationship between percent change in population of incorporated places in central Nebraska from 1930 to 1950 to size of place in 1930.

Nebraska, by size groups, coded to indicate their population losses or gains from 1930 to 1950. In addition there are charted on an area scale the acres of land use classes IV, V, VI, VII and VIII land in each county which are presently in crop production. In these two sets of data we can identify some probable adjustment areas in Nebraska which are as yet heavily occupied by

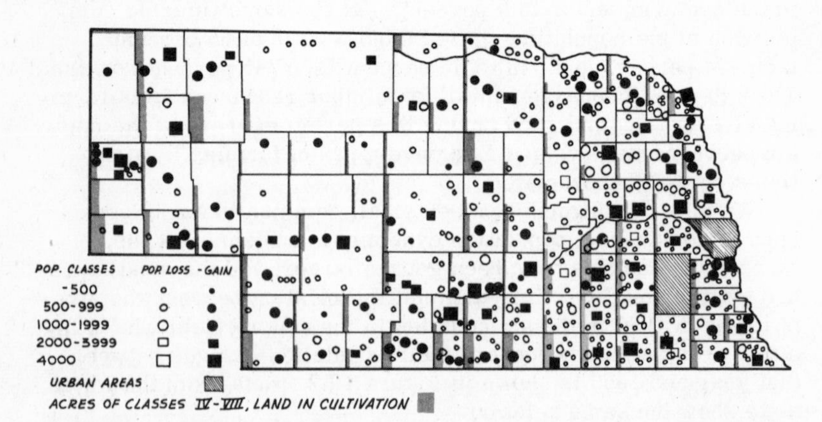

Fig. 19.3. Geographical distribution of incorporated places of different sizes in Nebraska, 1950, population changes between 1930 and 1950, and acreage of land use classes IV, V, VI, VII and VIII. Land Presently in Cultivation, by County, 1958.

small towns which will be affected by land withdrawal programs. It is these same communities which have lost population heavily during the past. I would suppose that some other areas in the Plains would be affected more severely than those shown in Nebraska.

The peculiar effects of a land withdrawal program on the rural communities affected will not occur because of the beginning of a population movement as such, but rather because of the "shock" aspects of the program. The people in most rural communities are presently concerned with problems associated with population withdrawals, and are reacting in one way or another. The land withdrawal program envisaged here would confront them with an enhanced version of the same problems. This is not to say that there is no need for policy attention to the impacts on these communities. On the contrary, policy attention is rationalized because of the newly created urgency of the same problems as well as the additional costs created by this urgency.

Specific Impacts

Several types of impacts will be felt in the local community as a result of a land withdrawal program. In the following discussion each of these is taken up in turn.

Movement of Farm Population

A land withdrawal program large enough to affect agricultural production will inevitably provide the impetus for the outmovement of farm people who are particularly susceptible to alternative opportunities. Various "susceptibility classes" can be suggested. In the first place, beginning owner-operators not fully established, or owner-operators on small farms, particularly those whose debt encumbrances are substantial, might find it expedient to sign up their entire acreages. Under a Soil Bank arrangement they would be free to engage in full-time work off the farm while continuing to live there, or to move to a farm-city, or to metropolitan areas near and far to take nonfarm jobs. They may do all three, in that order, over time. They would have similar incentives under a land easement program, under which they would either sell their land or lease to other farmers.

Tenants would be a second group which would be susceptible to such a program. Under a rental program landlords stand to gain more than tenants, even though they split the returns from the program with the tenant; there is evidence that they have not been unaware of the economics of this, even though they have been reluctant in many cases to take direct steps to force tenants off. Tenants would be equally vulnerable under an easement program, and would have the incentive either to secure the control of more land or to leave the farm.[4]

A third susceptible group would be those operators who are nearing retirement. The program would provide them with the incentive to disengage from active farming more quickly than would otherwise be the case. However, most of this group will remain on their farms, or in the community.

In a short run many of the whole farms which are placed under the program by owner-operators will be kept under the control of these operators, even though they assume an absentee status. In the longer run, as the younger men become established elsewhere, and the older farmers dispose of their farms, the land will pass into the control of remaining operators, and so the farm consolidation process will be enhanced, particularly under an easement program which will allow more extensive use of the land.

In addition to those placing their whole farms in a withdrawal program, there will be less-susceptible operators who will "sign up" parts of their farms. This process will be selective between land productivity classes, related to the type of payment schedules set up for various productivity classes. As time passes, these operators may decide to work part-time off the farm as a permanent arrangement, or in this way begin the process of moving out. Or, they may enlarge their total acreage by renting or buying more land.

On balance, a decrease in the farm population can be expected as farm land is withdrawn from production. This movement will tend to lag behind the "sign up" of land, but it will be sustained as people find the conditions propitious for a decision to leave.

Effect on Farm Income

With pressure for the disengagement of human resources, and a reduction in various capital resources, the initial impact of a land withdrawal program would likely be a reduction in gross

---

[4] In another context it is to be noted that tenants and owner-operators of smaller-than-modal farms were most common among those selling out in central Nebraska during the drought of 1956-57 than farmers of other types. Of a group of these sellers contacted by mail survey in 1956-57, with a 47 percent response, one-third left the state after selling out, and all of them left farming.

farm income in an area. Data from an analysis of the Conservation Reserve Program in Nebraska indicate that in two areas conservation reserve payments equalled about 75 percent of the gross income which would have been received had the land been farmed.[5] This reduction in gross income will have a direct impact on the nonfarm businesses handling the goods and services for which this increment would have been spent. The decrease in gross income in a given community will be more severe, of course, under a rental, nonuse program than under an easement-use extensification program.

On the other hand, net income per farm should be increased by a withdrawal program for several reasons. First, farmers signing up will presumably have decided that they are adopting the more profitable alternative. In the longer run, a second factor will be additional impetus toward farm enlargement because of the withdrawal of farm population. The community effects related to net farm income changes will depend on the distribution of that income, and on the items for which it is used — consumer goods, farm enlargement, expansion of farm working capital or outside investment. Also, to the extent that landowners move out of the community, their net income will in a large sense move with them, as long as they retain control of their land.

A final, less immediate income effect will presumably take place if the program is large enough to have the macro-effect assumed for it; that is, if a reduction in national feed production is accomplished the result will be an increase in farm prices, and a consequent gross income effect will accrue to the farm production activity left in the community.

Effect on Structure of Expenditures by Farmers

Several effects can be hypothesized. First, if the population outmovement is small enough, there may well be an increase in types of consumption expenditures by farmers for which income elasticities are relatively high, for example recreation, education and other items considered to be in the luxury class. Conversely a decrease in the total expenditures would be expected for those items for which income elasticities are relatively low; examples of these would be food, work clothing and small household appliances. Finally, there may well be a decrease in the farmer expenditures for production factors such as fuel, fertilizer and machinery.

---

[5] Ralph Johnson, "Some effects of the Conservation Reserve Program in selected counties of Nebraska," unpublished manuscript, 1960.

Unfortunately for the small town, there is considerable evidence that farmers tend to travel to larger trading centers – farm cities – for the first type of goods, relying on the small town for staples and convenience goods.[6] This means that the level of economic activity of small towns is affected more by population numbers than by level of income, as compared to larger centers.

Effect on Structure of Farm Marketing

Obviously a land withdrawal program in a cash grain area will decrease the volume of grain marketed. Grain typically moves through marketing facilities close at hand, in the small centers. On the other hand, livestock tends to move directly to larger marketing centers located either in farm cities or in stockyards cities. Small towns in ranching or livestock feeding areas are thus presently involved to only a limited extent in marketing activity, and will not be affected by a land withdrawal program. However, in a cash grain town direct contraction of business will result.

Banking is an activity which is carried on to an important extent in small towns. Any change which reduces the volume of business flowing through a town will affect it directly.

Differential Impacts on Private Service Sector of Small Community

Having outlined the impacts which will be generated at the farm level and which will affect the community, we can next translate them into effects on Main Street. The net effect of a land withdrawal program in a county will be decreased volumes of business and smaller resource returns to various types of town business; however, the impacts will be differentiated depending upon the type of business. The largest impact will fall on those businesses handling staple, convenience goods of various kinds, including both consumption and production items. Among these will be grocery stores, everyday clothing stores, auto repair shops, lumberyards, filling stations and feed and supply stores. Banks would be similarly affected. These businesses characterize towns of populations of 500 or less. Table 19.1 is illustrative.

[6] Edgar Z. Palmer, "Some economic problems of Clay Center, Nebraska," Univ. of Nebr. Business Res. Bul. 54, 1950; also A. H. Anderson and C. J. Miller, "The changing role of the small town in farm areas," Nebr. Agr. Exp. Sta. Bul. 419, 1953.

Table 19.1. Types of Businesses in Towns in Sherman County, Nebraska[a]

Types of business	Number of businesses by places					
	Total, all towns	Loup City	Litch- field	Ashton	Rock- ville	Hazard
	(1950 population)					
1950 Population	2,520	1,508	337	381	164	130
Heavy construction	1	1				
Electrical, masonry, stone-work, etc.	1	1				
Special trade contractors	1	1				
Partitions, shelving, lockers, etc.	1	1				
Meat packing	1	1				
Creamery	1	1				
Newspaper	1	1				
Dairy products store	1	1				
Car dealer	1	1				
Women's ready-to-wear	2	2				
Dry goods and gen. merchandise	3	3				
Family shoe store	1	1				
Men's and boys' clothing	1	1				
Jewelry store	1	1				
Hotel	1	1				
Cleaning and dyeing	1	1				
Machine shop	1	1				
Grocery or general store	12	3	2	2	2	3
Service station	11	6	1	1	2	1
General auto repair shop	7	2	2	1	1	1
Drinking places	8	3	1	2	1	1
Eating places	6	4	1	1		
Fuel dealer	3	1	1			1
Assembler (mainly farm prod.)	4	2		1	1	
Hardware store	3	2			1	
Farm equipment dealer	7	6		1		
Drug store	3	2		1		
Liquor store (packaged)	3	2		1		
Funeral director	3	2	1			
Electrical repair shop	5	3	2			
Blacksmith shop	2	1			1	
Hay, grain, feed	2		1	1		
Lumberyard	3	1	1		1	
Shoe repair shop	1		1			
Gen. repair shop	1		1			
Electric or gas utility	1		1			
Telephone system	1					1
Total types	---	31	13	10	8	6
Total establishments	106	60	16	12	10	8

[a] Source: Dun and Bradstreet.

On the other hand, there will be less decrease, perhaps no change, and even an increase in the expenditures for recreation items, education, professional services and luxury items; these items for the most part are obtained in the farm city of 2,500 people or more rather than the small town. The net effect on trade in these items will depend upon the relative magnitudes of population outflow and increase in net consumption increases of the people remaining. Of course, the farm city also serves as the source of staple consumption and production items for farmers in its immediate trade area and will be affected in this sector in a manner similar to the small town by land withdrawal and population movement. We have simply noted the existence of two types of trade areas for the farm city — the staple goods trade area of more modest circumference, and that for goods of higher income elasticity which extends further out and blankets the immediate trade areas of small towns.

The Community Multiplier

If we are to deal effectively with the impacts of land withdrawal on the nonfarm sector, some quantitive predictions of these impacts will be necessary. The notions of primary, secondary and tertiary economic activities are relevant.[7] In a purely agricultural community the farms would comprise a primary sector, while the townspeople would be engaged mostly in tertiary activity, with little secondary activity being carried on. A variation of this formulation is the derivative-basic ratio and the community multiplier.[8] In brief these terms imply that there are quantitive relationships between the basic, or "export" activities of a community, the derivative, or service activities, and the total economic activity of the community. Using employment as the symbol of economic activity the derivative is the quotient when derivative employment is divided by basic employment, while the multiplier is the quotient of total employment divided by basic employment. In the typical small communities with which we are concerned, the basic activities would be almost entirely agricultural, while derivative would include trucking, banking, trade, government and other activities whose economic output is not exported but is consumed internally.

---

[7]Colin Clark, Conditions of Economic Progress, (Rev. ed.), Macmillan Co., London, 1951.

[8]Edgar Z. Palmer (ed.), Gerald E. Thompson, Moon H. Kang and William Strawn, "The community economic base and multiplier," Univ. of Nebr. Business Res. Bul. 63, 1958.

Table 19.2. Total, Basic and Derivative Employment and Ratios for Selected Great Plains Farm-Cities, 1950

County	State	City	Employment Total	Employment Basic	Employment Derivative	Derivative ratio	Multi-plier
Pierce	N. Dakota	Rugby	2,818	1,434	1,385	.966	1.966
Tripp	S. Dakota	Winner	3,409	1,464	1,945	1.328	2.328
Clay	Kansas	Clay Center	4,512	1,616	2,896	1.792	2.792
Union	N. Mexico	Clayton	2,449	914	1,535	1.679	2.679

Source: Edgar Z. Palmer (ed.), Gerald E. Thompson, Moon H. Kang and William Strawn, "The community economic base and multiplier," Univ. of Nebr. Business Res. Bul. 63, 1958, p. 101.

There is little evidence available on these relations for small communities on the Plains area. However, some data from selected Plains counties whose boundaries coincide with the trade areas of small farm cities give some indication (Table 19.2).

In the counties which these towns dominate, 85 percent or more of the basic activity is agricultural; thus they are fairly "pure" examples. They illustrate magnitudes of what may be expected in rural communities. Thus, in Tripp County, South Dakota, where 90 percent of the basic employment is agricultural, about 1.3 persons were employed in derivative activity for each person in basic production activity, largely farming.

Admittedly, these data relate only to the labor resource. In moving labor out of farming and releasing land we will also release nonland capital. We need to know more about the quantitative effects of this total resource movement on the capital of the nonfarm business sector of the community, as well as on its labor. Such knowlege is lacking, and the research need is obvious.

Impacts on the Public Service Sector

Perhaps as important as the effects of land withdrawal on the private business sector will be its impacts on the public service sector. Typically public services are organized on a different geographical basis than is private business, with some, such as country roads, being set up on a county basis and others, such as power, in districts. These services may be operated as strictly governmental activities, or as public utilities.

A first impact will occur from the revenue side. With an out-movement of population, and assuming no changes in levies, revenues from personal property taxes will obviously decrease. With a change in the use of land, as under an easement program, there will undoubtedly be pressure to reduce real estate tax rates on the land affected. Utilities depending upon per capita payments, such as telephones, will experience direct loss of revenues with population shrinkage.

On the cost, or service side, a decreased need will occur for those services which are provided on a per capita basis, such as telephones, elementary and secondary education and consumption electricity. On the other hand, the cost per capita for these services will rise, due to the fixed components which will be divided among fewer persons. Some services represent fixed costs almost entirely, once they are established. Among the latter are roads and county government. The per capita cost of these items will rise in proportion to population declines, until some retrenchment takes place.

MEANS OF LESSENING THE IMPACTS OF LAND WITHDRAWAL

In the past, agricultural control programs have typically been oriented toward the individual farmer, and in most cases have ignored the nonfarm sector of the community in which the farmer lives. Inversely, the nonfarm part of the local community has been quite ignorant of the larger issues involved in economic development, resource adjustments in agriculture and need for action in the small town in the face of these adjustments. The more vociferous reaction in the small town in the face of changes like this, if one is to take the comments of country newspaper editors at face value, is that any loss of population is undesirable and is to be prevented at all costs. After having fought losing, if poorly planned, battles against such loss, many small towns awake to find themselves empty shells of their pasts. It would seem possible that small towns could benefit by taking as positive a view of these developments as possible, rolling with the punches, and capitalizing on any advantages which they may retain. We would suppose that deliberate policies could be initiated in conjunction with land withdrawal programs which could assist towns in the most feasible directions.

THE ROLE OF EDUCATION

Sometimes programs "break" with little warning or interpretation and are brought into being without adequate understanding on the part of the people affected. The first requirement of a land withdrawal program should be intensive educational efforts in the communities affected, probably carried on by extension services in cooperation with the action agencies. Such educational programs should leave the community clear as to the reasons for the particular program, the various effects which are expected, both in the aggregate and at the local level, and how the program will be carried on. Finally, the communities should be given some insights into the types of actions which might be taken locally. Implied here is policy education in its broadest sense.

COMMUNITY ORGANIZATION

An educational program of the type suggested above would logically awaken the community to the need for broadly conceived community or area planning. Desirably such planning should be oriented toward the natural economic areas organized around the farm city. In the process, villages should be made conscious of this broader economic area of which they are a part. Such planning activity should cut across the boundary lines of local units of government, and should encompass all major lines of economic activity, including agriculture, business and services. With it, people should be made to feel a sense of participation in working out their own economic and social adjustments in what may be in the large sense a strategic withdrawal.

An economic area planning organization might involve itself in many ways. It could estimate the number of farm people involved in a withdrawal program, and predict the nature of population movements which will result. It could analyze in detail the impacts of the program on the business and service sectors of the individual communities. It might make recommendations about the types of business enterprises which are likely to be the most viable in the long run. It might make recommendations to local governmental units concerning adjustments which should be made with respect to public services such as roads, schools and power, as well as local and county government *per se*. It might also make recommendations to such non-governmental corporate units such as churches, credit agencies, real estate agencies and the like. It might make recommendations about possible zoning of new business enterprises, as well as the location of rural residences.

STATE POLICIES

Policy consideration at the state level in connection with land withdrawal programs would be necessary. Educational and action activities should be coordinated here. The identification of communities to be affected heavily by withdrawal programs would logically be made on a state basis. Problems related to such things as the tax system, school system and county organization should receive cognizance at the state level.

FEDERAL POLICIES

Considerable federal activity would appropriately be directed at the community in connection with land withdrawal programs. It is obvious that different communities will be affected in different ways and to different degrees by a withdrawal program. Criteria would need to be set up in advance as to the conditions under which federal assistance would be forthcoming to affected communities. Such criteria might relate to (1) the proportion of land affected, or (2) the proportion of population which will be displaced, or both. We would suggest that such communities (for lack of a better geographical unit these would probably be counties) be designated as withdrawal communities, similar to the designation of disaster areas made during times of drouth or other emergency. Communities so designated would then be eligible for special types of assistance such as those suggested below.

Relocation Assistance for Farmers Who Elect To Change Occupations

The type of activity inferred under this heading has been a missing link in our collection of agricultural policies. The need for it will be simply increased by a land withdrawal program. Obviously a land withdrawal program is in the essence going to be a labor withdrawal program as far as agriculture is concerned if the long-run effects are to be consistent with our past analysis of the resource problems of agriculture. The "Homesteads in Reverse" approach appears feasible.[9] Involved in it might be several means. Subsidized retraining of a vocational nature

[9] Theodore W. Schultz, "An alternative diagnosis of the farm problem," Jour. Farm Econ., 38:1137-52, Dec., 1956.

might be provided through special courses in local schools or through vocational schools. Such training must be comprehensive, in line with abilities of the students, and also relevant to the needs of the nonfarm job market in the most sophisticated sense possible. Subsistence allowances might be provided during training in the same fashion as the GI training program for World War II veterans. Individual job placement assistance might be provided, going beyond the mere provision of information about job openings in various areas. This could be coupled with the payment of moving costs for men accepting a job in another location. A subsistence and rental allowance might be provided for a specified period such as one year, after a man has accepted a job, to offset various kinds of special costs accruing to people in the process of making this type of adjustment.

In terms of the kinds of societal resources which we are prepared to devote to a number of purposes from time to time, including other aspects of agricultural policy, it would seem that this is an example of an area for which our financial support has been rather meager, and to which we have devoted little imagination.

Relocation Assistance for Nonfarm Residents of Withdrawal Areas

The nonfarm sector or rural communities may have labor surpluses in the same way that we characterize agriculture. As in farming, we find people in small towns whose economic role may be justifiable only by their acceptance of very low imputed returns to their labor. The effects of resource withdrawal from a community's agriculture on the nonfarm sector should be a predictable phenomenon, and may be expressed in terms of the number of persons who may be displaced in the town by the withdrawal policy, assuming a minimum acceptable labor return in the town. Again, as in farming, the operators of businesses in the small town are of many economic types, including those who are getting started, those who are expanding and those who are contracting. In fact, a distinct class which appears to have come into being may be the retired farmer who starts a business, partly just to do something for which he gets a return low enough not to interfere with his social security payment. Thus, not everyone who operates a business or performs a service in a small town will choose to leave in response to either coercions or incentives. However, policy could be directed at assistance for some proportion within specified age limits who might choose to make a shift involving change of location or job.

Such means might be very similar to those already suggested for farmers, including retraining and moving subsidies. In the cases where the problem is one of moving a business to another location, or consolidation and reorganization, special credit might be made available through the Small Business Administration.

Industrial Development

Industrial development is regarded by some as a panacea for the cure of economic ills of small communities. There is a considerable amount of wishful thinking in many communities about the possibilities of attracting a new industry, and there are cases where uneconomic ventures have been subsidized heavily by a community for long periods of time only to prove incapable of survival.

Having introduced this note of caution, let us not, on the other hand, be too hasty in ruling out all possibilities for the introduction of industrial activities in rural communities. There are success cases, too. The development of industry in rural areas involves costs, but so does the outmovement of people. May there not be situations where new economic activity may be generated more cheaply in social terms in a rural area than the social costs of moving and reestablishing farm people, and setting up the educational and other facilities to service them, in already heavily industrialized areas?

This question calls for sophisticated analysis and planning on both national and state levels; it involves much more than salesmanship and brochures produced by chambers of commerce and state industrial development commissions. First there is needed research directed at the possibilities, resource requirements and limitations related to "industrial development" in rural areas. There has been some description of labor and natural resources in rural communities toward this end, but little analysis directed at the cause-effect relationships involved. It should be possible to classify rural communities with respect to the factors making up their potential for nonagricultural economic activity, and similarly to classify industries with respect to their adaptability to such communities. Perhaps for some kinds of industries the marginal factors relative to their location in rural communities may be less stringent than commonly thought.

Admittedly the rural community referred to here is the "farm city," rather than its surrounding satellite towns and villages. The latter will become more and more subsidiary to the farm city in a relationship similar to those between metropolitan areas and suburbs.

Let us assume for the moment the availability of information on social and private costs, and consequences associated with the locations of industrial activity, and that these facts bear out the hypotheses inferred above. It would appear that much more planning and policy attention could be given to the locational aspects of industrial development than has been the case in the past, particularly at the national level. Except in times of emergency, industrial development has gone its own way, with society following along and making such adjustments and additional investments as are forced upon it.

Grants-in-Aid to Local Communities

As we have seen, the type of economic retrenchment involved in a land withdrawal program will have definite impacts on various types of local governmental and quasi-governmental services. The problem, when the chips have all fallen, will be whether the local facilities can be left as effective in providing services for the people who remain as they were before the program. Admittedly this will call for reorganization on the part of these facilities. Grants-in-aid might facilitate the reorganization of the services, encourage changes which are presently desirable and keep the financial burden from descending upon those who remain. For example, aid might be given to counties to cover the expenditures associated with the closing of public roads in areas of heavy population loss. Similarly aid might encourage the consolidation of school facilities whose efficiency has been affected adversely. Funds might be used to purchase power and telephone facilities made excess by reduction in population; in addition, payments might be made to utility systems in lieu of lost revenues for a specified period, say for three years, under the condition that service to those who remain be unimpaired. The consolidation of counties in affected areas might be encouraged by funds for the movement of equipment and materials and renovation or construction of facilities designated as the permanent centers after consolidation. Perhaps both federal and local offices might be consolidated in this process. The longer the period given for the total adjustment, the more costs of this type which can be depreciated out, and the fewer which might have to be subsidized.

A NOTE ON THE STATE OF KNOWLEDGE

It has been obvious throughout the foregoing discussion that there is much we don't know about the economic and social causes and effects associated with the types of land withdrawal programs assumed as they relate to the affected communities. Some of the research needs implied are very complicated, and the data subjective. Yet it is to be hoped that programs of this type might be initiated and administered with the benefit of as much information as possible if the desired long-run effects are to be accomplished. Specifically, we need more data on which farm tenure types are most vulnerable and most apt to shift in response to the program. We need to know more about the types of community "multipliers" which hold for various types of rural communities so as better to predict the impacts of farm population withdrawal on the nonfarm sector. What are the per unit costs of services as related to population dynamics? What of the job market? Can we really do an effective job of identifying job opportunities in sectors in which growth is taking place, train human resources for these jobs and then bring man and job together satisfactorily? What kinds of training will actually make people useful in these growth sectors? How best can communities be organized to participate in the type of economic retrenchment activities which would seem on the surface to violate traditional values and orientations of city councils and chambers of commerce? Can this actually be done? What of the possibility of replacing agricultural production activity in the rural community with other types of economic activity which would absorb its surplus labor? These questions illustrate the complexity of the subject which has been covered rather hastily and superficially in this chapter.

Chapter 20

G. S. TOLLEY
North Carolina State College

Meshing Elimination of Agricultural Surpluses With Other Goals

WHATEVER MEANS are used, adjusting agricultural production to demand seems bound to inconvenience many persons and perhaps inflict serious hurts on some. Congress has proven to be sensitive to these inconveniences and hurts almost to the point of allergy, with a resulting inclination to try to live with excess production rather than face how to get rid of it.

Critics may oversimplify when they label the congressional position as just politics. The inference is that Congress does not reflect the social interest. There seems to be the notion that the socially desirable course is obvious if only an imperfect political mechanism would follow it. Often the critic of Congress identifies the social interest with norms concerning economic efficiency. But, though the political mechanism may not be perfect, it is democratic. Congressional hesitancy in eliminating surpluses in part reflects a realization that there is a more complex weighing of goals than to follow only one simplified set of norms. This chapter tries to suggest major considerations in weighing the goals.

The first part of the chapter concerns demand-supply characteristics for land and for the human input. The aim of this discussion is to contribute to understanding effects of agricultural control programs. Armed with this background, the second part considers goals related to surplus eliminations. These goals include: conservation, efficiency, rising gross national product, human and cultural development, income equity and regional equity. Then, in the third part, the goal-implications of alternative policy directions are analyzed.

RESOURCE EQUILIBRIUM IN RELATION TO SURPLUSES

Land

A hypothesis is that the long-run supply of agricultural land is well approximated as elastic over ranges likely. The supply of land is visualized to be perfectly elastic due to marginal land adjustments. Partly these adjustments take the form of marginal land going in and out of use. By marginal land is meant zero or low rent land. There are millions of acres of marginal land in the Southeast and the western Great Plains. In addition, in areas like the Corn Belt, there are marginal areas and marginal lands even on good farms. These marginal lands tend to go out of production when demand falls making residual returns negative. They tend to come into production if rents rise above the amortized costs of clearing and other investments necessary to make them suitable for farming.

Marginal land adjustments also include drainage, levelling and other improvements. These increase the effective amount of land. Similarly, with low rents, there may be a tendency not to keep land up, letting it erode and so forth. Even though land stays in cultivation, if it deteriorates, the effective supply is reduced.

The marginal or endogenous land adjustments that have been mentioned act as a governor on all agricultural land rents. This is because land use throughout the country is interrelated. The land is in competition producing for common national markets. High rent land — fertile, productive soil with good climate — tends to stay in regardless of demand for land. Due to competition between regions, adjustments to changes in demand may ramify around the country through chains of substitution. But these tend to work themselves out to places where marginal land adjustments are made that either increase or decrease the effective land supply as the demand situation calls for.

The marginal land adjustments and competition for land for common markets lead to depicting the aggregate supply of land in its horizontal position SS as shown in Figure 20.1.

In contrast to the marginal or endogenous land adjustments just discussed, other land supply adjustments may be referred to as exogenous and semi-exogenous. Decreases of this type include pre-empting of agricultural lands for urban and road uses. Increases include government land development activities — such as reclamation and flood control which increase product potential of flood plains. The exogenous land supply influences can temporarily move us from the demand-supply equilibrium O, where DD

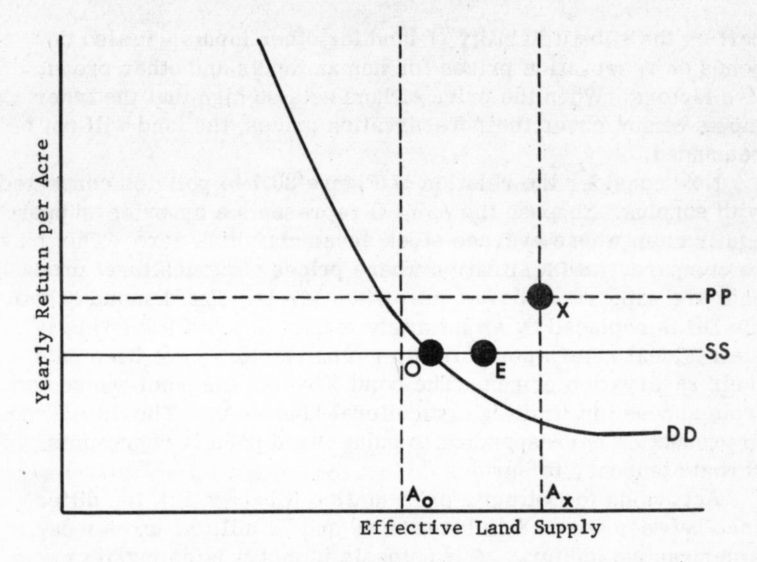

Fig. 20.1. Aggregate demand and supply for agricultural land.

crosses SS, to point E. But competition will result in marginal adjustments that bring the total effective supply of land back to equilibrium O. As an illustration of this type of adjustment, the effect of western reclamation may be to start competitive reactions that eventually drive out marginal areas elsewhere in the country. It has been estimated that for every 20 workers remaining in the southern agriculture, one has been displaced by western reclamation.[1]

What of the demand schedule for land? It is a derived demand depending on demand for farm products, farm technology and supply conditions for labor, purchased inputs and other productive factors. The degree of elasticity of the demand schedule DD remains conjectural. One reason we do not know much about the elasticity is that the supply curve SS, being horizontal, has kept rents from fluctuating enough to reveal much about adjustments to varying rent. That is, since the supply curve has not shifted much, there has been little opportunity to trace out empirically the demand curve DD. The elasticity of DD depends in

[1]The ideas presented thus far in this section are elaborated in my "Reclamation's influence on the rest of agriculture," Land Econ.,Vol. XXXV, No. 2, May, 1959, pp. 176-80; "Inter-area relations in agricultural supply," Jour. Farm Econ., Vol. XLII, No. 2, May, 1960, pp. 453-73 (with L. M. Hartman); "Alternative land development possibilities," Modern Land Policy, H. G. Halcrow (ed.), University of Illinois Press, Urbana (in press).

part on the substitutability of land for other inputs. It also depends on reservation prices for human inputs and other productive factors. When the price of land gets so high that the other inputs cannot cover their reservation prices, the land will not be demanded.

Now consider the relation of Figure 20.1 to policies connected with surplus. Suppose the point O represents a no-price-support equilibrium where average stock accumulation is zero. This may be compared with a situation where prices of agricultural products are supported above equilibrium levels. The demand schedule DD is replaced by an infinitely elastic demand PP. This is the residual return per acre after other factors have been paid their reservation prices. The point X shows the point where controls succeed in limiting agricultural land to A_x. The difference in production corresponding to point O and point X represents chronic tendency to surplus.

According to Bottum's presentation (Chapter 12), the difference between O and X is between 40 and 70 million acres today in American agriculture. A hypothesis is that it is no mystery why we are accumulating surpluses. We are supporting prices without fully controlling production. Three main failures to control production may be mentioned. First, supports on non-allotted corn. Second, the 55-million national minimum wheat allotment. Third, lack of cross-compliance requirements.

Determined acreage controls are represented by A_0 in Figure 20.1. Because of the substitution of other inputs for land, the line A_0 falls to the left of O. That is, because of the substitution of other inputs for land at above-equilibrium product prices and rents, final demand for agricultural products can be satisfied on fewer acres than with a no-price-support equilibrium. The substitutions include those that are reversible, such as fertilizer, and those that are irreversible, such as new plant varieties.

But the precise place where A_0 would fall is a detail. The important point is that production can be controlled through acreage restriction if farmers are willing to accept the restriction. We have had substitutions, but there is simply a limit to them. At least in tobacco, we appear to be near physical maximums on fertilizer, plants per acre, disease control and other cultural practices. Research may increase yield again by irreversible changes such as varieties. But these can be met by tightening up further. Tobacco is a prime example of a commodity supported at high levels which has escaped chronic surpluses through effective control even in the face of dramatic yield advances.[2] While

[2] Tobacco has had a better demand growth than wheat, for instance, so the needed adjustments in wheat may have been more severe than in tobacco.

yield increases economize the land input, they do not necessarily decrease other inputs and may even increase some such as fertilizer. Possibly, then, the difficulty of controlling output through land restriction can be over-emphasized.

Figure 20.1 suggests that the need for controls is not likely to disappear through time. As long as parity prices are above equilibrium, there will be pressures to increase agricultural production enormously. Some have expressed the hope that the surplus problem will be solved by growth in the demand for food. Favorable to this idea, suppose population growth is rapid while technological progress in agriculture slows. Then the free market demand schedule for land DD will shift to the right. More land will be needed to grow the nation's food. In relation to present acreage restrictions, the job of control will be made easier. In other words, surpluses might be avoided with present acreage, or increases in allotments might even be called for to increase effective land supply. But acreage controls would still be necessary, because the land response to parity prices is to make for an even greater increase. Growth in demand does not eliminate the gap between PP and SS making for indefinite increase in land supply.

Some may question that land supply is perfectly elastic as depicted in Figure 20.1. This possibility was considered in earlier research. Making the most extreme assumptions about upward slope of the supply of land and about growth in demand for land led to the conclusion that the maximum rise of agricultural prices that could be expected at the farm level due to land shortage was only about 8 percent over a 20-year period.[3] This suggests that the chance is not great for free market farm prices to rise to parity levels of their own accord.

Human Input

A long-run governor of the rate of pay of the human input is the amount that can be earned in nonagriculture. The human resource may therefore be visualized to have a supply schedule for agriculture that in the long run is perfectly elastic. But in the short run, the supply is not perfectly elastic. While the Ricardian idea of land being residual claimant may be acceptable for the long run, the residual claimant status in the short run is shared by the farm operator and sometimes even by hired labor. This is because cash- and share-rental arrangements are sticky and

[3] "Alternative land development possibilities," op. cit.

because the human resource is not instantaneously mobile. The short run may extend over many years.

By now analysis is familiar with the way economic progress aggravates human resource mobility problems for agriculture, the combination of low-income elasticity of demand and high rate of technological progress reducing the human resources required to meet demands on agriculture.[4] Since at least 1920 the combination has been operating jerkily. Sluggish response of the human resource to the demand and technological changes has been a chronic depressant to farmer income, and the uneven course of the changes has repetitively renewed the strain on farmer adjustability.

The imperfect mobility of human resources in agriculture suggests there might be chronic income problems for the whole of agriculture if the free market route to elimination of surpluses were followed. But at the same time it suggests difficulties of reducing agricultural production by overt government control. People who want to farm and have resistances to leaving are going to have to be induced to get out. Something on the order of 5 percent of the people now farming might have to leave to solve the agricultural surplus problem. Which 5 percent shall it be? That is the uncomfortable question we are discussing.

A concept that may need to be in the fore is human quasi-rents. It is significant that a Gallup Poll on people's goals and outlook for the decade of the '60's revealed a preponderance of optimism, except that the 50-year-old farmer was singled out for special mention as typical of persons who do not think the future looks bright. The concept of human quasi-rents is relevant for persons who have vested comparative advantage in their chosen occupation by dint of experience. Their earnings can sink considerably before alternative employments starting at the bottom of the ladder are as profitable. Earnings can sink still further before a person may be willing to face a total readjustment.

Economic growth processes are already pushing many out of agriculture through pressure on human quasi-rents making it more difficult to superimpose further adjustments. Unfortunately lag effects can last almost a lifetime. The young farmers who were attracted by the profitability of World War II and postwar years of temporary high demand are by now committed to the point where uprooting takes a major effort.

The 30 percent reduction in flue-cured tobacco allotments

---

[4] T. W. Schultz, The Economic Organization of Agriculture, McGraw-Hill, New York, 1953, Chap. XVIII, pp. 283-320; E. O. Heady, H. G. Diesslin, H. R. Jensen, G. L. Johnson (eds.), Agricultural Adjustment Problems in a Growing Economy, Iowa State University Press, Ames, 1958.

since 1955 provides a case study of human resource adjustment when agricultural controls are clamped down.[5] Approximately 20 percent of the families on tobacco farms in North Carolina left between 1955 and 1959. Sharecroppers, who have little property and who supply mostly labor rather than management, exited in greatest numbers. The croppers who remained and the managers of the large multiple units employing the croppers were in the fortunate position of being able to carry on much as before simply by taking over the allotments of croppers who left. Single-unit operators near industrialized centers increased off-farm employment substantially, whereas in parts of the state with few urban opportunities this type of adjustment was not great. Operators in good farming areas turned to alternative crops and livestock and were able to offset at least a part of the income cut in this manner. Farm operators in relatively poor and retarded predominantly agricultural areas tended to take the income cuts with little offsetting adjustments. It is fortunate that for the state as a whole there existed a large supply of unspecialized laborers that could, in effect, be pushed out readily. The evidence suggests that, without this valve, pressure against unadjustable operators with vested management and property interests in tobacco farming might have resulted in almost a full 30 percent income cut for farm families in many areas instead of the relatively moderate cut that was possible by spreading the allotments over fewer people. Even so, reductions in welfare impinged heavily on some farmers.

Most crops in other parts of the country are not so labor intensive as tobacco, and hence the valve of unspecialized labor to make adjustments permitting less pain to all can be counted on to lesser extent. An unanswered question is how difficult human adjustments would be to eliminate surplus production.

GOALS

Conservation

Conservation may seem at first glance to be closely related to surplus elimination. One may think of taking out of production land that most needs conserving. However, three hypotheses may be stated which are in line with the view that conservation

[5]For a fuller study of adjustments, see E. C. Pasour, W. D. Toussaint and G. S. Tolley, "North Carolina Piedmont and Coastal Plain tobacco farms: their changing characteristics, 1955-1958," A. E. Info. Series No. 71, Dept. of Agr. Econ., N. C. State College, Raleigh.

does not need to be given primary consideration in seeking ways to eliminate surpluses.

A first hypothesis is that one of the major beneficial roles for soil conservation concerns critical areas and problem situations. These include erosion and sedimentation. Their effects are costly to reverse and, for several reasons including ignorance and low management ability, farmers may not take preventive measures even though a case can be made for them in economic terms. If agricultural production were brought into line with demand, millions of acres would almost certainly come out of cultivation. Especially if land were abandoned, conservation problems might be increased through lack of care for the land. This might happen in situations where natural vegetation and runoff characteristics would not enable the land effectively to take care of itself if left alone. The important point is that surplus elimination might increase critical areas needing attention, but this does not imply that decisions on which land to take out of production should be geared to soil conservation.

A second hypothesis is that a major need is to undertake soil conservation simultaneously with other forms of technical assistance, primarily those that raise management's levels. That is, improvements in the land resource and the human resource may be complementary. For conservation to pay off may require improved decision-making ability to make use of the improved land input.

The third hypothesis is that soil conservation measures tend to have maximum beneficial results if they are kept in tune with the drift of agricultural adjustments. For instance, if the trend in an area is toward large mechanized farms and away from small backward farms, those types of measures that best fit in with the mechanized operation should be pushed. The future direction of agricultural adjustments in an area may depend in part on agricultural control measures. This is another example where surplus elimination may have important implications for soil conservation but not vice versa.

Efficiency

A situation where people engage in useful activity, i.e., produce things that will be consumed, is clearly more efficient than one where they spend their time producing products which society does not want and will not pay enough to remunerate the factors used in their production at an opportunity return. This is the kind of glaring inefficiency associated with surplus agricultural production. Economists, with their refined thinking about resource use, sometimes speak about a much more stringent kind of efficiency. This stringency has to do with carrying on production at minimum cost, that is, producing what is produced in the most efficient way. A balanced view about efficiency goals may be as follows. It is very undesirable, if not absurd, to produce commodities on a mass scale in excess of what will be used. The more stringent kind of efficiency — to produce at least cost — is a goal to be pursued, but not the only goal.

If the preceding paragraph is accepted, the most important efficiency problem is reflected in the 5 percent to 8 percent of resources in agriculture producing redundant agricultural commodities. One of the least important inefficiencies is the resource recombination associated with effects of agricultural programs on relative factor prices. Acreage controls give incentives to substitute other productive factors for land, and economists have called attention to the resulting divergence from conditions for optimum resource allocation. Tobacco offers an excellent example because the price of land having acreage allotments has been raised perhaps 20 times above non-allotment land by the tobacco program.[6] If land having a tobacco allotment were valued at the opportunity return of the land, it would bring something like $100 per acre instead of a current market price of $2,000 or $3,000. The dramatic increase in the relative cost of land as a factor input appears to have induced increases in fertilization, in plants per acre and in new high-yielding varieties. <u>However</u>, a recent study indicates that if the land cost were dropped to its opportunity return, only about a penny's worth of resources would be saved per pound of tobacco.[7] The study estimated the most profitable techniques of production under land price expected <u>with</u> and <u>without</u> the program. A finding was that the main effect of the tobacco program on cost of tobacco is the direct effect of increased land costs and not the quite minor increase in real cost of production due to factor substitutions induced by the program.

Though some have said that we should pity the consumer because of high price supports on agricultural commodities, probably rightly high retail prices are not a major issue in deciding farm policy. Carrying through the analysis mentioned in the preceding paragraph, one finds that the 15 cents to 16 cents

---

[6] F. H. Maier, James L. Hedrick and W. L. Gibson, "The sale value of flue-cured tobacco allotments," Tech. Bul. 148, Virginia Polytechnic Institute, Blacksburg, 1960.

[7] L. M. Hartman and G. S. Tolley, "Effects of federal acreage control on costs and techniques of producing flue-cured tobacco," forthcoming tech. bul. of N. C. State College, Raleigh.

increase in price of tobacco at the farm level due to the program accounts for only about $1\frac{1}{2}$ cents out of 25 cents that the consumer pays for a pack of cigarettes. There should be little wonder, then, that the loss in consumer surplus due to the federal tobacco program is not a widely debated social issue. Since the effect of federal controls on allotment values for tobacco have been profoundly greater than for other commodities, inefficiencies that have been discussed for tobacco may be even less important when considering other commodities.

The present system of acreage allotments based on historical production tends to freeze in the inefficient areas and hinders relocations of agricultural production as technological changes alter regional comparative advantages. This is almost surely significant and requires more study, but it is not a national calamity. There is more urgent need to bring production in line with demand than to make sure that we reach the optimum optimorum in the location of that production.

There is a potential conflict between most efficient location of agricultural production and easing the pain of adjustment involved in cutting back on production. Taking the least efficient areas out of production will require pushing more resources out of agriculture *in toto*. Indeed, to eliminate surplus production with the least displacement of resources, the most efficient resources should be taken out.

Temperance on the efficiency issue requires recognizing the distinction between holding efficiency as one of several goals and making efficiency the sole criterion by which to judge policies. This is all the more true because the differences in real national product do not appear large under alternative schemes to curtail agricultural production. The varieties of ways in which a given agricultural output can be produced in the United States contain many widely varying alternatives whose costs are of the same order of magnitude.

Rising Gross National Product

In speaking of efficiency we were considering maximization of product at any one point in time. Now let us consider growth of output through time.

An oft-heard argument is that an efficient agriculture is needed to contribute to the nation's economic growth. The contribution of agricultural efficiency may be determined largely by the size of the sector. Though growth in output per unit of input has been erratic and is difficult to measure, the average rates of increase do not appear terribly different for agriculture and nonagriculture. Suppose gross national product is being raised 2 percent per year because of growth in output per unit of input in all sectors. Then agriculture's contribution is one-tenth of 1 percent to national growth each year on the assumption that only about a twentieth of the nation's resources are used in agriculture. In other words, if all increases in output per unit of input in agriculture ceased, the rise in per capita income for the nation would be 1.9 percent instead of 2 percent per year. While the example is only illustrative, it is numerically realistic and perhaps suffices to help place in perspective the contribution of technological revolution in agriculture to national growth.

Education of youth in agriculture possibly constitutes the biggest contribution of that sector to growth.[8] Here also we may begin seriously to run into conflicts between growth and agricultural surplus solution. The reason is that, if through education people are made more productive generally, they will become better farmers. This will tend to shift downward the aggregate supply scheduled for agricultural products and so increase tendency toward surpluses.

To develop the human resources of the nation, particularly in the South where education is poor, we may need to undertake educational programs as measures to increase national economic growth. Per pupil expenditures run less than 50 percent in some of these states compared to states which invest relatively fully in education. If investment pay-off is anywhere near proportional to expenditure, productivity could be doubled by greater educational investments in many rural areas. In view of the lagging incomes of these persons, this estimate may be conservative. At any rate, the potential contribution to economic growth appears great, and at the same time there may be an aggravation of surplus problems considering that many of the educated youth may try to stay in agriculture.

Human and Cultural Development

Education and similar efforts mentioned in the preceding section are important as ends as well as contributors to economic growth. In agriculture those most neglected in this regard are

---

[8]On the increasing awareness of the importance of education to economic growth, see T. W. Schultz, "Investment in man: an economist's view," Soc. Serv. Rev., Vol. XXXIII, No. 2, June, 1959, pp. 109-17; A. G. Frank, "Human capital and economic growth," Economic Development and Cultural Change, Vol. VIII, No. 2, Jan., 1960, pp. 170-73.

often referred to as low income farmers living in rural slums — bypassed people culturally disadvantaged relative to the majority of Americans.[9] They are inarticulate and unable to help themselves effectively within the context of their present set of circumstances.

Education and technical assistance that would help these disadvantaged persons to a life fulfillment on a par with the rest of the nation can encounter a conflict with policies to eliminate surplus agricultural production. As already noted, if people are helped to become more effective individuals, they will be more effective farmers.

Results from the Egbert-Heady model (see Chapter 11) corroborate this contention. The model is intended to show where grain would be produced in the United States at least cost and in amounts that would just meet final demand. The ex-post model using actual production costs for 1954 shows no grain production in southern regions. However, the ex-ante model, assuming that all regions were to develop to the point where production techniques were as efficient as the best known today, shows substantial grain production in the South. The indication, then, is that in the 1950's the South was a relatively inefficient producer. If investments were made in the people of the South on a larger scale, they would become better farmers and contribute to surplus problems.

The best action seems clearly not to try to mesh these goals. If helping low income farmers will aggravate surplus problems, then we should simply try to live with aggravation.

Income Equity

In addition to the problems of culturally disadvantaged individuals mentioned in the preceding section, there is a pervasive income problem associated with agricultural adjustments in process of economic growth. Even the most successful commercial farmers are touched. This problem was suggested in the analysis of human resource adjustments earlier in this chapter. The implications were that the downward pressure on the farm labor force is resulting in low human quasi-rents in agriculture.

---

[9]An idea of the prevalence of this condition can be gained from C. E. Bishop, "Underemployment of labor in southeastern agriculture," Jour. Farm Econ., Vol. XXXVI, No. 2, May, 1954, pp. 258-72; W. E. Hendrix, "Size and distribution of the income of farm people in relation to the low income problem," Jour. Farm Econ., Vol. XXXVI, No. 5, Dec., 1954, pp. 1134-44; E. G. Davis, Low-Income Farm People: A Selected List of References (Washington: USDA, 1955).

In other words, there appears to be a tendency for persons of like ability to earn less in agriculture than in nonagriculture.

Achieving farm versus nonfarm income equality requires overcoming many obstacles. High price supports can funnel more income into agriculture, but it is difficult to ensure that the increased income will go to the human factor. Later in this chapter there will be further discussion of implications of the fact that increased income tends to be capitalized into land or certificates or whatever the instrument of control of production is.

Probably an even greater obstacle to achieving income equality is reflected in the fact that the general surplus resource situation of agriculture is superimposed on a complex, heterogeneous industry. Managers are old and young, and they are efficient and inefficient. Demand shifts and technological changes make agriculture one of our most dynamic industries. Changing regional competitive advantages are constantly causing shifts in the regional concentration of production.

The income incidence of various ways of cutting back on agricultural production might be termed the unfaced heart of the farm problem. This is especially true if income is considered more important goal-wise than resource allocation in choosing among alternative farm policies.

Regional Equity

All the goals discussed so far are at least in principle well defined. Additional considerations to which the legislative process is sensitive include the repugnance to congressmen of losing constituents and to influential merchants of losing business associated with farm population. It is popular cynically to write off these considerations as imperfect politics. While this view makes for an intellectually simple world, should we definitely rule out the possibility that there is some social rationality in the machinations associated with balancing of regional and other group interests?[10] Without going more deeply, it may be noted that society will act as if important goals were being reflected. These considerations cannot afford to be ignored by those interested in giving serious counsel on solution of surplus problems.

---

[10]Economic costs and community and personal problems connected with outmigration are considered by C. L. Leven, "Regional economic development," Iowa Farm Policy Forum, Vol. 12, No. 3, 1959-60, pp. 22-32.

POLICY IN LIGHT OF GOALS

Acreage Control Versus Certificate Schemes

Acreage controls have in their favor that they can effectively restrict production. There is a misconception to the contrary, the idea apparently being that there is no limit whatever to the amount of substitution of other inputs for land that can take place. Reasons for present excess production were brought out earlier in this chapter. In a nutshell, the fault is not so much in the type of control as it is in the fact that the controls have not been applied firmly enough.

The present system of trying to keep production in bounds through acreage restriction has further in its favor that it is an accepted means of control. In this sense it works.

Economists have a penchant for recommending the control of production through saleable certificates entitling the bearer to the production of so much of a commodity. Arguments that have been advanced supporting this type of scheme are (1) that it permits agricultural production to be geographically mobile through sale of the certificates and (2) it does not induce the yield-increasing substitutions of other factors for land that is characteristic of acreage controls. The discussion of the efficiency goal in the preceding part of this chapter tried to bring out that these reasons are not or should not be the major considerations in shaping agricultural policy. Further, certificates have against them that they appear radical. Farmers and farm organizations are suspicious of them, and legislators who are against complete geographical mobility of production oppose them on these grounds. Certificates make it clear that something "artificial" is involved in federal programs.

Certificates schemes need to face the problem, which is not discussed by most of their advocates, that regardless of the form of control, there is going to have to be a substantially reduced number of resources producing in agriculture in order to bring production in line with demand. In short, who is going to produce less? Certificates will not magically accomplish this any more than acreage control does. In fact, if saleable certificates encourage more efficient production, particularly in permitting geographical movements of production, they may increase the excess resource problem over what it is with the system of acreage controls because they permit a given amount of production with less resources. The more significant question is whether production will be controlled, not the form of the controls.

Incidence of Production Restrictions

Three routes for the effects of production controls may be noted. First, people may work less. Second, they may engage in off-farm work to use the time freed by the decline in farm output. Third, there may be migration from an area, tending to leave those remaining carrying on the same amount of farm production per person as before imposition of controls.

The second and third routes help to mitigate income decline associated with having to produce less. Conditions conducive to the second and third routes are as follows.

A general factor influencing all parts of agriculture is general business conditions that affect the entire urban labor market. When there is a plenitude of industrial jobs, off-farm work and migration are both facilitated.

The influence of most of the other factors can be expected to vary greatly from area to area. Off-farm work availability depends on proximity to industry. Even more conducive to this route may be location in industrializing areas where there is active expansion of opportunities for nonfarm employment.

In view of the mechanism of farm to city migration, previous mobility from an area would seem to favor further mobility. Though migrants often move long distances, they tend to go along established paths, the first move to a new area often being arranged with the help of friends or relatives who have moved there previously. Thus, if the mobility valve is already open, it may be relatively easy to keep open.

The age-tenure displaceability of labor is probably an even more important factor affecting migration. Hired labor and sharecroppers are at the most mobile end of the scale. These people bring little but unspecialized labor to the productive process. They do not have much comparative advantage in agricultural as opposed to nonagricultural occupations, and so there is limited possibility for large human quasi-rents such as can be associated with high management skill in farming. Since they are hired by the very persons who may wish to displace them, the mechanism for the displacement is easy and direct. When production is cut back, operators can hire less labor and take over more of the chores. Managers of multiple units can reduce the number of croppers taking over some of their land. At the other end of the mobility scale from hired labor and croppers are old owners. They need to be able to take over from others, and when there are so many of them that this is difficult, the adjustment and income problems for an area may be particularly serious.

Adjustment problems may be increased by father-son leaks into farming. On the assumption that a working career is 40 years, on the average, about $2\frac{1}{2}$ percent of farmers must be retiring each year. If there were no entering farmers, this would more than take care of the reduction in farm labor force that has been witnessed in many recent years. Perhaps it is too bad that a moratorium cannot be put on entry into the farm labor force. But there is probably too much feeling that a father should be able to pass along a farm as may happen when father and son operate for a time in partnership.

This discussion of age-tenure displaceability calls attention to the mixed effects that can ensue from the population profile of an area. Consider an area where high birth rates make it appear there is much population pressure. This can have a double-barreled favorable effect on farm incomes. First, it ensures that the mobility valve will be open. Second, large families make it difficult for any one heir to acquire ownership and hence discourage father-son leaks into farming. These factors offset to some extent the unfavorable influence, namely, that high farm birth rates may increase the number of persons entering the labor force who have a determination to farm.

To proceed to another condition that helps offset unfavorable income effects of production restrictions, <u>substitute farm enterprises</u> may be available in some areas. In the past, failure to control all agricultural production and the lack of cross-compliance requirements have made this an important form of adjustment greatly contributing to surplus problems, as was brought out earlier in this chapter. With effective production control, this form of adjustment would be minimized.

Finally, adjustment to production restriction will be made more difficult if there are large <u>existing pressures on the man-land ratio</u> of an area due to mechanization and other changes in production technique. These pressures are already reducing the demand for the human input and so are already taxing the adjustability of some areas.

The foregoing list of possible income adjustments in response to production restrictions emphasizes the widely differing incidence that controls may have. Consider now the further complication to the income effects engendered by the level of price supports, if any, that goes with the controls. A central consideration is that capitalization effects make it difficult to ensure that increased income will go to the human input. Many have stressed that acreage controls lead to capitalization of income effects of agricultural programs into land, whereas with the certificate scheme, capitalization would be into the value of the certificates.

While the capitalization phenomenon is often considered an undesirable result of programs, perhaps there are both pros and cons. After all, there is some overlap between farmers and owners. The older farmer tends to be an owner. These are the people most likely to be hurt by agricultural adjustments associated with growth. The capitalization might not be deleterious to anyone, if the agricultural sector was comprised entirely of owner-operators each of whom had one heir who was male and would take over the farm. In reality, benefits tend to be diffused among many heirs. The undesirability of this can be overstated. Does not attention to human quasi-rents suggest that it is older farmers whom society should be primarily interested in helping rather than their offspring?

A frequent criticism of the capitalization effects associated with acreage or certificate control is that they hinder young people from getting into farming. In seriousness it may be said that this is a good effect. The more important criticism of these schemes may be that they do not make it difficult enough for the young people to get into farming.[11]

How can an optimum incidence of income effects of controls be arranged? This section has served to emphasize the difficulty of answering the question. Most suggested solutions would have a potpourri of effects. Large windfalls might be given via high price supports in areas where off-farm work is readily available or where labor push-out occurs easily. On the other hand, cutbacks, even if accompanied by substantial rises in price support levels, might not succeed in avoiding harm in areas of low mobility and little possibility of off-farm work.

The discussion of goals in the earlier part of this chapter suggests that important criteria in cutting back on production may be income equity and regional balancing of interests. Adherence to these criteria is blocked by lack of knowledge of the income effects of alternative programs.

A suggestion: self-financing entry control for agriculture. As brought out above, acreage controls and certificate schemes have the disadvantage in common that — no matter the level at which agricultural prices are supported — the programs cannot be expected to eliminate the disparity between returns to the human

[11]However, the present control program is having some effects in restricting entry to farming in addition to land price effects. Customary share rental arrangements make the rental market at least a little imperfect so as to discriminate against the younger farmer. The landlord and tenant share the products on a customary fractional split. The landlord knows that the more experienced farmer will get better results and so rents to him rather than the younger farmer where there is a choice. This has the good effect of encouraging the younger farmer to go to town.

resource in agriculture and nonagriculture. Increased incomes due to the programs will tend to accrue not to labor but to owners of the instruments of program control, via capitalization.

Let us distinguish three types of equilibria. Suppose, under all of them, that average stock accumulation were zero, i.e., production were in line with demand. First, there is the equilibrium that might occur under acreage or certificate restriction of production. The value of allotments or of certificates would depend on the level of price support, but the return to the human input in agriculture would be below that in nonagriculture due to the adjustments associated with economic growth. The differential would be associated with the continued outmovement of the human input from agriculture. A second type of equilibrium is a free market equilibrium. In this situation there would be no allotment value, and the value of land would be determined largely by marginal adjustments in land as discussed earlier in this chapter. The tendency of the rate of pay of the human input in agriculture to be below that in nonagriculture might be just about the same as in the first type of equilibrium. Finally, a third type of equilibrium might be referred to as a Pareto factor equilibrium where the human resource in agriculture receives a rate of pay equal to what it could receive in nonagriculture. This would have to be accomplished by a different kind of government program. There would be direct financial inducements to adjust the number of persons in agriculture. While the taxpayer might bear this expense, perhaps the better alternative would be to have high enough price supports so that the scheme could be self-financing within agriculture. A part of the receipts from agricultural production could go into a fund for controlling entry into farming. This fund would be used to attract people out of agriculture. This idea is a variant of the homesteads-in-reverse proposal of T. W. Schultz.[12]

If the scheme mentioned in the preceding paragraph raised agricultural prices only enough to finance the outmovement of people to attain equal factor rewards, the welfare criterion for economic efficiency ought to come closer to being satisfied than under the free market equilibrium. But this is not the primary motive for suggesting the scheme. The primary motive is to eliminate income disparity.

The proposal does not solve the key problem of which resources are to be moved out of agriculture. However, it proposes to get them out by financial incentives, which ought to

---

[12] T. W. Schultz, "Homesteads in reverse," Iowa Farm Policy Forum, Vol. 8, No. 5, 1956, pp. 12-14.

minimize the inconveniences and hurts as compared with arbitrary quantitative effects associated with acreage controls or certificate schemes. The proposal is suggested as a general direction for policy that needs investigating. The details could take on many forms. There would undoubtedly be many problems of implementation in view of the heterogeneity of agriculture.

To avoid giving the impression that the aim is to "get people out of farming," legislation might be framed in terms of licenses to farm. Entry into farming would be controlled by purchase and sale of these permits. In times of surplus accumulation the government would raise the price of the permits so that more farmers would be induced to sell their permits to the government.

In view of inelasticity of demand for farm products, there seems little doubt that the revenue to finance the net payments for outmovement could be raised through higher prices of farm products so that costs to the United States Treasury could be eliminated. This would have the advantage of discouraging the habit of agriculture as an interest group using the tax dollar which is so badly needed for other purposes.

CONCLUSION

Highlights

A purpose of the first part of the chapter was to show that attempts to control agricultural surpluses should be made taking cognizance of the nature of resource use equilibration in agriculture. The equilibration is influenced by highly elastic long-run supply curves for land and for the human input. In the short run, imperfect mobility leads to inelasticity of supply of human input so that labor shares a residual claimant status with land. The human immobility, together with chronic downward shifts in the demand for human input in agriculture, means that many do not earn as much in agriculture as earned by persons of equal ability in nonagriculture.

Discussion of the goals of policy in the second part of the chapter brought out the following contentions relevant to current policy debates:

(1) The kind of inefficiency most to be avoided is waste of product. Another kind of inefficiency, failure to achieve least-cost production, does not appear to merit overriding consideration in formulating agricultural policy in view of the smallness of losses to consumers associated with it.

(2) To contribute to the nation's economic growth, to further the human and cultural development of many disadvantaged citizens and to raise the level of living of rural-slum farmers, education and other assistance are needed in poor areas. Elimination of agricultural surpluses seems less important than the goals just mentioned. Helping farmers in poverty can contribute to surplus problems. The analysis suggests this should be allowed to happen.

(3) One of the most important goals of agricultural policy may be to achieve equal incomes for persons of comparable ability. Another related goal is to achieve an equitable balancing of regional interests. Due to economic growth adjustments leading to low human quasi-rents, an income disparity problem pervades the efficient commercial segments of agriculture as well as the poverty-stricken segments. Lack of knowledge about the income incidence of various ways of cutting back on agricultural production is a major hindrance to formulating desirable policies.

The third part of the chapter considered policy alternatives. A conclusion was that acreage restrictions have been overmaligned as a method of controlling production. They can be made to work, and they have the advantage, over restrictions on physical quantities of marketings, that they are a more accepted means of control. Instead of centering on method of control, the more important policy questions may concern who shall produce less in eliminating surpluses. Ease of adjustment in different areas might most desirably influence this choice. Factors affecting ease of adjustment are: off-farm work availability, previous mobility from an area, age-tenure displaceability of labor, substitute farm enterprises and existing pressures on the man-land ratio.

The discussion of alternative policies closed with a suggestion to try self-financing entry control for agriculture. This ought to be more effective than direct production controls in eliminating low human quasi-rents in agriculture. The scheme proposes to restrict production through payments to enter or leave farming financed by price supports high enough to avoid drain on the United States Treasury.

Economists' Contributions to Policy Formation

The discussion of this chapter suggests two major needs for analysis of policies. The first need is to attack more vigorously the technical job of estimating the income incidence of various ways of cutting back on agricultural production. The object would be to supply information enabling decision-makers better to face the immediately pressing problem of getting rid of surplus production.

The second need, more in the realm of social philosophy, is to devise policies in light of social goals and values. In this way, a contribution can be made to achieving a longer-run satisfactory solution for agriculture. A burden of this chapter has been to show that this latter task will be aided if efficiency is not taken as the only goal but instead is seen in perspective as one of several goals.

Chapter 21

DONALD R. KALDOR
Iowa State University

Adjusting Land Inputs and Use Toward Production Control and Increased Returns to Farmers

TWENTY CHAPTERS have been presented on various technological and economic aspects of land use and its relation to the problem of disequilibrium in the farm industry. In the aggregate, they represent a prodigious volume of ideas, hypotheses, facts and projections. My assignment is to summarize and comment on this mass of material.

FARM PROBLEM

The farm industry is in serious economic difficulty. On this there seems to be general agreement among the authors. It is characterized by surpluses, low prices and disparities in income-earning opportunities. These, however, are but the outward manifestation of a more basic problem — an excess supply of resources. The amount of disequilibrium created by such forces as rapid technical progress, changing input prices, growth in per capita income and a decline in export demand has been more than the industry could digest. While adjustments have been taking place at a fast pace, the rate of resource adaptation has lagged far behind the rate of disequilibrium creation. As a result, we have an industry that is producing too much output at too high a total resource cost.

The level of output is excessive in the sense that it cannot clear markets at a level of prices that will permit comparable returns to labor and capital on well-organized farms. If markets were allowed to clear, returns on such farms would fall substantially below opportunity cost levels. In producing a more optimum level of output, fewer resources will be needed.

Because of outmoded technology and inefficient resource combinations, resource costs per unit of output are extremely high on many farms. As a result, total farm output could be increased significantly, even with some reduction in total input and no new technical knowledge. Fewer resources also will be needed if the present level of output is to be produced at a total resource cost approaching the feasible minimum. This condition is one of the chief obstacles to effective production control via a modest reduction in inputs. I am inclined to disagree with the view expressed by Tolley (Chapter 20) that this is a relatively unimportant kind of inefficiency in agriculture.

In brief, this seems to be the present situation. Without special programs, is it likely that the problem of excess resources will disappear with the passage of time? Several chapters have focused on future technological and economic developments. What impressions do they leave?

LONG-RANGE OUTLOOK FOR THE GENERAL ECONOMY

Knowles (Chapter 2) presented a number of projections of gross national product. They suggest that the future rate of potential growth is high, appreciably higher than the historical rate. Real gross national product in 1975 could be nearly 90 percent greater than the level in 1959. In the year 2000 it could exceed the trillion dollar level.

The realization of these levels will require, among other things, a sufficient expansion in aggregate demand to maintain full employment, and a high capacity for resource adaptation. This kind of growth is likely to have a big impact on the structure of demand for resources.

The assumption of a maximum level of unemployment of 4 percent may be somewhat optimistic. Although the chances of a really serious depression are pretty small, the probabilities of some significant departures from full employment appear fairly high. Nevertheless, the long-range outlook for a high and reasonably steady rate of increase in per capita income is bright.

OUTLOOK FOR FOOD AND FIBER

The demand for food and fiber in the years ahead will continue to expand with the growth in population and rising incomes. However, the upward trend in per capita income is likely to add a declining increment to demand because of the diminishing income elasticity for food.

The growth in per capita income also will modify the pattern of demand for farm products. Demands for the higher income elasticity products such as meat and poultry will expand faster than the demands for the lower income elasticity products such as eggs and milk. Inasmuch as the income elasticity for cereals and potatoes is apparently negative, the demands for these products will increase only as long as population growth offsets the effect of rising income. Population growth is likely to be rapid enough to expand the total demand for these products, but the rate of expansion will be smaller than for most farm commodities. So much for the qualitative aspects.

The projections presented by Koffsky (Chapter 3) indicate that with a medium population increase, farm output in 1980 would need to be about 45 percent larger than in 1958 to meet projected requirements. This is equivalent to an annual rate of increase in total requirements of about 1.75 percent. In 1980 domestic use would be up 68 percent for meat animals, 49 percent for dairy products and only 33 percent for cereals and potatoes. Farm exports in 1980 are projected to be 27 percent higher than in 1958.

Two additional effects of rising incomes should be noted. As a result of the higher income elasticity for the services associated with food, the proportion of the consumer's food dollar spent on farm products is likely to continue its downward trend. Again because of differences in income elasticities, growth in per capita income will increase the demands for nonfarm products more than the demand for farm products. In the competition for resources, nonfarm industries will be in a position to outbid the farm industry. Unless offsetting factors come into play, this is likely to mean some continuous cost-price squeeze in farming.

As pointed out by Koffsky, the range of possibilities in projecting long-run demands for food and fiber is large. Different assumptions about the rate of growth of population can have a big effect on the level of requirements. Apparently some of the recent demographic developments are prompting some speculation about the continuation of the high rate of population growth.

What is the outlook on the supply side? Here the uncertainties are even greater, partly because less is known about the supply function than the demand function, and partly because there is less basis for predicting the future levels of the variables entering the supply function. Until we can do a better job of explaining past changes in farm output, there is little basis for projecting future output. This is a research job that will require the joint efforts of physical scientists and economists. A breakthrough is badly needed.

The consensus of the authors seems to be that farm output will continue its upward trend in the absence of a more vigorous public effort to restrain the forces of expansion. This is a reasonable expectation in view of (1) the size of the technological gap and the possibilities of tightening internal efficiency in the farm industry, (2) the likelihood that more resources will be poured into research, (3) the high rate of transformation of research resources into improved production methods and (4) the continued improvement in the quality of the labor-management input.

On the crucial question of the rate of increase in output, one can find more diversity of opinion. Over the short run, say 5 to 10 years, the balance of professional judgement seems to support the view that farm output will continue to grow at a rate at least as high as that of the recent past. The studies of production, prices and incomes under conditions approximating free markets, conducted in the USDA and Iowa, gave results that are reasonably consistent with this view. The presentations by agronomists do not seem to contradict the belief.

For the longer run, the range of opinion widens considerably. Some argue that because of non-repetitive factors, the longer term rate of expansion is likely to be less than that of the recent past. I gather from Bressler (Chapter 13) that he is still inclined to this view. On the other hand, it is not hard to find other competent scientists who will argue that the rate of technical progress is rising, that we are on the verge of important new discoveries which will greatly expand our capacity to produce and that the technological gap is becoming smaller and smaller. Obviously, we need more research on which to base projections of future output if these conflicting beliefs are to be resolved.

With respect to comparative rates of growth of output and demand in the absence of effective control programs, the consensus seems to be that supply will continue to press heavily on demand for at least a decade. Present output capacity probably exceeds the current long-run equilibrium level by 6 to 8 percent. Thus, it would take several years for demand to catch up, on the assumption that output remained at recent levels. Even if output were to grow at a slower rate than in the past, this would add several more years. If at the same time stocks were to be reduced to more normal levels, the time at which supply and demand were brought into balance at a long-run equilibrium, prices would be pushed still farther into the future.

OUTLOOK FOR OTHER LAND-USING ACTIVITIES

A growing population and rising per capita income also will expand future demands for recreational facilities, forest products, transportation service and space for living and conducting business. Apparently the income elasticity of demand for most of these goods and services is moderately to substantially higher than for food and fiber. The income elasticity for recreation services is especially high. Thus, future demands for these things might be expected to grow more rapidly than the future demand for farm products.

The supplies of outdoor recreation facilities, forest products, transportation services and space for urban development are determined to a large extent by the actions of public bodies. It is undoubtedly true that our political machinery is less efficient than the price system in providing increased supplies to meet increased demands. The situation in education is perhaps a good example. Thus, the amount of resources devoted to the production of those public goods and services experiencing secular increases in demand may be substantially less than the economic optimum. This seems to be especially true with respect to outdoor recreational facilities.

Clawson (Chapter 4) presented projections of land needs for recreation, transportation and urban development for the year 2000. Adding these figures together gives a total land need of about 115 million acres. This is equivalent to an annual rate of increase of about 2 percent. If these requirements were to be met, it would mean that in the year 2000 the amount of land devoted to these activities would be more than double the level of recent years.

Held's figures (Chapter 14) are for 1985. He puts the total for that year at about 65 million acres. The amount of cropland involved is estimated at only 16 or 17 million acres, however.

The projections for forest products given by Hopkins (Chapter 10) are for the year 2000 and are based on a Forest Service study. For the medium level of consumption they show a 45 percent deficit in total growing stock and a 76 percent deficit in saw timber. While I have some reservations about these figures, they are suggestive. These gaps were not translated into land requirements. However, I gained the impression that a large part of the projected deficits might be met most economically by additional investment in and better management of existing forest lands. This view seems to be reasonably consistent with that expressed by Held (Chapter 14).

LAND REQUIREMENTS PER UNIT OF OUTPUT

A number of the authors have recognized that the amount and quality of land used per unit of output varies widely among the principal land using activities. In order to gauge the future structure of demand for land, one needs to know, among other things, both the future structure of demand for the products of land and the future production coefficients -- how much of what quality land will be used per unit of each kind of product.

Heady (Chapter 1) stressed the point that the amount of land used per unit of farm production has been declining over the years. Advances in farm technology have raised the marginal productivity of capital relative to that of land and encouraged a substitution effect. Since 1940 the substitution of capital for land has also been stimulated by a relative decline in the price of capital. These developments have tended to reduce the relative demand for land in farm production.

I am not aware of any comparable changes in the production of other important land-using products. Undoubtedly, there have been some, but none perhaps as dramatic as the developments in farm production. However, there have been some improvements in other land-using activities that have had the opposite effect. For example, the development of bigger and faster airplanes has required larger landing fields.

LAND POLICY GOALS

In part, this volume has been concerned with the specification of needed land use adjustments. Such an activity implies some image of an optimum, or at least a more optimum, allocation and use of land resources. This requires, among other things, the identification and ordering of policy goals. In view of this, it is somewhat surprising that more attention has not been given to the goals of land use adjustment. Tolley (Chapter 20) does the best job on this score.

What is society trying to accomplish in land policy? Are the goals competitive and/or complementary? What are the relations between the goals of land policy and other policy goals? What are the marginal rates of substitution? The answers to these questions are necessary for the rational programming of land resources.

It is reasonably clear that recent land policies have involved a number of goals, including regional development, higher farm income, conservation, economic efficiency, distributive justice and family farming. It is equally clear that the effort to achieve all these goals via land policy has produced some serious inefficiencies. For example, the policy of encouraging short-run output-increasing capital investment in land on grounds of conservation and regional development has been working at cross purposes with the policy of reducing farm output through land retirement.

There seem to be two goals especially relevant to the subject matter of this volume: (1) the social goal of achieving a maximum real national product and (2) the farm policy goal of achieving a solution to the imbalance problems of the farm industry. These goals are implicitly or explicitly recognized in a number of the chapters dealing with land use adjustments. However, it makes some difference whether one approaches the problem of land use adjustment from the viewpoint of national income or from the viewpoint of surplus farm production.

If the approach is from the standpoint of national income, the critical questions are: (1) what adjustments in land use will contribute most to increasing the national income and (2) to what extent will these adjustments contribute to the solution of the output imbalance problem of the farm industry?

In approaching the problem from the viewpoint of farm surpluses, the principal question concerns the amounts and qualities of land that need to be removed from farm production to balance supply and demand at "satisfactory" prices. By and large, this is the approach of the Soil Bank and other proposals for land retirement. A secondary question sometimes raised in connection with these proposals is how the land retired from farm production can best be used to enhance the national income.

NEEDED LAND USE ADJUSTMENTS

Both approaches are likely to give some of the same land use adjustment answers. Given the technological and economic outlook for the 1960's, it seems clear that the amount of land devoted to farm production should be reduced. Likewise, the proportion of farm land devoted to labor and capital intensive crops should be decreased, whereas the proportion devoted to hay and pasture should be increased.

From the viewpoint of national income, the land withdrawn from agricultural uses should be employed in other land-using activities which have a greater value productivity. Most of it probably should go into recreational uses, much smaller quantities into urban development and forestry and a very small amount to transportation. However, most of the proposals to reduce farm production through land retirement make no provision for getting land withdrawn from agriculture into more productive nonfarm uses.

When it comes to the matter of quantities, the two approaches are likely to give quite different results. If one starts with the question — how much land should be taken out of farm production to solve the output imbalance problem — the answer will involve an amount of land withdrawn from farm production which is almost certain to be larger than the amount that would be withdrawn to maximize the real national product. The reason is clear. More of the output-reducing effect will be induced by the decrease in land input and less by the decrease in other inputs.

Heady (Chapter 1) and Chryst and Timmons (Chapter 17) made the point that land use adjustments cannot be specified independently of adjustments in labor and capital inputs. If we reduce farm output to the equilibrium level by withdrawing land, there is a range of possible effects on the input of labor. If whole farms are withdrawn, the reduction in labor input per unit of land withdrawn will be equal to the average ratio of labor to land on the farms taken out of production. This method is likely to induce the largest reduction in labor input. Toward the other extreme would be a land withdrawal program that distributed the reduction in land input among all farms. This type of program is likely to have little effect on labor input.

But even in the most favorable case — that of withdrawing whole farms — the reduction in the amount of labor is likely to be too small in relation to the reduction in land input for the most efficient residual combination of resources. The farms withdrawn from production are likely to be units with too high a ratio of labor-to-land for low-cost production, partly because of selectivity effects and partly because there are many more of these farms.

For years, farm management specialists have emphasized the importance of having an adequate land base in achieving a well-organized unit. However, if farm size is to be increased, it means that the ratio of the reduction in labor input to the reduction in land input must be greater than the ratio of labor-to-land on the average farm. Only then will more land be available per unit of labor. What seems to be needed from the standpoint of national income is a relatively large reduction in labor input and a small reduction in land input with heavy emphasis on more extensive use of agricultural land.

A land withdrawal program may affect national income in another way. If land is simply retired from all productive use, it makes no contribution to the national product. From the standpoint of national income, it is better to produce food that has some value than to produce nothing. Of course, if people attach a lower value to the increment in food than they attached to the increment of other products that could be produced with the resources, it is even better to produce the increment of other products.

During the 1960's a land withdrawal program of the size needed to reduce output to an equilibrium level is likely to involve more land than can be efficiently employed in other major land-using activities. Undoubtedly, some land needs to be reallocated from farm production to these activities on the ground of increasing the national income. However, this amount is probably small in relation to the quantity that would need to be withdrawn from farming to achieve an equilibrium level of output. If more than this amount were allocated to these uses, the marginal social cost would exceed the marginal social benefit. In terms of national income, too many resources in these employments can be just as bad as too few.

While land retirement might rate as only a "third or fourth best solution" from the standpoint of national income and its distribution, it undoubtedly rates higher in terms of political acceptability. Moreover, if properly designed, it could make some positive contribution to needed long-run adjustments in resource use in the farm industry. Egbert and Dumenil (Chapter 11) present some useful ideas and information along this line.

If a land retirement program is to make its maximum contribution to needed resource adjustment, land should be withdrawn as whole farms in areas at the extensive margin. However, such a program is likely to magnify the secondary adjustment problems in areas of heavy land withdrawal. These problems have been pointed up by Ottoson (Chapter 19). For this reason, many people in these areas are likely to oppose this kind of land retirement program. It now appears that if Congress does provide for a big increase in the Conservation Reserve, it is likely to emphasize land retirement on all farms. While this might be more acceptable at the moment than other variations, it is also likely to be the least efficient alternative and the most difficult to make effective.

Raup and Learn (Chapter 16) presented an interesting analysis of the land use effects of a generalized marketing quota program with salable marketing certificates. This type of program is likely to give more effective control over market supplies than a land retirement program. However, the output-reducing effect is achieved in the same way — by unemploying or underemploying resources. The big difference is that the input of land is likely to be cut back less, and the input of labor and capital more, with a generalized marketing quota program. Within the farm industry, the forces of competition would still determine the allocation of output and input among producers.

From the standpoint of national income, its chief weakness is its failure to provide any effective mechanism for getting unneeded land, labor and capital in agriculture re-employed in more productive nonfarm employments and for easing the stresses and strains associated with such an adjustment. Moreover, it is likely to provide the most benefits for those who already have the highest incomes. On this score, it falls in the same class as other programs, including land retirement, which distribute the increase in farm income among individual producers in almost direct proportion to the amount of resources owned and controlled.

Chapter 22

W. ROBERT PARKS
Iowa State University

Political Acceptability of Suggestions for Land Adjustment

AS I APPROACHED my assignment of analyzing and appraising the proposals for public action in terms of their political acceptability, and became increasingly aware of all of the frustrations and difficulties involved in such an undertaking, I could not but recall the classic reaction of Thomas Carlyle when told of the favorite statement of the New England transcendentalist, Margaret Fuller. To her proclamation: "I accept the universe," Carlyle's grim comment was, "Gad! she'd better!"

This is not to intimate that I am undertaking this analysis with the exuberant and expansive confidence and optimism with which Margaret Fuller accepted the universe. Rather, in Carlyle's grim spirit of inevitability, I think that "I'd better" recognize and accept at the outset those difficulties and frustrations which are inherent in the problem. I think it is the better part of academic wisdom immediately to face up to the limitations which such an analysis must have and the criticisms to which it can legitimately be subjected.

Such an analysis must, of course, be highly subjective in its definition of terms, in its selection of the factors which determine political acceptability and in its interpretation of the meaning and weight of these factors. In the first place, how is political acceptability itself to be defined? The meaning of political acceptability might be subjected to various refinements. For purposes of discussion here, however, let us pragmatically define a proposal as politically acceptable whose goals or purposes and the methods and procedures prescribed for achieving these goals are such that the proposals (1) could be enacted into law by the policy-determining machinery of government and (2) would be sufficiently acceptable to the broad masses of citizens affected by it that it would be enforceable. (The classic example of legislation which met the first, but not the second, of these pragmatic tests of acceptability was, of course, prohibition legislation.)

This is an example of government's being called upon merely

to restrain the citizen. Today, however, public action — particularly in the field of agriculture and natural resources — usually requires more in the way of consent from the citizen than merely refraining from taking action. Rather, he is expected to cooperate in a positive fashion — as is typified in the "sign up" in many agricultural programs. The second test of acceptability, therefore, is growing increasingly important.

A second question is: How is a proposal's "acceptability potential" to be measured? That is, which factors or forces in the policy-making process are critical in determining a proposal's political acceptability? The factors an individual selects as critical will depend upon his views of the nature of representative government, of the relationships between government and citizens and upon his interpretation of the workings of the decision-making process of government.

For example, does he view the decision-making process as power politics in the raw, a process in which political might makes policy? How much weight does he assign to the interplay of party politics? Commodity politics? Executive-congressional politics? Does he think that political acceptability could be determined if we could accurately measure the relative strength of the various blocs of power in the representative process? Does he feel that our elected representatives reflect the psychology and the views, and the needs and the interests, of the persons and groups of persons they are purported to represent? Or does he believe that the whims and fancies of the human personalities who are manning the policy machinery play a determining role? To what extent does he feel that the personal predilections of elected representatives, the shadows on the wall which congressmen and executive officials sometimes see as reality, the web of personal relationships, loyalties, obligations, friendships and personal antipathies affect the political acceptability of a proposal?

Clearly, one's answers to such questions as these will influence one's judgment upon the political acceptability of a proposed public action. Moreover, even if we could all agree on the relative weight to assign to each of the forces at work in the policy-determining process, we, as students, still have not sufficiently refined our tools so that we could precisely measure and predict how the interaction of these various forces would affect a given policy proposal.

The measurement of political acceptability is made still more difficult because the acceptability potential of a particular proposal is not static. Its acceptability varies with the particular point in time at which it is introduced in the decision-making process. In terms of time, a proposal's political acceptability depends upon much more than where it occurs upon the time continuum of American social progress. Obviously, ideas are politically acceptable today which would have been feared and hated in the days of McKinley, let us say. Many of the collective actions taken by Franklin Roosevelt's New Deal would have been totally unacceptable in the days of T. R.'s Square Deal. Thus, the political acceptability of some proposals for public action, which probably would not be approved by the machinery of government today, should be evaluated by projecting our social progress continuum over a 20, 30 or perhaps even 50 year future period.

Also, a proposal's political acceptability, in terms of time, will depend upon more than the social climate of the times. We all know that proposals for governmental action which are politically acceptable in a period of major economic depression, which generates a spirit for social pioneering, would be completely unacceptable in a period of prosperous, sluggish complacency, such as the 1950's. For example, nationalization of the United States banking system would probably have been politically acceptable, according to both tests which we have set up, in the early dark spring days of 1933. But can you imagine with what abhorrence such a proposal would be greeted today?

In short, it does not take a long period of changing social values and attitudes toward collective action, or even a national crisis such as a major depression or a military emergency, to change a proposal's acceptability potential. It does not even take a congressional or presidential election. The political patterns in the decision-making process which determine whether a particular proposal will be accepted are like a child's kaleidoscope. They are endlessly shifting as the multiplicity of factors in the policy-making process form and reform into differing prevailing opinions. The patterns of prevailing opinion shift and change as the perceptions, aspirations, fears, ambitions, loyalties and antipathies of the human personalities, the interest groups, the political parties and even the branches of government change. These patterns can be transformed, almost overnight, by such occurrences as the publication of the findings of a public opinion poll, a readjustment in the relationship between Congress and the executive, the flaring up of personal animosity between the secretary of agriculture and key congressmen in his own political party, a new rapport among several commodity interests in Congress, a sharp falling off in the price of hogs, the prediction of a bumper wheat crop, even the death of an influential senator.

For all of these reasons, any sort of *ad hoc* operational analyses of how, in particular instances, the forces within the decision-making process might combine to determine the acceptability of particular proposals could only be highly speculative. Moreover, I think that it would be more meaningful and useful if we could view political acceptability more broadly and in longer-range terms — that is, if we could discover and define the confining socio-political frameworks which, under our American system of representation, set the outer bounds and determine the norms for political acceptability. Such frameworks are the broad, containing political patterns within which the lesser and more temporary political patterns form and reform. They, too, are in a process of change. But they are less ephemeral and transient. These frameworks might be compared with the great cyclonic storm systems which move slowly across the continent, with many lesser cyclonic circulations swirling around and changing patterns within their bounds. If they could be meaningfully and accurately defined, these frameworks could, I believe, provide broad measurements or guidelines for determining any proposal's acceptability potential.

These broad, containing forms which confine, shape and regulate our day-to-day and even year-to-year political behavior might be defined and classified in various ways. I realize that one's definitions will depend upon one's views of the nature of the political process. For purposes of preliminary discussion here, however, I shall suggest these four: (1) the frame of prevailing social attitudes, (2) the frame of the American constitutional system, (3) the frame of the two-party system operating in a nation of continental proportions and (4) the frame of basic interest. I do not insist that these are the only important containing frames, or that they are accurately defined or interpreted. I offer them tentatively, as suggestions which may stimulate further thinking and analysis.

The broadest and most fundamental containing framework is, I believe, the frame of basic social values. There is, I think, a force of broad, popular thinking which sets the limits within which the governmental decision-making process must find its policies. Unorganized, amorphous, groping uncertainly to understand its needs and wants, there is a body of mass opinion which, although influenced and sometimes distorted by the symbols and propaganda of organized groups and institutions, is somehow under and apart from the organized entities of society. This broad opinion is not to be interpreted in terms of an expression of individual or group interest alone; it is not the result of the weighing of particularized pressures; it is more than the sum total of special interest. Over the years, this broad stream of public opinion has rolled along, sometimes sluggish, muddy, unclear, and at other times turbulent and demanding. But, at all times, it has, I believe, in the long run, framed and set the norms for political acceptability.

The first set of social values which, I think, helps to explain the shape and content of many of our agricultural policies today is a series of attitudes which arise out of what Felix Frankfurter once called the "unresolved inner conflict." This is the conflict within the individual between the traditional picture he has in his head of the proper and suitable role of government, on the one hand, and on the other hand, his increasing need for and reliance upon government brought on by the new environmental coercions he is experiencing.

Americans still quite commonly hold to a concept of government developed during their revolutionary past when their ancestors were trying to break the bounds of an arbitrary, if not tyrannical, government. This is a concept of government which, for over a hundred years, fitted Americans' needs quite well, because of the peculiarly open nature of economic opportunity in a rich and sparsely settled continent. It is a concept of government developed out of the eighteenth century enlightenment belief that there are natural economic and social laws which, if unrestricted by government, will efficiently work out men's salvation. The free market is, of course, the earthly manifestation of these natural laws. Therefore, government must be considered a "necessary evil." The government which is best is the government which governs least. A citizen has natural rights, including the right of property, which are outside the grasp of the state. Government generally is to be feared, distrusted and restricted to narrow limits.

At the same time, however, that the citizen holds to these eighteenth century concepts of the good government, he has found it necessary to go, albeit unwillingly, to government, seeking its assistance and protection against the new hazards his twentieth century environment is creating. What, then, has been the effect of this mass social schizophrenia upon resulting public policy? What limits has it set upon political acceptability? I am aware of the danger of reducing social behavior to an over-simple formula. Nevertheless, I believe that the conflict between the way we view the role of government in the broad, and the things we want from government for ourselves as individuals has been a powerful limiting force in determining what is politically acceptable — in determining what government should do and how it should do it.

First, it has limited the political acceptability of long-range programming. It has caused the political process to reject long-term solutions in favor of short-term palliatives, although such palliatives may be both costly and ineffective. For, if one believes in the efficacy of an unfettered economy, then the economic maladjustments and particular hardships which the individual experiences must be considered to be mere temporary abnormalities which do not require long-term solutions. One goes to government merely to seek immediate relief from a temporary hardship. One does not, for example, see the need for a long-term land retirement program.

In defense of our political process, I must say, however, that I do not think that it is only "original sin" — in the form of an unresolved inner conflict — which leads our elected representatives frequently to reject long-term programs. Often, I think, it is because our laymen politicians are astute enough to realize that the experts themselves are confused by the complexities of the problems of agricultural adjustment, and sometimes are even in conflict as to what are the best solutions. Consequently, they are reluctant to commit government's power and resources, on a long-term basis, to any programs, based upon what Ray Bressler (Chapter 13) describes as "simplified and partial analysis," which sometimes is the best that the expert can offer the politician. Professor Bressler, in introducing his paper at the conference, frankly and modestly pointed out: "The end product will be a far cry from the 'ideal land use pattern' suggested by the Program Committee, but it will exhaust my abilities in that direction." With equal frankness, D. B. Ibach (Chapter 9) explained: "I have attempted to outline some of the factors by which we might project economic potentials in agriculture. For crop production, I have ventured some quantitative evaluation in relation to projected needs for 1980. Five years from now, probably sooner, I may want to alter the picture as presented for purposes of this discussion." Similar modest disclaimers can be found in many of the other chapters. Now, I submit that these honest statements from recognized experts are no way to "buck up" a politician's courage to vote for a long-term program! Seriously, however, I do think that the failure to adopt long-term programs may not be primarily a political failure, but a failure in our "expert knowledge."

Secondly, our social schizophrenia has limited the use of planning as a process for developing public policies. If long-range programs are not needed, then, it clearly follows that a planning process for developing such programs is also unnecessary. Planning as an organized entity in the process of government is still suspect as being the insidious enemy of an unrestricted economic order. As James Knowles (Chapter 2) pointed out, certain activities in a planning process have, over the past two decades, gained respectability. He began his chapter with this statement: "In the last two decades the use of long-range projections of the growth possibilities of the American economy has become standard practice in many areas of public and private decision-making. Its use has become commonplace in the areas of agricultural policy, water resources development...and various other public programs...." Mr. Knowles emphasizes the "calm, routine character of such projections compared to the controversies of only a decade or so ago...."

We who were in the Bureau of Agricultural Economics during the 1940's — when even economic fact-finding stirred congressional furor and deeper budget cuts — can well appreciate what a significant step forward the public decision-making process has taken. However, fact-finding and projections are only the initial stages in a planning process. I rather suspect that the planning organizations in government today are still only tolerated as long as their activities are narrowly circumscribed and their personnel is circumspect.

Third, our belief in narrowly limited government lessens the acceptability of comprehensive and inclusive programs, within which the goals and methods used for solving particularized agricultural problems can be integrated into a consistent overall pattern of action. As Earl Heady (Chapter 1) pointed out: "We have created a maze of programs which simultaneously subsidize improvements of land to (1) increase current production at the expense of the future, (2) pay farmers for withholding land from current production and (3) conserve the land for future periods." These program inconsistencies have developed, in part at least, because of the refusal of the political process to view the variety of agriculture's maladjustments except as particularized emergencies which can be met on an ad hoc, piecemeal basis.

Today, within the political process, there is growing recognition and acceptance of the hard fact that agriculture's maladjustment is long term and fundamental. In the 1960 political campaign, the leadership of both political parties publicly attested to the need for long-range programs of broad agricultural adjustment.

Nevertheless, although the political process will undoubtedly recognize increasingly the basic nature of agricultural maladjustment, it cannot, I think, be expected in the near future to adopt those comprehensive and inclusive programs which could eliminate program inconsistencies. For, I submit, the inconsistencies we find as between the particularized programs, and also between the goals and the means adopted for their achievement within a single program, are more than the accidental by-products of initiating programs on an ad hoc, piecemeal basis. Such program inconsistencies are, in a sense, the hedges which the political process has made against the danger of public action changing the structure of agriculture or the pattern of agricultural production unwisely or too radically. Program inconsistencies, then, are the counterbalances which tend to keep our total agricultural policy within an established norm. Standing in opposition, they limit change.

The governmental process may, as the political patterns in the decision-making process reshape themselves in the 1960's, seek to develop more horizontally inclusive programs which encompass the whole complex of adjustment, conservation, income and welfare. Conflicting and duplicating public actions may be thus, in part, eliminated. However, it is doubtful — because of the basic inconsistency in our attitude toward the proper role of government — if American politics is yet ready to adopt programs which are truly comprehensive in the sense that they are vertically consistent in terms of: (1) the adoption of means adequate for achieving prescribed goals and (2) the depth of program consequences which are recognized and dealt with.

The most politically acceptable programs — however inclusive they may be horizontally — are probably those which are oriented toward immediate ills and toward the individual farm or farm family. Programs which are vertically comprehensive and consistent, in that they foresee and attempt to cope with the circle of indirect consequences which broaden out from the first remedial action, are generally less politically acceptable than those which stop with the initial problem. The ratio between political acceptability and the degree to which a program broadens out to encompass the indirect consequences of initial remedial actions is probably inverse.

Thus, programs, such as Howard Ottoson (Chapter 19) suggests, which face up to and attempt to ameliorate the impact of land withdrawal on the nonfarm sector of rural communities and even of whole regions, or programs which deal with the need for retraining and relocating those human beings displaced by land retirement, are probably less acceptable than land retirement programs which ignore the residual problems ensuing from land withdrawal. For Americans' felt need for public actions to deal with the broad consequences of proposed programs is generally not strong enough to break through their stereotype of narrowly restricted government and make politically acceptable those comprehensive governmental actions which such residual problems frequently require. Broad, comprehensive programs of action, which could achieve both horizontal and vertical consistency, probably involve changes in the agricultural structure and patterns of production which depart too widely from established norms to be politically acceptable at present.

Fourth, the conflict between Americans' general concept of government and their demands for government's assistance in meeting their particularized problems has limited the types of governmental actions which are politically acceptable. It has meant the development of programs limited in terms of (1) government's interference with the rights of landowners to make decisions concerning the use of their land, (2) the use of governmental police power to control the use of land and (3) the ways in which government resources are used to correct agricultural maladjustments.

The adjustment programs which have been most politically acceptable have been those which interfered least with the rights of fee simple ownership. Our political reluctance to interfere with property rights in land resources is evidenced by the half-way manner in which we have reluctantly adopted such land retirement devices as acreage allotments, marketing quotas and the Soil Bank, which divest the farmer of some of his property rights to determine the use which is to be made of his land. Moreover, even these use-control measures were considered to be politically acceptable only when accompanied by cash bounties. That the degree of land use control these measures achieve is not commensurate with the cash subsidies used to pay for such control is evidenced by the piling up of both unmanageable agricultural reserves and of government costs.

Walter Chryst and John Timmons (Chapter 17) reason persuasively that production controls which would not build government benefits into the price of the land could be achieved if government-alloted marketing rights and benefits — which now attach to individual parcels of land — were to "run with the person" rather than the land. Property rights are not a bundle of rights which are indivisible. Nevertheless, the reluctance with which the political process has curtailed use rights in property as a means of limiting production suggests that measures which stripped land of its marketing rights and attached them to the person would, at the present at least, be viewed as too radical an interference with traditional property rights. Moreover, as the owners of government-granted marketing rights became separated from the property to which these rights had previously been attached, the political pressures to give land, thus stripped of its marketing rights, new marketing privileges would build up to proportions which Congress probably could not withstand.

It goes almost without saying that the types of rural land adjustment which have thus far been politically acceptable have been limited to "voluntary" programs — programs which obtain adjustment through land purchase or leasing, money payments for compliance and technical assistance incentives. The only national effort to restrict an owner's use of his land through the police power — the Soil Conservation Service's attempt to obtain the adoption of local land use ordinances — has been almost a complete failure.

It is entirely possible, however, that as the balance of political power shifts to urban representatives in both our state and national legislatures, the political concern for a farmer's "fee simple rights" may well decline. For, after all, city people are by now completely accustomed to being restricted in the use of their property. Therefore, if the cost of agricultural adjustment reaches what city people consider an unfair drain on the national treasury, we may well see rural land use adjustments which are backed by the police power of the state. Moreover, as the cities billow out into the countryside, farmers and rural people themselves may increasingly turn to the police power to zone out undesirable developments.

Finally, the bounds of political acceptability limit the ways in which, program-wise, money resources may be used. When one considers the magnitude of the cost of present agricultural programs, one might reasonably contend that the concept of limited government sets no real bounds on the use of government resources. Yet, the bifocal way in which most citizens view government does limit the uses which can be made of government resources in bringing agriculture into adjustment with the rest of the economy.

Clearly, it is not now politically acceptable to pay agricultural labor to be idle. Earl Heady remarks in Chapter 1: "I never expect to see a time when payments direct to agricultural labor become an acceptable means for reducing or shifting farm output." However, Chryst and Timmons (Chapter 17) and Ottoson (Chapter 19) indicate the real need for programs which subsidize labor withdrawal. Ottoson suggests such measures as subsidized retraining of displaced agricultural labor, individual job placement, payment of moving costs and subsistence and rental allowances during a relocation period.

We have already found unemployment compensation in the industrial sector politically acceptable and administratively feasible. Increasingly, as the squeeze which is forcing excess labor out of agriculture tightens and affects more citizens, programs which give those who must migrate out of agriculture personalized professional guidance, and even perhaps some economic assistance, will, I think, come within the bounds of political acceptability.

Because of our concept of a narrowly limited state, the use of resources to correct agricultural maladjustment through any widespread use of consumption subsidies has been generally unacceptable. Consumption subsidies have thus far been acceptable only for limited uses which involve strong countervailing symbols, such as the school lunch. Foreign aid to underdeveloped areas, partly because it provides a relatively painless way out, may rapidly develop into another such symbol which justifies consumption subsidization.

If Americans' unresolved inner conflict over the nature and functions of government was the only controlling social attitude which determined political acceptability, the prospect for future social progress would, indeed, be a dreary one. We know, however, that our political process has adopted vast programs of economic and social adjustment which are reasonably long term, broadly consistent and reasonably equitable and effective.

Such social progress has been made possible, at least in part I think, because we are slowly developing another picture of government which parallels and seemingly can live in peace with our traditional concept of narrowly limited government. Through this view, government is not viewed as a total entity. Rather, it is looked at pluralistically. Government is seen as operating as a series of functional blocs.

Under this pluralistic view of government, the bounds which confine political acceptability can be pushed outward, by a sort of transference process. It is a process which permits a governmental function, after its need and usefulness have been broadly and thoroughly established, to be transplanted outside our total concept of narrowly limited government. These transplanted functions are not subject to the same bounds of political acceptability. They, themselves, are powerful public symbols which command men's loyalties and allegiance.

Thus, over the years, such functions as public education, conservation, social security, have become established as areas of government which are not narrowly limited. Therefore, the political acceptability of any land adjustment program is increased if it can march under the symbol of "conservation." Although many economists and soil scientists may wish a clarification of terminology which would exclude some of the things done under the name of "conservation," it should be realized that activities which they believe should not be called conservation might suffer politically from disassociation with the conservation symbol.

The point which I wish to make here, however, is that there is a growth process at work in our political symbolism which is pushing out the bounds of political acceptability. Because of our dual vision of government as a total entity, and government as a series of functional blocs, individual functions of government are able to escape from the confining concept of the narrowly limited state, and are able to develop into powerful symbols for further public action. This is a continuous growth and transference process. One by one, as our functions of government grow and develop, they frequently take on a symbolism which puts them outside the restriction of the narrowly limited state concept and, theoretically at least, permits the development of broad, consistent and effective programming in these areas. Thus, just as "conservation" has become a symbol which makes for political acceptability, it is very possible that the day will come when "agricultural adjustment" will be a powerful symbol which permits broadly consistent and long-term policy development. Therefore, I believe that the political acceptability potential for programs of agricultural adjustment must be projected over at least a 10-year period.

Another set of social attitudes which prevents political acceptability from being determined by power politics alone is a belief in certain "rules of the game" -- such ethical values as a sense of national welfare, a feeling of responsibility to future generations, a belief in equity and fair play and a sympathy for the underdog. Even political analysts who do not admit the force of public interest in policy development, usually concede that there are certain "rules of the game" which, although they exist outside the arena of pressure group politics, nevertheless influence the course of policy development.

One of the most important of these rules of the game in determining political acceptability is, I believe, our sense of equity, our desire for fair play. After all, the belief that all men should have approximate equality of opportunity is as much a part of our democratic heritage as is the concept of the negative state.

Our sense of equity is reflected in present agricultural programs, and it will undoubtedly limit the political acceptability of proposals for future action. We all realize that geographical and commodity politics have insisted upon national program uniformity in acreage reductions, regardless of soils and locations. However, our sense of equity has also been a factor in making such program uniformity possible. It is the belief that farmers across the nation should share on an approximately equitable basis in agricultural relief, and that sacrifice in terms of restrictions on land use should also be equitably shared. The use of the historical base for determining program benefits and acreage restrictions is, of course, also grounded in this concept of equity.

This concept of equity will undoubtedly limit the political acceptability of proposals for developing new land use patterns which are more consistent with national economic development. For shifts in the use of land which fall with differing weight upon different geographical and social regions will be contrary to our generally held criterion of equity. As Earl Heady (Chapter 1) pointed out, such shifts would "mean concentration of major land use adjustments in particular locations. It would mean a much less intensive agriculture and a further and more rapid shrinkage in farm and nonfarm populations in these locations."

Such proposals which threaten not only to close out whole farms but whole farming areas, whole groups of communities, and to upset the customary pattern of economic life in such areas, are bound to meet with fierce political opposition. Donald Boles and Ross Talbot (Chapter 18) have described the political furor which has been created because the Soil Bank program has taken whole farms out of production and disturbed economic activity in the community centers. This congressional reaction is a forewarning of the type of opposition such proposals will likely encounter. Of course, much of this opposition must be interpreted in terms of geographical politics. But it is being justified on equity grounds as well as in terms of agricultural fundamentalism. From the standpoint of our equity concepts, land use "extensification" in marginal areas, such as Howard Ottoson suggests, would probably be more acceptable than land withdrawal programs.

Here again, however, I think the politicians' reluctance to disturb the existing patterns of land use is also explainable in terms of our lack of sufficient expert knowledge. Ray Bressler (Chapter 13) pointed up the complexities in arriving at new land use adjustments which are more consistent with national economic development: "... it is clear that any serious attempt at solution must involve general equilibrium — interrelations between agricultural and nonagricultural sectors of the economy, between land and other resources and between farm and nonfarm uses of land. We visualize a complex interaction of available resources, technology, alternative uses, consumer demands and preference -- all in a spatial context with appropriate interconnections in the form of transfer, processing, and marketing costs. The model should be dynamic, of course, to allow for changes in technology and tastes, for interactions between and within major sectors and for all the serial interconnections of these variables."

Perhaps the seminar on which this book is based, and others like it, may begin to throw enough light on these complex interrelationships so that our lawmakers may begin to see some reliable guidelines in moving toward a new type of land adjustment policy.

Americans' concepts of equity will in the future, I think, work to put further limitations on the shape and nature of agricultural adjustment programs. As the urban representation in Congress strengthens, our concepts of equity will work with urban representatives in making politically unacceptable the programs of land adjustment which make inequitable demands upon the rest of the economy. Again, our sense of equity may cause a nonfarm legislative majority with its large representation of low income groups in the urban economy to reject regressive formulas for distributing program benefits among the various agricultural classes.

Closely allied to Americans' sense of democratic equity is their humanitarian feeling for the needs of the underdog. Although frequently this social feeling for the underdog has been weakly reflected in our legislative actions, it is another rule of the game which sets limits upon political acceptability.

At least up until World War II, this sense of sympathy for the underdog served a chronically depressed agriculture well. Moreover, as the farmer's political strength weakens, it perhaps will be increasingly important in making programs of agricultural adjustment, which must be implemented with financial subsidies, politically acceptable.

However, it may be difficult to sell, on the basis of equity, the idea of adjustment subsidies if the size of farms keeps enlarging. For it may be difficult for the public to see the big farmer as an underdog — even though he may be caught in the cost-price squeeze on each of the hundreds of acres he owns. Moreover, it will also be difficult for the public to view the growing number of part-time farmers, who make good wages in industry and are protected by labor unions, as suitable objects for public assistance in a land adjustment program.

Finally, I do not think I should leave the problem of the underlying social attitudes which confine and control political acceptability without at least mentioning a social value which is rather particularized, in that it has force only upon policy developments affecting agriculture. This is the force of agricultural fundamentalism. Americans' feeling for the fundamental importance of agriculture as the basis of all of our economic activity and as the source of a virtuous national life has been one of the controlling social attitudes throughout our history. It has consistently and broadly affected the shape and content of our agricultural programs.

It has been an important factor in obtaining consistent support from the national treasury for agricultural programs. It has committed the government to programs designed to keep people on the farm. Our agricultural fundamentalism has made us politically reluctant to face the proposition that our advancing agricultural technology is making it necessary for people to leave farm life. In part, at least, the political reaction against taking whole farms out of production under the Soil Bank program was a response to agricultural fundamentalism. Americans' reluctance to accept the fact that a substantial part of our farm population must leave the life of the farm and make its living in cities will probably be a limiting factor in obtaining programs for guiding and assisting people in their farm-to-city migration.

Our agricultural fundamentalism has also made programs more politically acceptable if they help to keep the little farmer in business. Agricultural fundamentalism, which glorifies family farm life, has committed our political process to the preservation of the family-sized farm. Building programs of land adjustment which do not conflict too radically with the family farm symbol are made more difficult by the fact that, although, for the economist, the family farm is an elastic concept which expands with an advancing technology, the size of the family farm as a political concept is not so easily expandable.

Thus far I have discussed only one of the four frameworks which I originally outlined as setting limits on political acceptability. I intend to treat the remaining frameworks only in summary fashion.

Both our constitutional and our two-party systems complement and reinforce our prevailing social attitudes in setting bounds upon political acceptability.

All I want to point out about our framework of constitutional powers is that whereas it was once a narrowly restricting frame which prevented action, since 1937 court decisions have so broadened it out that today any proposals which qualified agricultural economists would deem wise and feasible would probably come within the limits of government's constitutional powers. Donald Boles and Ross Talbot (Chapter 18) have outlined the constitutional means through which land adjustment can be accomplished. They pointed out that "no major legal or constitutional obstacles presently exist to prevent programs aimed at removing excess agricultural cropland from production."

However, the force of our constitutional system of checks and balances is to drive proposals for public action toward the central norm in political acceptability. Only proposals with a relatively high "acceptability potential" can usually successfully run the gamut of both houses of Congress and the presidency.

Our two-party political system, operating as it does over a continental area, also serves as a force which prevents radical departures from established patterns of action. Because both parties, to achieve a majority coalition, must compete for the vote of all groups and sections of our society, they must strive to strike the "great average" in political attitudes. Neither party can afford to adopt a policy which appears to be a radical departure from present norms and habits of mass political thinking.

Finally, we come to the framework of basic interest. Henry Adams once said that practical politics consists in ignoring facts. But the force of basic interest in our representative process is one large fact which no politician can afford to ignore. Regardless of the prevailing social climate, regardless of which political party is in power and regardless of the political coalitions which pressure-group politics may be forming in Congress, political acceptability will, at least approximately, reflect the relative strength of the basic interests of our society.

The fact that the political strength of agriculture, as a basic interest, is on the decline is the large political fact that those who are proposing new policies for agriculture cannot afford to ignore if they wish such policies to be politically acceptable. As we all know, in the 1950's the farm population declined more than 15 percent and will probably continue to shrink as agricultural technology marches on. Moreover, the nature of the farm population's occupational interests is changing. The shrinking and changing of the nature of the farm population cannot but weaken agriculture's political strength.

Today, there are only 263 congressional districts whose working farm population comprises 5 percent or more of the people in the district. By 1971, it has been estimated by the Census Bureau, seven of our ten most rural states will have lost ten more congressional seats. Moreover, the urban interest in these so-called "farm districts" is strong. Not only do such "farm districts" frequently contain such large urban centers as Des Moines, Iowa, but the occupational interests of the growing number of part-time farmers, who also are frequently wage earners in town or even industrial workers in the city, are divided. It has been suggested by one of our shrewdest national politicians, holding one of our highest offices, that today only 100 of our 437 congressmen are directly affected by the farm vote.

The question, here, then is: How will the decline in the political strength of the basic agricultural interest affect the political acceptability of future proposals for agricultural adjustment? During recent years the voting record of urban-based congressmen on farm legislation indicates that, if they are not coerced by their political party, they are inclined to vote against farm programs which seem costly to urban consumers and taxpayers. Moreover, their voting record also reveals that it is becoming increasingly difficult for the political party to persuade such congressmen to vote even for party-sponsored bills. As the farm population continues to decline, there is a growing possibility that the political party itself may feel that the farm sector is no longer a major partner in the group coalition on which it is depending to win elections. Thus, the political acceptability of agricultural proposals increasingly cannot be measured on the basis of farmer majority strength.

The problem of agricultural policymakers, in the future, will be to develop programs which will be politically acceptable to an urban-oriented Congress and presidency. The solutions which in the long run will be politically acceptable within this developing new frame of basic interest, I believe, (1) must have some coincidence with our commonly held concepts of the general welfare, (2) must be effective in actually solving the farm problem, (3) must not be excessive in cost in terms of other demands upon the national budget and (4) must not have an inequitable impact upon other groups in the population.

Curiously enough, the force of basic interest may, in the future, be a force which pushes out some of the bounds of political acceptability which certain of our prevailing social attitudes have set. The force of basic interest may insist upon agricultural programs which are not costly, uncoordinated, stop-gap measures. It may neutralize the agricultural fundamentalist belief that changes in the economic structure of agriculture can be held back by political fiat. In short, the force of changing basic interest may compel our political process to modify the boundaries which have been set on political acceptability. It may make increasingly acceptable those proposals for agricultural adjustments which are more consistent with national economic development.

Index